# AN INTRODUCTION TO RELATIVITY PHYSICS

# AN INTRODUCTION TO RELATIVITY PHYSICS

by

# R.L. Gerl

ELTON-WOLF PUBLISHING

Cover designed by David Marty
Text designed by Terry Bain

04 03 02 01          5 4 3 2

ISBN: 1-58619-025-3
Library of Congress Catalog Number: 2001-086269

Second Printing September 2001
Printed in Canada

Published by Elton-Wolf Publishing
Seattle, Washington

ELTON-WOLF PUBLISHING

2505 Second Avenue Suite 515   Seattle, Washington 98121
Tel 206.748.0345  Fax 206.748.0343
www.elton-wolf.com  info@elton-wolf.com

This book is dedicated to my parents and grandparents.

# Contents

# Foreword

*An Introduction to Relativity Physics* is written for people interested in making the transition from classical physics to relativity physics. It is also written for people who simply want to learn about Albert Einstein's discoveries in enough detail to really understand them. Each chapter explores different aspects of relativity without the extra burden of a lot of unneeded material. Therefore, learning relativity is something that can be done in a reasonable amount of time. This book serves as a comprehensive and straightforward introduction to the special and general theory of relativity.

# PART 1

## *Relativity*

# CHAPTER I

## *Introduction*

THE THEORY OF RELATIVITY, which comprises the general theory of relativity and the special theory of relativity, is generally very difficult to learn. While this book is designed to help those newly initiated to the theory, a background in vector and tensor calculus is necessary to understand the general theory of relativity, which is analyzed through tensor calculus. The special theory of relativity can be understood with algebra and a solid grasp of calculus. An overview of some vector and tensor calculus is given in this book, but does not cover these topics in detail. For a solid understanding of these subjects readers should consult books dealing exclusively with this material.

The primary impetus of this book is to cover the foundations and basic principles of relativity. Other topics related to relativity, such as current ideas about the early universe or speculations about backward time travel, are not explored in depth. For discussions of these highly conjectural areas, readers can consult references at the end of this book. A good historical account of the development of relativity is *Subtle Is the Lord*, by Abraham Pais.

Special relativity, which explains the hyperbolic shape of space-time, has been so thoroughly confirmed through scientific experiments that it is effectively proven. The amazing character of the theory is that so much physics can be derived from so little. Two fundamental physical laws, the principle of special relativity and the principle of the constancy of the speed of light, produce many consequences: the inter-convertibility of matter and energy; the relative slowing of time; the increase in relative mass with relative motion; the aberration of star light; the unification of space and time; a fuller unification of electromagnetism; and so on.

While the general theory of relativity has been less thoroughly tested than the special theory, there are no grounds for doubting its correctness, and astronomers continually put it to further tests. In general relativity a huge amount of physics follows from the principle of equivalence and the principle of general relativity: black holes; the expanding universe; the deflection of light by gravitational bodies; the relative slowing of time in gravity fields; the curvature of space-time; gravitational waves; and explanation of the structures of white dwarf and neutron stars.

Even though the theory of relativity explains a great deal, we should be cautious about drawing social or moral conclusions from it. Relativity is solely a physical theory about the nature of things such as mass-energy and space-time. It has no consequences for moral issues and does not support the idea of moral relativism. To this writer moral relativism is false.

## Quantum Theory and Its Relation to Relativity

Another great revolution in physics is quantum theory, the equations and concepts of which are consistent with relativity. They are used together, for example, in quantum field theory. The often-stated difference between the two theories is that quantum theory is non-deterministic, while relativity can be consistent with either deterministic or non-deterministic views. Mathematically speaking, relativity is a deterministic theory, allowing for no uncertainties. Given exact initial conditions and boundary conditions, relativity gives exact results, while quantum theory does not. For this reason, many scientists feel that a broader theory uniting the forces of nature and incorporating both relativity and quantum theory is yet to be discovered. The principle of relativity says that the laws of physics are the same in every frame of reference, but this does not mean that all of those laws must be deterministic. Further, while the principle of equivalence says that gravity and inertia are the same thing, this does not preclude the possibility of a quantum nature for gravity and inertia. Rather, any non-deterministic behavior of inertia must be identical to any non-deterministic behavior of gravity, because these are not two separate phenomena. Thus relativity does not preclude quantum indeterminacy, and quantum indeterminacy does not preclude relativity.

### *Review of Some Properties of Vector Fields*

Relativity studies space-time by use of tensor fields, which are generalizations of vector and scalar fields. Some crucial properties of vector fields, which are used heavily in electromagnetism and other areas, are reviewed here. The equality of mixed partials holds for scalar functions. For example, if $f = f(x, y, z, w)$, then for any two variables, say $x$ and $z$:

$$\frac{\partial^2 f}{\partial x \partial z} = \frac{\partial^2 f}{\partial z \partial x}$$

For a multi-variable function, the multivariable chain rule is used. For functions of the form

$$z(x) = f(g(x),\ h(x),\ i(x),\ j(x))$$

the derivative is:

$$\frac{dz}{dx} = \frac{\partial f}{\partial g}\frac{dg}{dx} + \frac{\partial f}{\partial h}\frac{dh}{dx} + \frac{\partial f}{\partial i}\frac{di}{dx} + \frac{\partial f}{\partial j}\frac{dj}{dx}$$

And for functions of the form

$$a(x, y, z, w) = f(g(x, y, z, w), h(x, y, z, w), i(x, y, z, w), j(x, y, z, w))$$

the partial derivatives are:

$$\frac{\partial a}{\partial x} = \frac{\partial f}{\partial g}\frac{\partial g}{\partial x} + \frac{\partial f}{\partial h}\frac{\partial h}{\partial x} + \frac{\partial f}{\partial i}\frac{\partial i}{\partial x} + \frac{\partial f}{\partial j}\frac{\partial j}{\partial x}$$

$$\frac{\partial a}{\partial y} = \frac{\partial f}{\partial g}\frac{\partial g}{\partial y} + \frac{\partial f}{\partial h}\frac{\partial h}{\partial y} + \frac{\partial f}{\partial i}\frac{\partial i}{\partial y} + \frac{\partial f}{\partial j}\frac{\partial j}{\partial y}$$

$$\frac{\partial a}{\partial z} = \frac{\partial f}{\partial g}\frac{\partial g}{\partial z} + \frac{\partial f}{\partial h}\frac{\partial h}{\partial z} + \frac{\partial f}{\partial i}\frac{\partial i}{\partial z} + \frac{\partial f}{\partial j}\frac{\partial j}{\partial z}$$

$$\frac{\partial a}{\partial w} = \frac{\partial f}{\partial g}\frac{\partial g}{\partial w} + \frac{\partial f}{\partial h}\frac{\partial h}{\partial w} + \frac{\partial f}{\partial i}\frac{\partial i}{\partial w} + \frac{\partial f}{\partial j}\frac{\partial j}{\partial w}$$

A vector $\bar{w}$ with components $(w_1, w_2, w_3, w_4)$, each a function of time, $x_1(t)$, $x_2(t)$, $x_3(t)$ and $x_4(t)$, can be written as:

$$w_i = w_i(x_1(t),\ x_2(t),\ x_3(t),\ x_4(t))$$

Here the values of the index $i$ range from one to four. The time derivative of the $w_i$ component is:

$$\frac{dw_i}{dt} = \frac{\partial w_i}{\partial x_1}\frac{dx_1}{dt} + \frac{\partial w_i}{\partial x_2}\frac{dx_2}{dt} + \frac{\partial w_i}{\partial x_3}\frac{dx_3}{dt} + \frac{\partial w_i}{\partial x_4}\frac{dx_4}{dt}$$

Or:

$$\frac{dw_i}{dt} = \sum_{k=1}^{4} \frac{\partial w_i}{\partial x_k}\frac{dx_k}{dt}$$

This equation is true by virtue of the fact that each $w_i$ takes the same form as the equation $z(x) = f(g(x),\ h(x),\ i(x),\ j(x))$, considered previously. Functions of the form given above by the equation $a(x, y, z, w)$ and its partial derivatives can be written more generically as:

$$z_i = z_i(y_1(x_1,x_2,x_3,x_4), y_2(x_1,x_2,x_3,x_4), y_3(x_1,x_2,x_3,x_4), y_4(x_1,x_2,x_3,x_4))$$

with the index ranging from one to four. The $x_j$ partial derivative of $z_i$ is given by:

$$\frac{\partial z_i}{\partial x_j} = \frac{\partial z_i}{\partial y_1}\frac{\partial y_1}{\partial x_j} + \frac{\partial z_i}{\partial y_2}\frac{\partial y_2}{\partial x_j} + \frac{\partial z_i}{\partial y_3}\frac{\partial y_3}{\partial x_j} + \frac{\partial z_i}{\partial y_4}\frac{\partial y_4}{\partial x_j}$$

Or, more briefly, as:

$$\frac{\partial z_i}{\partial x_j} = \sum_{k=1}^{4} \frac{\partial z_i}{\partial y_k}\frac{\partial y_k}{\partial x_j}$$

Consider the set of functions $z_i = z_i(x_1,x_2,x_3,x_4)$, where the index ranges from one to four, and their inverses $x_i = x_i(z_1,z_2,z_3,z_4)$. The $z$'s can be expressed as functions of themselves: *(substitute $x_i$ for the four $x$'s)*

$$z_i = z_i(x_1(z_1,z_2,z_3,z_4), x_2(z_1,z_2,z_3,z_4), x_3(z_1,z_2,z_3,z_4), x_4(z_1,z_2,z_3,z_4))$$

Taking the partial derivative with respect to any $z$ and applying it to this equation gives:

$$\delta_{ij} = \frac{\partial z_i}{\partial z_j} = \frac{\partial z_i}{\partial x_1}\frac{\partial x_1}{\partial z_j} + \frac{\partial z_i}{\partial x_2}\frac{\partial x_2}{\partial z_j} + \frac{\partial z_i}{\partial x_3}\frac{\partial x_3}{\partial z_j} + \frac{\partial z_i}{\partial x_4}\frac{\partial x_4}{\partial z_j}$$

Or:

*orthogonal*

$$\delta_{ij} = \frac{\partial z_i}{\partial z_j} = \sum_{k=1}^{4} \frac{\partial z_i}{\partial x_k}\frac{\partial x_k}{\partial z_j}$$

*Kronecker Delta*

Here $\delta_{ij} = 0$ if $i$ does not equal $j$ and $\delta_{ij} = 1$ if $i=j$. These equations can easily be generalized for greater numbers of variables by simply increasing the range of the index sum. The cross product is another heavily used quantity in physics. Consider two vectors, $(a_x, a_y, a_z)$ and $(b_x, b_y, b_z)$. Their cross product is defined

$\vec{a} \times \vec{b}$

to be $(a_y b_z - a_z b_y, a_z b_x - a_x b_z, a_x b_y - a_y b_x)$. Differential equations can be written in two forms, differential form or integral form. For example, the equation

$$\frac{dx}{dt} = v(t)$$

is written in differential form. The same equation in integral form is:

$$x = \int v(t) dt$$

In this case, ordinary calculus allows one easily to switch between integral and differential form. For many vector equations, integral and differential form can be interchanged by using the divergence theorem and stokes theorem. These theorems are given below.

*The Divergence Theorem:*

$$\iiint_T div \overline{F} dV = \iint_{\partial T} \overline{F} \bullet d\overline{S} = \iint_{\partial T} (\overline{F} \bullet \overline{n}) dS$$

*The Stokes Theorem:*

$$\int_{\partial S} \overline{F} \bullet d\overline{l} = \iint_S (curl \overline{F}) \bullet d\overline{S} = \iint_S (curl \overline{F} \bullet \overline{n}) dS$$

To see how these equations can convert between differential and integral forms, consider the conservation of mass law in classical physics. Consider a closed surface, $T$, and let $M$ be the amount of mass inside $T$ at any given time. Let $\rho(x, y, z, t)$ be the density of mass at any point and let $v(x, y, z, t)$ be the speed of a differential region of mass at any point. The flux of mass through the surface $T$ is:

$$\Phi = \iint_{\partial T} \rho \overline{v} \bullet \overline{n} dS = \iint_{\partial T} \rho \overline{v} \bullet d\overline{S}$$

This is simply the surface integral of mass flux at any point integrated over the

$$\frac{kg}{m^3} \qquad \frac{m}{s}$$

kg per square meter per second

surface of $T$. If mass is conserved, the rate at which the mass of $T$ changes should equal the negative of the total mass flux through the surface:

$$\frac{dm}{dt} = -\Phi$$

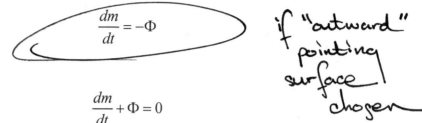

*if "outward" pointing surface chosen*

Or:

$$\frac{dm}{dt} + \Phi = 0$$

The decrease in the mass of $T$ equals the negative of the mass flux through the surface of $T$. If this equation holds true, then mass is conserved. This equation $dm/dt + \Phi = 0$ can also be viewed as constraints on $\rho$ and $\bar{v}$. Because the mass of $T$ is the volume integral over the mass density, the above equation represents the integral form of the conservation of mass. It can be rewritten as:

$$\frac{d}{dt}\iiint_T \rho \, dV + \iint_{\partial T} \rho \bar{v} \bullet d\bar{S} = 0$$

Applying the divergence theorem to the right-hand side, and bringing the time derivative under the first triple integral, this equation becomes:

$$\iiint_T \frac{\partial \rho}{\partial t} \, dV + \iiint_T div(\rho \bar{v}) dV = 0$$

Or:

$$\iiint_T [\frac{\partial \rho}{\partial t} + div(\rho \bar{v})] dV = 0$$

*wow*

Since the integral must be zero at all times and for all volume regions, the integrand must always be zero. Thus, the conservation of mass is transformed to differential form:

$$\frac{\partial \rho}{\partial t} + div(\rho \bar{v}) = 0$$

Conservation equations of this type can apply to quantities other than mass, such as electric charge. In this case mass density becomes charge density and momentum density becomes current density. Any conservation equation of this form is called a continuity equation. For one final example, consider converting Maxwell's equations between differential and integral form, using both the divergence theorem and stokes theorem. Let $\Phi_B$ be the total flux of a magnetic field through a surface $S$ and $\Phi_E$ be the total flux of an electric field through a surface $S$. By definition:

$$\Phi_E = \iint_S \overline{E} \bullet d\overline{S}$$

$$\Phi_B = \iint_S \overline{B} \bullet d\overline{S}$$

The integral forms of Maxwell's equations are:

$$\iint_{Sc} \overline{E} \bullet d\overline{S} = \frac{q}{\varepsilon_0}$$

$$\iint_{Sc} \overline{B} \bullet d\overline{S} = 0$$

$$\int_{\partial S} \overline{E} \bullet d\overline{l} = -\frac{d}{dt}\Phi_B$$

$$\int_{\partial S} \overline{B} \bullet d\overline{l} = \mu_0 \varepsilon_0 \frac{d}{dt}\Phi_E + \mu_0 i$$

Here $S_C$ refers to a closed surface and $S$ refers to an open surface such as a disk. The charge can be written as a volume integral of the charge density, $q = \iiint \rho\, dV$, and current, $i$, can be written as the flux of current density through a surface, $i = \iint \overline{j} \bullet d\overline{S}$. Substituting these and the flux definitions into the above integral equations and applying the divergence theorem and stokes theorem, we can rewrite Maxwell's equations in differential form:

$$div\,\overline{E} = \frac{\rho}{\varepsilon_0}$$

$$div\,\overline{B} = 0$$

$$curl\,\overline{E} = -\frac{\partial \overline{B}}{\partial t}$$

$$curl\,\overline{B} = \mu_0 \varepsilon_0 \frac{\partial \overline{E}}{\partial t} + \mu_0 \overline{j}$$

no magnetic monopoles

While the integral form explains what electric and magnetic fields do over regions of space and time, the differential form explains what the electric and magnetic fields are doing at a given point.

### Newton's Laws, Inertial Frames, and Science

In the study of relativity, it is vitally important to understand how inertial frames relate to forces. From Newton's three laws of motion comes the notion of an inertial frame. In Newtonian mechanics the velocity of an object does not change unless a net external force acts upon it. This also holds true in relativity. When an object has no net external force acting on it, it resides in an inertial frame. Its velocity does not change, and any other object traveling with the same velocity is in the same inertial frame. A coordinate system can be established to identify locations within the frame. Usually a rectangular Cartesian coordinate system is employed in three-dimensional space for a given inertial frame. Any object residing in a given inertial frame has no velocity with respect to the coordinate axes for that inertial frame.

In science, measuring devices are used to study natural phenomena. To make measurements for a given inertial frame, the devices must be stationary with respect to that frame. They can then measure both things that are moving and stationary relative to that inertial frame. Examples of measuring devices are well known: thermometers measure temperature; clocks measure time; rulers measure distances; ammeters measure electric current; voltmeters measure potential differences in circuits; and so on. The essential point is that all of these devices make measurements for the inertial frame in which they are stationary. This simple point plays an important role in the theory of relativity.

# CHAPTER 2

## *The Fallacy of Absolute Simultaneity*

THREE OF THE MOST IMPORTANT DISCOVERIES of classical physics were Newton's laws of motion, Newton's universal law of gravitation, and Maxwell's equations for electromagnetism. Classical physics held that motion was absolute—some objects are intrinsically at rest and other objects are intrinsically moving—and that simultaneity was absolute. But, as will be seen shortly, neither motion nor simultaneity is actually absolute. Experiments at the beginning of the twentieth century yielded results that could not be explained solely by Newton's and Maxwell's theories. Further, the relationships between Maxwell's equations and the inertial frames of classical Newtonian physics—also called Galilean inertial frames—were unclear. When motion occurs along the $x$-axis alone and the $x$-axes coincide at all times, Galilean inertial frames are related by the equations:

$$x' = x - vt$$
$$y' = y$$
$$z' = z$$
$$t' = t \qquad\qquad\qquad 2.1$$

The equations in (2.1) assume that the origins coincide at time $t = 0$. Maxwell's equations, which unite electric and magnetic fields, imply that waves of light, or, more generally, electromagnetic waves, should always travel from their sources at the same speed: $3.00 \times 10^8$ meters/second. Yet in Galilean inertial frames the speed of light can be less than this. In fact, in an inertial frame traveling at exactly the speed of light, the speed of light can be zero. A way to account for the wave-like properties of light, classical physicists thought, was to view light as waves of a fluid-like medium, "aether," which was conjectured to permeate all of space. However, quantum mechanics accounted for the wave-like properties of light and so, like relativity, made the concept of aether unnecessary. Experiments on the aberration of starlight—the change in angle of starlight due to the earth's changing motion—showed that physics required new fundamental ideas. So did the Michelson-Morley experiment, which sought and failed to find changes in the speed of light. Classical physics had assumed that motion was absolute: that one inertial frame was "really" at rest and all other inertial frames were "really" moving. The conjectured aether was assumed to be stationary with respect to "absolute rest."

When Albert Einstein asked whether absolute rest really existed, he meant: is motion absolute or relative? Because Maxwell's equations are not the same in different Galilean inertial frames, classical physicists deemed it reasonable to use electromagnetic observations to determine absolute rest, and hence the absolute motion of objects. Except for Maxwell's equations, all the findings of classical physics were consistent with the idea that motion is relative. The Galilean principle of relativity states that the laws of physics are the same in all Galilean inertial frames. But Maxwell's electromagnetic laws are different in different Galilean inertial frames. Faced with the incompatibility between Galilean relativity and Maxwell's equations, Einstein had three choices: to discard the concept of relative motion, to modify Maxwell's equations so that they would remain the same in all Galilean inertial frames, or to modify the

Galilean transformations of space and time. Because Maxwell's equations had been tested very thoroughly, the second option was ruled out. Einstein's discovery, that motion is actually relative, meant that every law of physics must be the same in every inertial frame. For this to hold for Maxwell's equations, Einstein saw that the Galilean transformations of space and time must be modified. These modifications are the foundations of special relativity, which shows that uniform motion is relative. The general theory of relativity extends this truth for non-uniform motion, *i.e.*, gravitational fields.

For the ancient world there was absolute up, absolute down, absolute east, west, north and south. But Columbus and Newton showed that direction and position are relative. The discovery of the spherical shape of the earth, together with Newtonian gravitation, shows there is no "absolute up" or "absolute down." Angles in space are relative. While two straight lines intersect at a certain angle, each line is inclined relative to the other by the same angle, neither line is actually or absolutely inclined by that angle. In special relativity, motion is relative in the same way the inclination angle between two lines is. Two objects in space travel with a relative velocity to each other but neither is actually traveling at a specific velocity. For example, relative to the earth, the earth is stationary and Jupiter is moving at a certain speed. But, relative to Jupiter, Jupiter is stationary and the earth is moving with that speed. Each case is equally true: they move only in relationship to each other.

To understand why motion is relative, imagine a boxcar on a railroad track, traveling at a constant speed relative to the ground. Inside the boxcar, an observer throws a billiard ball straight up into the air. To that observer the billiard ball travels on a straight line up, momentarily comes to a halt, and travels back down again on a straight line. However, to someone standing beside the railroad track the billiard ball travels on the curve of a parabolic path. Which path does the billiard ball actually follow, a straight line or parabolic path? In the classical view, there was a privileged inertial frame— absolute rest—and all other inertial frames were absolutely in motion. If there really were an absolute rest frame, and the boxcar were in that privileged rest frame, then the billiard ball would move along a straight line. The parabolic path observed by someone on the ground would simply be an inaccurate perception or illusion. It is hard to believe that the parabolic path measured by observers on the ground is an illusion. Further, measurements of the speed and momentum of the billiard ball suffer errors in accuracy in all inertial frames except that of absolute rest. These errors become greater and greater as the speed of inertial frames differs more and more from that of absolute rest. Like momentum, measurements of the kinetic energy of the billiard ball become less and less accurate the greater the speed of the observer's inertial frame.

In the classical view of absolute motion, then, measurements of many physical quantities are correct only when they are made in the inertial frame of absolute rest. But this idea requires that measuring devices in all other inertial frames give false readings for many physical quantities, and therefore implies that all experimental science is unreliable. It is hard to believe that measuring devices would measure unreal physical quantities. Einstein solved this confusion in his theory of special relativity by stating that motion is relative and neither absolute rest nor aether exists. Measurements of a physical quantity such as motion in one inertial frame are just as correct and accurate as (differing) measurements made in another inertial frame. In this sense the principle of special relativity defends all of experimental science.

So the billiard ball is not actually traveling on a parabolic path nor a straight-line path. Relative to the inertial frame of the ground, it travels on a curved parabolic path; relative to the inertial frame of the boxcar it travels on a straight-line path. Both sets of measurements of its motion are equally correct, but neither is absolutely so, because billiard ball's motion is relative, not absolute. The same thing holds for other physical quantities, such as momentum. Like motion, the momentum of the billiard ball is relative and depends on the inertial frame of the observer. In the boxcar the billiard ball has no horizontal momentum, but to the ground it does. Both measurements of its horizontal momentum are equally right. If motion were absolute, observers on the ground would measure the horizontal momentum of the billiard ball with an accuracy error equal to the mass of the ball times the absolute speed of the inertial frame of the ground (because the boxcar is assumed to be in absolute rest). Thus the relativity of motion is embodied in the statement, "a measuring device, stationary in any inertial frame, makes measurements that are just as correct as measurements made by the device when it is stationary in another inertial frame." Accuracy error is still the difference between the true value and the measured value of a physical quantity. But the true value of a physical quantity is relative to inertial frames.

As a further illustration, the earth travels relative to the sun at a speed of 30 kilometers per second as it travels around the sun. If the sun were absolutely at rest then the earth would be moving absolutely at 30 km/sec. But an observer on the earth, sitting on the top of a mountain, measures the speed of a nearby mountain at zero km/sec. If motion were absolute then those measurements would suffer an accuracy error of 30 km/sec (for this example the earth's spin is ignored). Since motion is relative, both speeds are equally correct and neither measurement of the mountain's speed suffers an accuracy error. The mountain has a speed of 30 km/sec, relative to the sun, and the same mountain has a speed of zero km/sec, relative to a nearby mountain. Because physical quantities such as speed, momentum, and kinetic energy are relative, the laws of physics must be the same in every inertial frame. If the laws of physics were not the same, from inertial frame to inertial frame, then that could be exploited to determine a specific inertial frame and hence the "absolute motion" of that inertial frame. The laws of physics are necessarily the same in all inertial frames because absolute motion does not exist. Now, because the laws of physics are the same in all inertial frames, this must include Maxwell's laws for electromagnetism. But Maxwell's laws require that light always moves away from its source at the same speed of $3.00 \times 10^8$ meters/second in the vacuum of space. Therefore the constancy of the speed of light should be a law of physics.

Special relativity is based on two fundamental physical laws: *the principle of special relativity*, which is based on considerations of motion, and the *principle of the constancy of the speed of light*, which is based on electromagnetic considerations. The principle of special relativity can be stated as discussed above: any measuring device, stationed in any inertial frame, measures reality with the same correctness and accuracy that it does stationed in any other inertial frame and, in every inertial frame, all physical laws are the same. The principle of the constancy of the speed of light, as asserted by Maxwell's laws for electromagnetism, can be stated as follows: in the vacuum light always travels at the same speed of approximately $3.00 \times 10^8$ meters/second, regardless of the motion of its source.

A consequence of these two physical laws is that the speed of light is the same in every inertial frame. This is because the laws of physics are the same in all inertial frames, and the constancy of the speed of light is itself a law of

• nearly

physics. Since the speed of light is the same in each inertial frame, it must be measured to have the same speed in each inertial frame. But aren't these two principles incompatible with each other? In fact the two principles are compatible only if time itself is relative. There is no such thing as absolute duration of time, nor does time flow at an absolute rate. Likewise, simultaneity is not absolute. Time is relative, just as are motion, momentum, kinetic energy, direction, and many other physical quantities.

While later chapters will elaborate on this further, a brief explanation is in order here. The principle of special relativity requires, for example, that a clock must measure time as accurately in one inertial frame as in any another. Because clocks are used to measure the speed of light, and because the speed of light is actually the same in each inertial frame, a clock in one inertial frame will run at a rate different relative to a clock in another. Clocks synchronized in one inertial frame are not synchronized in another. Hence, time is relative. These ideas clash both with ordinary human experience and with the principles of classical physics. While the classical ideas of absolute space and absolute time were based on ordinary human experience, relativity shows those ideas to be wrong. Classical physics inadvertently gave to the concept of absolute simultaneity an ontological status it did not deserve. It should not be too surprising that superficial human understanding needed to be corrected by relativity. Most discoveries in science do correct human misperceptions. For example the spherical nature of the earth and its revolution about the sun were incredibly counterintuitive after their initial discovery and, after relativity, the quantum theory was discovered with its incredibly counterintutitve ideas. The consequences of relativity can be thought of as an extension of the Copernican principle: just as the Earth is not the center of the universe, so human perception is not at the center of a true understanding of space and time.

The importance of special relativity for science cannot be overstated. If absolute simultaneity existed, then special relativity would be in error, along with Maxwell's equations, quantum field theory, general relativity and many other things. Measurements would be intrinsically unreliable, as would the whole of observational science, the big bang theory, and the structure of black holes. But experiments have thoroughly demonstrated the correctness of the theory of relativity and scientists consider special relativity as firmly established.

Special relativity's two fundamental physical laws of physics are summarized below.

## The Law of Special Relativity

The accuracy of any measuring device is independent of the inertial frame it is stationed in and, in every inertial frame, all physical laws are the same.

## The Law of the Constancy of the Speed of Light

In the vacuum light always travels in straight lines and always at the same speed, $2.99792458 \times 10^8$ meters/second, regardless of how its source moves through the inertial frame.

# CHAPTER 3

# *Consequences of Relativity*

THE PRINCIPLE OF SPECIAL RELATIVITY, together with the constancy of the speed of light, can be paraphrased simply: the accuracy of a measuring device, the laws of physics, and the speed of light are the same in all inertial frames. As previously stated, relativity requires that the speed of light is the same in each inertial frame. But how can a wave of light, or an individual photon (the quantum parcel of light), have the same speed in every inertial frame?

Imagine a car traveling north on a freeway at a speed of fifty-five miles per hour. That is, relative to the freeway, the car is traveling at fifty-five miles per hour heading north. Now, imagine a car traveling south at forty miles per hour on the same freeway. Relative to the southbound car, the northbound car moves at ninety-five miles per hour. This makes perfect sense and accords with the principles of classical physics, as the speeds are simply added. Thus the concept of a constant speed of light for all inertial frames seems just as counter-intuitive as if we claimed that, relative to the car traveling south at forty miles per hour, the car traveling north were moving at fifty-five miles per hour both in relation to the ground and freeway, and in relation to the southbound car!

Imagine a space ship traveling through space at one-half the speed of light, relative to the earth, and, also relative to the earth, a wave of light traveling at its usual speed of about $3.00 \times 10^8$ meters/second toward the spaceship. Relative to the space ship, the wave of light travels toward it at the speed of $3.00 \times 10^8$ meters/second! Why does the wave of light not travel at one and one half times the speed of light relative to the rocket, if the wave moves at the speed of light relative to the earth? The answer, as was explained partially in the previous chapter and will be clarified presently, is that time itself is relative. The rate at which time and clocks run can be different for different inertial frames, as can the synchronization of two different clocks. To understand the counterintuitive aspects of relativity, it is best to start with the principle of special relativity and the principle of the constancy of the speed of light and derive how the world must be if both are true. Because the speed of light is always the same in every inertial frame, its constancy can be used to create a clock. The traditional "thought experiment" goes as follows: a large box contains two mirrors, one at the top and the other at the bottom. A photon of light leaves the bottom mirror and travels to the top mirror. Once there the photon is reflected by the top mirror and travels back down to the bottom mirror. It takes a certain amount of time for the photon to travel on this journey. Due to the constancy of the speed of light, the amount of time required for the photon to go back to the bottom mirror must be double the amount of time it takes to travel from the bottom mirror to the top. The photon, after returning to the bottom mirror, repeats the journey an arbitrary number of times.

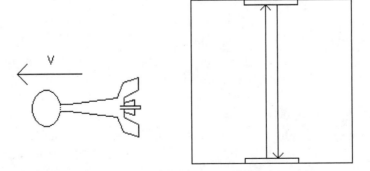

The box, then, becomes a clock, measuring time. Call the time it takes light to go from the bottom mirror to the top mirror $t$. It follows that the height of the box is $ct$, where $c = 3.00 \times 10^8$ meters/second. To a rocket in a different inertial frame, traveling with constant speed, $v$, horizontal to the box, how would the "box-clock" look? Relative to this new inertial frame the box is traveling with a speed of $v$ and the photon of light is traveling on a diagonal line, as in the diagram.

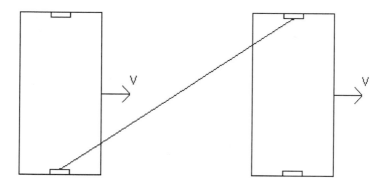

Relative to the rocket, the distance light travels from the bottom mirror to the top mirror is greater than the distance between those mirrors in the rest inertial frame of the box. But the speed of light must always be $3.00 \times 10^8$ meters/second, even in the rest inertial frame of the rocket. Therefore, in the rest frame of the rocket, light takes longer to go via the diagonal line between the two mirrors. Because the laws of physics are the same in both rest frames, to observers in the rocket time passes more slowly inside the box. But, to observers stationed inside the box, time runs more slowly in the rocket because it takes light a longer period of time to go from the ceiling of the rocket to its floor. (Here the ceiling and floor of the rocket are perpendicular to the rocket's direction of motion.) Is time really running slower in either the box or rocket? Not in an absolute sense. Relative to the box only, time aboard the rocket has slowed down, and relative to the rocket only, time in the box has slowed down. Each perspective is just as correct as the other. Measurements made in both inertial frames, that of the rocket and box, are equally true and equally right. The principle of special relativity requires this because the laws of physics are the same in all inertial frames. This is what is meant by the statement that time is relative, not absolute.

This thought-experiment allows us to calculate how much relative time-slowing occurs between the box and rocket. Consider the behavior of the box-clock in the rest frame of the rocket. Let $t'$ be the time it takes a photon of light to travel between the two mirrors, and $vt'$ the distance the box moves during the time the photon travels between the two mirrors. The geometry is given in this diagram:

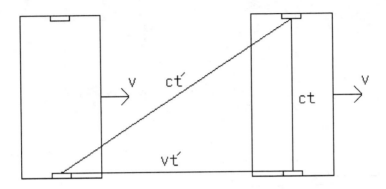

The height of the box, $ct$, is expressed as a function of the amount of time it takes light to move between the mirrors in the rest frame of the box. From the diagram it is clear that the relationship between $t$ and $t'$ can be calculated by simply using the Pythagorean theorem:

$$(ct')^2 = (vt')^2 + (ct)^2 \qquad 3.1$$

Or:

$$t' = \frac{t}{\sqrt{1 - v^2/c^2}} \qquad t' = \gamma t \qquad 3.2$$

This calculation assumes that the height of the box does not change with speed. The dimensions of an object perpendicular to the direction of motion must be the same as in the rest frame of the object; otherwise there would be a contradiction. Imagine two identical boxes, like the box above, passing each other with a relative horizontal speed, with the top and bottom of each box passing right next to the other's. Suppose the top of each box leaves a scratch mark on the other box as they pass. If that scratch mark were beneath the top of the other box, then by the principle of special relativity each would leave a scratch mark below the other's scratch mark. This is a contradiction.

Equation (3.2) relates the amount of time required for light to move from the bottom to the top of the box in both inertial frames. But, relative to the rocket, if the amount of time that elapses in the box is called $t'$ then it is related to $t$ (the amount of time elapsed in the rocket) by this equation:

$$t' = t\sqrt{1 - \frac{v^2}{c^2}}$$

3.3

This time-slowing effect in relativity is called *time dilation*. It was derived using the constancy of the speed of light with the principle of special relativity, which requires that any clock undergo time dilation, not just clocks using light. But there are additional consequences to special relativity's two laws of physics, including the relative contraction of the length of an object in the direction of its motion. To see why this must be, consider another kind of box with four mirrors, on the top, bottom, left, and right. The box has a length and height of $2L$. In the middle of the box a flash bulb flashes and radiates light waves out to each mirror.

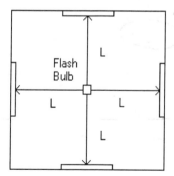

Imagine that the flash bulb goes off. Because the speed of light is constant, photons traveling in all four directions hit each mirror simultaneously after a time $t = L/c$, then reflect off the mirror and return to the flash bulb at twice this amount of time. The flash bulb must be hit from all four sides by the returning photons simultaneously. As before, suppose that a rocket travels at a constant speed $v$ relative to the box. In the rest frame of the rocket, the box travels with this same constant speed and its height is $2L$, just as it is in the rest frame of the box (by the previously mentioned scratch mark reasoning). But suppose, relative to the rocket, that the length of the box in the direction of its motion is not $2L$ but $2L'$. In the rest frame of the rocket the situation appears as in the diagram below:

*initial assumption*

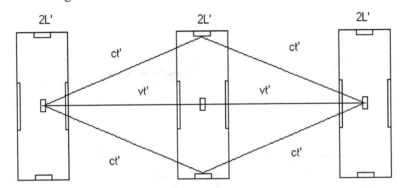

The time required for the photons of light to travel from the flash bulb to the top and bottom mirrors and back to the flash bulb again is $2t/\sqrt{1-v^2/c^2}$, where $t = L/c$. This follows from doubling the time in equation (3.2). It is also clear that the box moves a distance of $2vt'$. Because the speed of all photons is $3.00\times10^8$ meters/second for any rest frame, photons traveling in the same direction as the box must traverse $L'$ in the amount of time $L'/(c-v)$. And, by the same reasoning, photons traveling in the opposite direction of the box traverse $L'$ in the amount of time $L'/(c+v)$. All photons emitted from the flash bulb must return to the flash bulb at the same time in both inertial frames. Photons emitted in the direction of, or opposite to, the box's motion must travel out to their mirrors and bounce back to the flash bulb. Mathematically speaking, in the rocket's rest frame they will both return to the flash bulb at the same time because they both must travel a distance of $L'$ opposite to and in the direction of the motion of the box. But for these photons to get back to the flash bulb at the same time as the photons coming from the top and bottom mirrors, $2t/\sqrt{1-v^2/c^2}$, those two times must be equal. Setting those times equal gives:

$$\frac{2t}{\sqrt{1-v^2/c^2}} = \frac{L'}{c+v} + \frac{L'}{c-v}$$

3.4

Solving these equations by substituting $t = L/c$ into equation (3.4) and simplifying allows us to find $L'$:

$$L' = L\sqrt{1 - \frac{v^2}{c^2}} \qquad L' = \frac{L}{\gamma}$$

3.5

Clearly, then, an object of a given length contracts in the direction of its motion by the amount given in this equation, relative to the inertial frame in which the object travels. This length contraction is a requirement for the speed of light to be the same in all inertial frames. But, though the contraction is not an illusion, it is not absolute. In the rest frame of the box, the box has not contracted in length at all. Observers on two objects in relative motion each say that the other object contracts in the direction of its motion. Both are right. The contraction is relative as well as real. The term $\sqrt{1-v^2/c^2}$ is called the *contraction ratio*. This effect of relativity is called *length contraction*.

### Relativity of Simultaneity

Consider the box as above, but now imagine clocks at all four mirrors. When the bulb flashes all four clocks read zero.

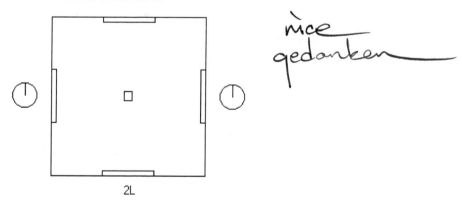

*nice*
*gedanken*

2L

When the photons reach the mirrors all four clocks will read $L/c$, the amount of time elapsed equaling the travel time of the photons from the flash bulb to the mirrors.

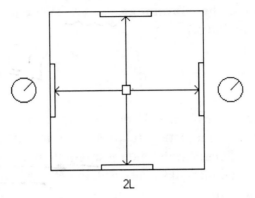

2L

Now, what is the character of this situation for the rocket traveling at a constant speed $v$, relative to the box? Consider the left and right clocks from the rockets' rest frame. From the flashbulb they are each stationed at a distance of $L'$, given in equation (3.5), but light coming from the flashbulb will reach the left-most clock first because of the constancy of the speed of light. The left side of the box is traveling toward its approaching light wave. Because the right side is moving away from its approaching light wave, its light is chasing after the right side of the box. Therefore, in the inertial frame in which the rocket is stationary, light reaches the left side of the box in $L'/(c+v)$ amount of time and the right side in $L'/(c-v)$ amount of time.

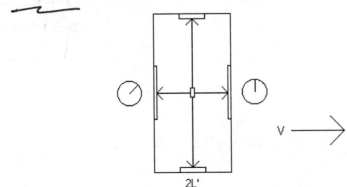

2L'

Because each clock reads $L/c$ the instant that light from the flash bulb strikes the mirror, the left and right clocks are not synchronized relative to the rocket. Rather, the left clock is ahead because the left side of the box is in an era of time ahead of the right side. But in the rest frame of the box, the clocks are synchronized. Are the clocks synchronized or not? This question is invalid because it presupposes absolute simultaneity and there is no absolute answer to it. And simultaneity is not absolute but relative. The lack of synchronization between the clocks from the rocket's rest frame is just as real and true as is their synchronization in the box's rest frame: neither situation is absolutely true, both are equally true in their respective inertial frames. Like length contraction or time dilation, relative simultaneity is necessary in order for the speed of light to be the same in every inertial frame. In the rocket's rest frame it is easy to calculate how much time will pass between the moment when the wave of light strikes the left mirror and when it strikes the right mirror:

$$\frac{L\sqrt{1-v^2/c^2}}{c-v} - \frac{L\sqrt{1-v^2/c^2}}{c+v} = \frac{2Lv/c^2}{\sqrt{1-v^2/c^2}}$$

3.6

And because the length of the box is $x = 2L$, the time difference between the front and back of the box in the rocket's rest frame is:

$$\tilde{\Delta t} = \frac{xv/c^2}{\sqrt{1-v^2/c^2}}$$

3.7

The major consequences of relativity can be summarized as follows: the rate at which time passes, the simultaneity of events, and the duration of time intervals are all relative in character. Distances are also relative and so, by extension, are volumes and areas. However, if the relative speed between two objects—such as the cars traveling north and south—is small in comparison to the speed of light, the relativistic effects of time dilation, length contraction, and lack of simultaneity are negligible. When this is true, all of the equations given above reduce to equations similar to those of classical physics.

$$\gamma = \frac{1}{\sqrt{1 - v^2/c^2}} \approx 1$$

$$t' = \frac{t}{\gamma} \approx t$$

$$L' = \frac{L}{\gamma} \approx L$$

$$\tilde{\Delta t} = \frac{xv}{c^2}\gamma \approx 0$$

3.8

Human experience and classical mechanics, then, are good approximations for small speeds.

Consider how the relativity of time and length apply to rockets traveling through space at speeds comparable to the speed of light. A rocket travels a distance $L$ at a speed $v$, relative to the earth, taking a total amount of time $L/v$. To observers on the earth time runs slow for the rocket, the astronauts on board the rocket age by the amount:

$$T_{trip} = \frac{L}{v}\sqrt{1 - v^2/c^2}$$

3.9

Equation (3.9) gives the amount of time that passes during the trip on board the rocket. Equation (3.5), however, gives the distance traveled from the astronauts point of view as $L'$ because the distance being traversed is itself moving and so is foreshortened by length contraction. In the rest frame of the astronauts they are at rest during the whole trip, their trip time is the foreshortened distance, $L'$, divided by the constant speed $v$ for a total trip time equaling the amount in equation (3.9). This is the same amount of time observers on earth see the astronauts age. Both parties agree that the astronauts age by the amount of time given in (3.9), but disagree about the reason why. For observers on earth, the trip time for the astronauts derives from the slowing of time on the rocket. But the astronauts say that it derives from the fact that the distance traveled is length-contracted and no time dilation is involved. Which is right? Does time really slow down for the astronauts or is the travel distance length-contracted? Once again, the question itself presupposes absolute space and time. Each answer is right relative to its own inertial frame, and there is no absolute truth for the situation. That neither absolute time nor absolute space exists has other important consequences, to be explored in subsequent chapters. But first the discoveries discussed above must be explored more thoroughly. It will be necessary to show that the speed of light is the same not only perpendicular to and in the direction of relative motion, but in all directions.

## Exercises

1.  Calculate the length of a rocket, one thousand kilometers in length in its rest frame, traveling at each of the following speeds: 10% $c$, 50% $c$, 87% $c$, 99% $c$.

    *995 km, 866, 493, 141*

2.  At what speed would a rocket have to travel so that for every thousand years of earth time, twenty years pass in ship time?

    $\gamma = 50$. $1 - v^2/c^2 = 1/2500$ $v = .9998c$

3.  Two events occur simultaneously, separated by a distance of ten kilometers, in an inertial frame. In another inertial frame traveling at 90% the speed of light, relative to the first rest frame and along the ten-kilometer line of the events, the events are not simultaneous. What is the time interval between the two events in this second inertial frame?

    *13 μs* *6.8872 × 10⁻⁵ s (69 μs)*

    $\gamma x v/c^2$. $(0.4359)(10\,km)(.90)/299792.458\,\frac{km}{s}$ *2.29*

4.  Show that the volume of an object in an inertial frame is $B' = B\sqrt{1 - v^2/c^2}$ where $B$ is the volume of the object in its rest frame. $\iiint dx'dy'dz' = \iiint \frac{dx}{\gamma}dydz$

5.  A spacecraft travels at 99.99 percent the speed of light from earth to the center of the galaxy, 30,000 light years away. During this trip, how much time elapses on the spacecraft?

    $\gamma_{9999} = 70.71$ *l contraction to: 424.25 light yrs.* *424.29 years*

6.  A rocket coasts from earth to a star in the Andromeda galaxy two million light years away at a speed of $(1 - 5.00 \times 10^{-13})c$. How long does the trip take relative to the rocket?

    $\gamma = 10^6$ $2 \times 10^6\,ly \rightarrow 2\,ly$

    *2 years*

# PART 2

## *Space and Time*

# CHAPTER 4

## *Transformations of Space and Time*

AS WILL BE SEEN LATER, the world of space and time consists not of a three-dimensional space moving through time, as classical thought assumed, but space and time together comprise a four-dimensional manifold. Events are points in this four-dimensional manifold, each located by four co-ordinates $(x, y, z, t)$.  Any event takes place at a location in space $(x, y, z)$ and at a particular time, $t$. But the coordinates of an event $(x, y, z, t)$ are specified for a given inertial frame. In a different frame the same event would have different coordinates $(x', y', z', t')$. Given a relation between two inertial frames, what will be the coordinates of an event $(x, y, z, t)$ in the other frame $(x', y', z', t')$? To simplify the calculations determining the transformation, it is customary to make the $x$ and $x'$ axes parallel, superimposed on each other. Let the constant relative speed between the two inertial frames be $v$, and let the origins of the two inertial frames coincide at the time $t = t' = 0$. At this time all primed coordinate axes are superimposed on their unprimed counterparts, but only at this time, and the two origins move further apart over time. Because of the relative motion, the origins move apart with constant speed $v$. By convention, at the time all axes coincide, time in both inertial frames is zero. To observers stationary in each inertial frame, clocks everywhere in that inertial frame are set at zero. In classical physics the transformation of events is described by the Galilean transformation:

$$x' = x - vt$$
$$y' = y$$
$$z' = z$$
$$t' = t$$

4.1

As discussed previously, this transformation is incompatible with Maxwell's equations and the two laws of special relativity. To replace (4.1) we must find the transformation that is compatible with special relativity. Here Einstein utilized the fact that the speed of light is the same in all inertial frames. When the coordinate axes of the two inertial frames coincide, their origins coincide and the x-axes are superimposed on each other. At that time a flash bulb located at their mutual origins flashes, emitting an expanding sphere of light. It does not matter in which inertial frame's origin the flash bulb is stationary. It does not have to be stationary at the origin of either inertial frame, but simply to be at their mutual origins at time $t = t' = 0$. Now at any time after the flash, the origins have moved apart by some distance because of the constant relative speed between the coordinate axes of the inertial frames. Because the speed of light is constant in both inertial frames, the origins in both inertial frames are always at the center of the expanding sphere of light. To repeat, both origins constantly move further and further away from each other and yet both origins are always at the center of the expanding sphere of light. Although this seems to conflict with human experience, there is no actual contradiction because the relative character of space and time, explored in the previous chapter, makes this a logical possibility. So the mathematical problem is to find the transformation from $(x, y, z, t)$ to $(x', y', z', t')$, such that the origins of both inertial frames are always at the center of the expanding sphere of light. Because the radius of the expanding sphere of light is $ct$ in the unprimed inertial frame and $ct'$ in the primed inertial frame, both of these equations are true:

$$x^2 + y^2 + z^2 = c^2 t^2$$
$$x'^2 + y'^2 + z'^2 = c^2 t'^2 \qquad c' \equiv c$$

4.2

Now, consider a fixed $x$-value in the unprimed inertial frame. Its $x'$-value in the primed inertial frame should be proportional to $x - vt$. In the primed inertial frame, the unprimed inertial frame is traveling in the opposite direction. By the principle of special relativity the laws of physics, which include transformation laws, must be the same in both frames. For a fixed $x'$-value, then, the corresponding $x$-value should be proportional to $x' + vt'$. Also, by the principle of special relativity, the constant of proportionality should be the same. So two of the transformation equations should be of the form

$$x' = \gamma(x - vt)$$
$$x = \gamma(x' + vt')$$

4.3

where $\gamma$ is a function of $v$ alone and $v$ is constant. Solving for $t'$ gives us:

$$t' = \frac{1}{v}\left(\frac{x}{\gamma} - x'\right)$$

4.4

Substituting the first equation from (4.3) into (4.4), the result simplifies to:

$$t' = \gamma\left[t + \frac{x}{v}\left(\frac{1}{\gamma^2} - 1\right)\right]$$

4.5

Again, substituting the first equation from (4.3) and equation (4.5) into the primed quantities of equation (4.2) yields an equation with no primed quantities. (Because spatial dimensions perpendicular to the direction of motion are not affected by motion, $y'=y$ and $z'=z$, as demonstrated in the previous chapter). Only unprimed quantities remain, allowing the calculation of $\gamma$.

$$x^2\left[\gamma^2 - \frac{c^2\gamma^2}{v^2}\left(\frac{1}{\gamma^2} - 1\right)^2\right] - 2xt\gamma^2\left[v + \frac{c^2}{v}\left(\frac{1}{\gamma^2} - 1\right)\right] + y^2 + z^2 = t^2\gamma^2\left(c^2 - v^2\right)$$

4.6

Now this equation must match the unprimed equation in (4.2) and, by matching coefficients between (4.2) and (4.6), $\gamma$ must be related to $v$ according to (4.7).

$$\left[\gamma^2 - \frac{c^2\gamma^2}{v^2}\left(\frac{1}{\gamma^2}-1\right)^2\right]=1$$

$$\left[2v\gamma^2 + \frac{2c^2\gamma^2}{v}\left(\frac{1}{\gamma^2}-1\right)\right]=0$$

$$\gamma^2(c^2-v^2)=c^2$$

4.7

The first equation of (4.7) is a polynomial of degree four with the four roots $\pm1$ and $\pm1/\sqrt{1-v^2/c^2}$. The remaining two equations each have the latter two roots. Because $\gamma$ must satisfy all three equations, $\pm1$ is ruled out. And as the transformation equations must approximate the Galilean transformations when the speed is small in comparison to light, $v \ll c$, $\gamma$ must be the positive value of the remaining two options. Hence:

$$\gamma = \frac{1}{\sqrt{1-v^2/c^2}}$$

4.8

Substituting this into (4.5), the result is $t' = \gamma(t - xv/c^2)$. The complete transformations are now calculated:

$$x' = \gamma\,(x - vt) = \frac{x - vt}{\sqrt{1-v^2/c^2}}$$

$$y' = y$$

$$z' = z$$

$$t' = \gamma\left(t - \frac{xv}{c^2}\right) = \frac{t - xv/c^2}{\sqrt{1-v^2/c^2}}$$

4.9

These equations are called the *Lorentz transformations,* after H. A. Lorentz, who independently studied their mathematical properties. The inverse transformations are partly found from (4.3) and (4.8). Solving for $t$ in the first equation of (4.3), we get:

$$t = \frac{1}{v}\left(x - \frac{x'}{\gamma}\right)$$

4.10

Substituting the latter equation of (4.3) and equation (4.8) into (4.10) and simplifying the result gives $t = \gamma(t' + x'v/c^2)$. The complete inverses are then:

$$x = \gamma\,(x' + vt') = \frac{x' \oplus vt'}{\sqrt{1 - v^2/c^2}}$$

$$y = y'$$

$$z = z'$$

$$t = \gamma\,(t' + x'v/c^2) = \frac{t' \oplus x'v/c^2}{\sqrt{1 - v^2/c^2}}$$

4.11

These equations hold not only for events denoting the expanding sphere of light but for all events, because in any $z$-$y$ plane all events are simultaneous. Thus an event constituting the expanding sphere of light is simultaneous with all other events in any $z$-$y$ plane. These inverse Lorentz transformations could also be obtained by inverting the Lorentz transformations or by letting $v$ become $-v$ and swapping the primed and unprimed quantities in accordance with the principle of special relativity. A geometric feel for these equations can be obtained by visualizing the coordinate axes for the two inertial frames and remembering the length contraction effect:

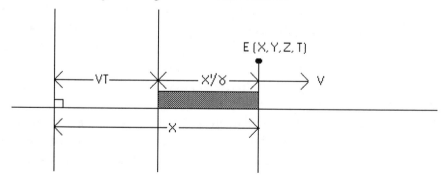

Consider the coordinate axes of two inertial frames. An event occurs at location $(x, y, z, t)$. In the unprimed inertial frame the distance between the origin of the primed inertial frame and the $x$-coordinate of the event is $x - vt$. If an observer in the unprimed inertial frame puts a mark in the primed inertial frame ($x$-coordinate) at the location of the event, an observer in the primed inertial frame measures the $x$-distance from its origin to the event to be $\gamma$ times $(x - vt)$ because of length contraction. Therefore the first equation of (4.9) is true by construction, and, as before, the first equation of (4.11) by the principle of special relativity. Inverting these two equations gives the last equations of (4.9) and (4.11). The other components are $y' = y$ and $z' = z$, as before. Derivations for length contraction and time dilation (in the previous chapter), as well as differences in simultaneity, allowed the speed of light to be constant. But this calculation only considered two directions: that perpendicular to and that parallel with the direction of relative motion. With the transformations given above, the constancy of the speed of light follows for *all* directions in space, not simply those perpendicular to and parallel with relative motion.

The Lorentz transformations allow events in one inertial frame to be transformed to another and provide us with time and place for events in each frame. But they do not provide the time and place at which these events are *observed* in the frame, because they do not take into account travel time of light. Observers in the same inertial frame do not necessarily see events at the moment they take place, because it takes time for light from those events to travel to the location of each observer. For example, an event occurring at $(x, 0, 0, 0)$ will not be seen by an observer at the origin until $x/c$ amount of time (travel time from the event time to the origin) elapses in that inertial frame. Stated differently, although an event occurs at $(x, 0, 0, 0)$, its real time and place in this inertial frame, an observer stationed at the origin of this frame sees this event at a later time $x/c$. Lorentz transformations transform the real locations and times of events, between inertial frames, but does not account for the travel time of light. To do this generally: find the spatial distance between the event and observer anywhere in the inertial frame and divide by the speed of light.

Further, the Lorentz transformations assume that the $x$ and $x'$ axes coincide. But the axes do not necessarily coincide in all cases, nor must the components be in rectangular Cartesian coordinates. For example, the spatial coordinates could exist in cylindrical coordinates, spherical coordinates, or some other coordinate system. In these other cases the transformations become more complex. In general, a Lorentz transformation is any transformation from $(w, x, y, z)$ to $(x'_1, x'_2, x'_3, x'_4)$ meeting the following requirement:

$$w^2 - x^2 - y^2 - z^2 = \sum_j \sum_i N_{ij} x'_j x'_i$$

4.12

Here the fourth coordinate is the time axis $w = ct$. But when changing some coordinates from rectangular coordinates to, for instance, cylindrical coordinates, the primed quantities are just as real as the unprimed quantities. The fact that $t'$, in the transformations of (4.9), is just as real as $t$ led Einstein to discover relativity. Measurements and coordinates in one inertial frame are no less correct than measurements and coordinates in another inertial frame. The Lorentz transformations are used extensively in relativity to solve problems and it is now useful to look at some examples.

## Examples of the Uses of Lorentz Transformations

Consider five stars scattered through space. Relative to a given inertial frame, those stars explode as supernovas at different times and places. Let $Y$ = one year and $L$ = one light year. Because $c$ is the speed of light, $cY = L$. The five supernova events are given below:

$$
\begin{array}{llllll}
A = ( & 0, & 2L, & 3L, & 3Y & ) \\
B = ( & -6L, & -4L, & 7L, & 6Y & ) \\
C = ( & 3L, & 0, & 5L, & 9Y & ) \\
D = ( & 0, & -L, & 8L, & 12Y & ) \\
E = ( & 18L, & -3L, & -10L, & 15Y & )
\end{array}
$$

In another inertial frame, moving at $(4/5)c$ relative to this one, at what places and times do the supernova explosions occur? In this problem the previous standard assumptions (coincidence of the $x$-axes of the inertial frames, and so on) apply. One way to expedite the calculation is to write the Lorentz transformation in matrix form. This is called the *Lorentz matrix*:

*Lorentz Matrix*

$$\begin{bmatrix} x' \\ y' \\ z' \\ t' \end{bmatrix} = \begin{bmatrix} \gamma & 0 & 0 & -v\gamma \\ 0 & 1 & 0 & 0 \\ 0 & 0 & 1 & 0 \\ -v\gamma/c^2 & 0 & 0 & \gamma \end{bmatrix} \begin{bmatrix} x \\ y \\ z \\ t \end{bmatrix}$$

4.13

Now, with $v = (4/5)c$, the matrix becomes:

$$\begin{bmatrix} x' \\ y' \\ z' \\ t' \end{bmatrix} = \begin{bmatrix} 5/3 & 0 & 0 & -4c/3 \\ 0 & 1 & 0 & 0 \\ 0 & 0 & 1 & 0 \\ -4/3c & 0 & 0 & 5/3 \end{bmatrix} \begin{bmatrix} x \\ y \\ z \\ t \end{bmatrix}$$

4.14

And substituting $(x, y, z, t) = (0L, 2L, 3L, 3Y)$ for supernova $A$ gives $(x', y', z', t') = (-4L, 2L, 3L, 5Y)$. Applying the same process for the remaining supernovas and collecting the results gives us:

$$
\begin{array}{lrrrrl}
A = ( & -4L, & 2L, & 3L, & 5Y & ) \\
B = ( & -18L, & -4L, & 7L, & 18Y & ) \\
C = ( & -7L, & 0, & 5L, & 11Y & ) \\
D = ( & -16L, & -L, & 8L, & 20Y & ) \\
E = ( & 10L, & -3L, & -10L, & Y & )
\end{array}
$$

Notice that in the unprimed inertial frame the supernova explosions occur in the order $A, B, C, D, E$ and in the primed inertial frame the supernova explosions occur in the order: $E, A, C, B, D$. As before, in what order do the supernova explosions actually occur? The question is invalid because it presupposes that time is absolute, as if asking the political affiliation of the number eight. Just as numbers have no political affiliations, there is no actual temporal ordering of the supernovas. The order of explosions in the primed inertial frame is just as true as in the unprimed frame. Likewise, there is no

*Betelgeuse has already super-novaed ... not in "this IRF," but in another.*

actual time duration between the explosions. In the unprimed inertial frame the supernova $B$ occurs three years after supernova $A$, and in the primed frame supernova $B$ occurs 13 years after supernova $A$ and both durations are equally correct. The relativity of simultaneity can be seen here as well: There is no fixed truth as to whether supernova $E$ comes before or after $A$.

The Lorentz transformations can also be used to calculate many other things. The speed of an object in one inertial frame, for instance, can be calculated by its speed in another inertial frame. Normally an object's velocity is calculated by noting two position vectors at different times and dividing the difference of the vectors by the time difference. This assumes the velocity of the object is constant; otherwise it is an average velocity. Consider a rocket that travels at a constant velocity and detonates two explosions along its straight-line path. The two explosion events are Event One = $(0, 2L, 0, 0)$ and Event Two = $(0, 5L, 0, 12Y)$ in one inertial frame. Consider another inertial frame traveling at a speed of three-fifths the speed of light relative to the first inertial frame, and assume that the $x$-axes coincide. Now calculate the rocket's speed in each inertial frame. As before, $c$ is the speed of light, L is one light year, and Y is one year. Clearly $cY=L$, as in the previous example. In the first inertial frame the speed of the object is:

$$u = \frac{\sqrt{(x_2 - x_1)^2 + (y_2 - y_1)^2 + (z_2 - z_1)^2}}{t_2 - t_1} = \frac{\sqrt{(5L - 2L)^2}}{(12Y - 0)} = \frac{1}{4}c$$

Using the Lorentz transformation on Event 1 and Event 2, with $v = (3/5)c$, we get:

$$( \quad\quad 0, \quad 2L, \quad 0, \quad 0 \quad )$$
$$( \quad -9L, \quad 5L, \quad 0, \quad 15Y \quad )$$

And calculating the speed in the second inertial frame is simple:

$$u' = \frac{\sqrt{(x_2' - x_1')^2 + (y_2' - y_1')^2 + (z_2' - z_1')^2}}{t_2' - t_1'} = \frac{\sqrt{(-9L - 0)^2 + (5L - 2L)^2 + (0 - 0)^2}}{(15Y - 0)} = c\sqrt{\frac{2}{5}}$$

Well, perhaps it already has in this frame inertial, the light not yet having reached up.

## Changes in Relative Velocity Between Inertial Frames

In classical physics velocities can simply be added. A rocket traveling at a speed $v$ by the earth emits another object, traveling at speed $w$ relative to the rocket. The velocity of the second object is $v+w$ relative to the earth. In relativity, this velocity addition applies only as a very good approximation for speeds much smaller than the speed of light. Consider an object moving in the $x$-direction only, with a constant speed. In a given inertial frame its velocity is:

$$u_x = \frac{x_2 - x_1}{t_2 - t_1}$$

4.15

The speed in another inertial frame can be found by applying Lorentz transformations to the four variables in the right-hand side of (4.15).

$$u'_x = \frac{x'_2 - x'_1}{t'_2 - t'_1} = \frac{\gamma(x_2 - vt_2) - \gamma(x_1 - vt_1)}{\gamma\left(t_2 - \frac{x_2 v}{c^2}\right) - \gamma\left(t_1 - \frac{x_1 v}{c^2}\right)} = \frac{(x_2 - x_1) - v(t_2 - t_1)}{(t_2 - t_1) - \frac{v}{c^2}(x_2 - x_1)}$$

4.16

After multiplying top and bottom by ~~the differences~~ *the inverse of* the differences between the two times and substituting (4.15) into (4.16), the result is:

$$u'_x = \frac{u_x - v}{1 - \frac{u_x v}{c^2}}$$

4.17

This equation holds true for $x$-velocity components even if $y$ and $z$ velocity components exist. The $y$ and $z$ velocity components are calculated in the same manner:

$$u_y = \frac{y_2 - y_1}{t_2 - t_1}$$

$$u'_y = \frac{y'_2 - y'_1}{t'_2 - t'_1} = \frac{y_2 - y_1}{\gamma\left(t_2 - \frac{x_2 v}{c^2}\right) - \gamma\left(t_1 - \frac{x_1 v}{c^2}\right)}$$

$$u'_y = \frac{(y_2 - y_1)/(t_2 - t_1)}{\gamma\left[1 - \frac{v}{c^2}\left(\frac{x_2 - x_1}{t_2 - t_1}\right)\right]} = \frac{u_y\sqrt{1 - \frac{v^2}{c^2}}}{1 - \frac{u_x v}{c^2}}$$

4.18

The $z$-component calculates to the same form as the $y$-component:

$$u'_z = \frac{u_z\sqrt{1 - \frac{v^2}{c^2}}}{1 - \frac{u_x v}{c^2}}$$

4.19

These velocities were computed for cases of constant speed. For variable speed, this method calculates the average velocity.

For non-constant velocities, a different method can be employed. Differentiating the first and fourth equations of (4.9) with respect to $t$ gives us:

$$\frac{dx'}{dt} = \gamma\left(\frac{dx}{dt} - v\right)$$

$$\frac{dt'}{dt} = \gamma\left(1 - \frac{v}{c^2}\frac{dx}{dt}\right)$$

4.20

Letting $u_x = dx/dt$ and noting that $dx'/dt' = (dx'/dt)(dt/dt')$ by the chain rule, the result is:

$$u'_x = \frac{dx'}{dt'} = \gamma(u_x - v)\frac{1}{\gamma\left(1 - \frac{u_x v}{c^2}\right)} = \frac{u_x - v}{1 - \frac{u_x v}{c^2}}$$

4.21

We see that this method gives the same equation as in (4.17). Remember that these equations describe how an object with varying $x$-speed $u_x(t)$ transforms to a different inertial frame.

This should not be confused with the case of a changing inertial frame. That case is handled by general relativity. Transformations of acceleration can be derived in a straightforward manner. Let $a_x = du_x/dt$ and use the chain rule to compute the $x$-component of the acceleration in the primed inertial frame, with the help of (4.20).

$$a'_x = \frac{du'_x}{dt'} = \frac{dt}{dt'}\frac{du'_x}{dt} = \frac{dt}{dt'}\left[\frac{\left(1 - \frac{u_x v}{c^2}\right)\frac{du_x}{dt} + (u_x - v)\frac{v}{c^2}\frac{du_x}{dt}}{\left(1 - \frac{u_x v}{c^2}\right)^2}\right]$$

$$a'_x = a_x\frac{\left(1 - \frac{v^2}{c^2}\right)^{3/2}}{\left(1 - \frac{u_x v}{c^2}\right)^3} = a_x\frac{\gamma^{-3}}{\left(1 - \frac{u_x v}{c^2}\right)^3} = \frac{a_x}{\left(\gamma - \frac{\partial u_x v}{c^2}\right)^3}$$

4.22

Because of symmetry, the $y$ and $z$ components of acceleration have the same transform form. Let $a_y = du_y/dt$. The $y$-acceleration in another inertial frame is given by:

$$a'_y = \frac{du'_y}{dt'} = \frac{dt}{dt'}\frac{du'_y}{dt} = \frac{dt}{dt'}\frac{d}{dt}\left[\frac{u_y}{\gamma\left(1-\frac{u_x v}{c^2}\right)}\right]$$

$$a'_y = \frac{a_y}{\gamma^2\left(1-\frac{u_x v}{c^2}\right)^2} + \frac{a_x v u_y}{\gamma^2 c^2\left(1-\frac{u_x v}{c^2}\right)^3}$$

4.23

The equation for the $z$-component transformation is identical to the equation for the $y$-component in (4.23), except that the acceleration and velocity components have subscript $z$. Inverses for all these velocity and acceleration transformations can be calculated by using the inverse Lorentz transformations, or by replacing $v$ with $-v$ and then swapping the primed quantities with unprimed quantities. Doing this for the velocity components gives:

$$u_x = \frac{u'_x + v}{1 + \frac{u'_x v}{c^2}}$$

$$u_y = \frac{u'_y\sqrt{1-\frac{v^2}{c^2}}}{1 + \frac{u'_x v}{c^2}}$$

$$u_z = \frac{u'_z\sqrt{1-\frac{v^2}{c^2}}}{1 + \frac{u'_x v}{c^2}}$$

4.24

And the inverse acceleration transformations are:

$$a_x = a_x' \frac{\left(1 - \dfrac{v^2}{c^2}\right)^{3/2}}{\left(1 + \dfrac{u_x' v}{c^2}\right)^3}$$

$$a_y = \frac{a_y'}{\gamma^2 \left(1 + \dfrac{u_x' v}{c^2}\right)^2} - \frac{a_x' v u_y'}{\gamma^2 c^2 \left(1 + \dfrac{u_x' v}{c^2}\right)^3}$$

$$a_z = \frac{a_z'}{\gamma^2 \left(1 + \dfrac{u_x' v}{c^2}\right)^2} - \frac{a_x' v u_z'}{\gamma^2 c^2 \left(1 + \dfrac{u_x' v}{c^2}\right)^3}$$

4.25

With these we can calculate some examples. For instance, calculate the $y$ acceleration in the primed inertial frame if, in the unprimed inertial frame, only $y$-component motions exist. What is the transformation equation covering this case? In equation (4.23), if $x$-acceleration and $x$-velocity are both zero, then the equation for $y$-component acceleration reduces to:

$$a_y' = a_y \left(1 - \frac{v^2}{c^2}\right)$$

4.26

$$\forall (a_x, v_x) = 0 \; ; \quad a_y' = a_y / \gamma^2$$

## Further ~~Calculations of Relativistic Transformations~~

Time dilation, length contraction, and lack of absolute simultaneity can be derived here from the Lorentz transformation. Consider an interval of time in an inertial frame $t_2 - t_1$ at any location $(x_0, y_0, z_0)$. This interval is denoted by two events, $(x_0, y_0, z_0, t_1)$ and $(x_0, y_0, z_0, t_2)$. In another inertial frame those events are:

$$(\gamma(x_0 - vt_1), y_0, z_0, \gamma(t_1 - x_0 v/c^2))$$
$$(\gamma(x_0 - vt_2), y_0, z_0, \gamma(t_2 - x_0 v/c^2))$$

The interval of time in the other inertial frame is the difference between the time components:

$$t_2' - t_1' = \gamma(t_2 - x_0 v/c^2) - \gamma(t_1 - x_0 v/c^2) = \gamma(t_2 - t_1)$$ 

4.27

Or:

$$\Delta t' = \gamma \Delta t = \frac{\Delta t}{\sqrt{1 - v^2/c^2}}$$

4.28

The interval of time is greater in the new inertial frame by the same amount calculated in the previous chapter.

Length contraction can be calculated in a variety of ways. Consider a rod of length $L$, with one end of the rod next to the origin in the unprimed inertial frame.

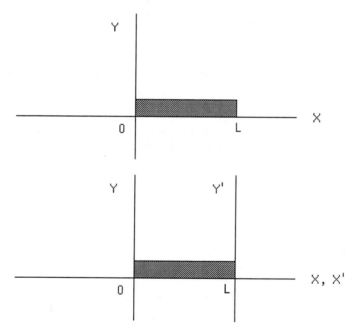

One way to determine the length of the rod is by using events. At time $t = 0$ the origins of both inertial frames coincide and, as usual, the x-axes are parallel with relative velocity $v$ along the $x$-axis. At the time the origins coincide an explosion takes place at the origin. That event is denoted by $(0,0,0,0)$ in the unprimed system. The primed inertial frame is traveling at a constant speed $v$. After an amount of time $L/v$ in the unprimed inertial frame, the origin of the primed inertial frame is at the other end of the rod. At this time another explosion event occurs there, denoted by $(L, 0, 0, L/v)$. It is easy to calculate the length of the rod in the unprimed system by using the events $(0, 0, 0, 0)$ and $(L, 0, 0, L/v)$. The time taken to cross the rod is simply the difference of the two event times, and $L$ equals this time difference multiplied by the speed $v$: $(L/v - 0)v = L$. Now, transform these two events to the primed inertial frame and use the same procedure to calculate length. The events in the primed frame are $(0, 0, 0, 0)$ and $(0, 0, 0, \gamma[L/v - Lv/c^2])$. The length of the rod in the primed inertial system is $(\gamma[L/v - Lv/c^2] - 0)v$, which simplifies to:

$$L' = \gamma\left(\frac{L}{v} - \frac{Lv}{c^2}\right)v = \gamma\left(L - L\frac{v^2}{c^2}\right) = L\sqrt{1 - \frac{v^2}{c^2}}$$

4.29

This is the same equation we found in the last chapter. Observers in one inertial frame measure the rod as length $L$ while observers in another inertial frame measures the rod as length $L'$ because these are actual lengths of the rod, in each inertial frame, even if the rod is unmeasured in those inertial frames.

The lack of absolute simultaneity is also a feature of the Lorentz transformations. While the supernova example given earlier shows this, we can calculate it more generally. Consider two explosions in the unprimed system:

$$(\qquad 0, \quad 0, \quad 0, \quad 0 \qquad)$$
$$(\qquad x, \quad 0, \quad 0, \quad 0 \qquad)$$

In the unprimed system these two explosions occur at the same time, *i.e.* at time zero. Applying Lorentz transformations to them gives:

$$( \qquad 0, \quad 0, \quad 0, \quad 0 \qquad )$$
$$( \qquad \gamma x, \quad 0, \quad 0, -\gamma x v / c^2 \qquad ) \qquad 4.30$$

Thus the explosions are not simultaneous in the primed system. The first explosion occurs before time zero, at $\gamma x$ on the $x$-axis, at time $-\gamma x v / c^2$; the second explosion occurs at the origin at time zero. The relativity of simultaneity is part of the Lorentz transformations.

For a more complicated example of how motion transforms, consider another example that uses Lorentz transformations to calculate the angle and velocity vector of an object. An object travels at a constant speed $u$ from the origin to a point in the $x$-$z$ plane, in an amount of time $t_1$. The $y$-coordinate is always zero.

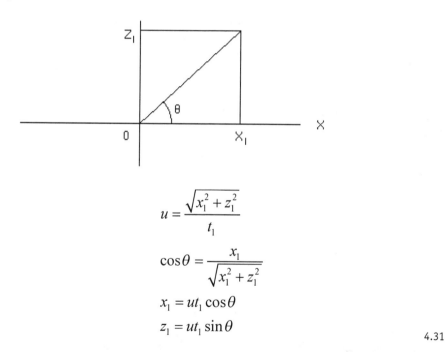

$$u = \frac{\sqrt{x_1^2 + z_1^2}}{t_1}$$

$$\cos\theta = \frac{x_1}{\sqrt{x_1^2 + z_1^2}}$$

$$x_1 = ut_1 \cos\theta$$

$$z_1 = ut_1 \sin\theta \qquad 4.31$$

This motion is denoted by two events, $(0, 0, 0, 0)$ and $(x_1, 0, z_1, t_1)$. Applying Lorentz transformations to these two events gives $(0,0,0,0)$ for the first event. The second event is calculated in (4.32):

$$x_1' = \gamma(x_1 - vt_1) = \gamma(ut_1\cos\theta - vt_1)$$
$$y_1' = y_1 = 0$$
$$z_1' = z_1 = ut_1\sin\theta$$
$$t_1' = \gamma\left(t_1 - \frac{x_1 v}{c^2}\right) = \gamma\left(t_1 - \frac{vut_1\cos\theta}{c^2}\right)$$

4.32

The speed of the object in the primed system, $u'$, is:

$$u' = \frac{\sqrt{x_1'^2 + z_1'^2}}{t_1'} = \frac{\sqrt{\gamma^2 t_1^2 (u\cos\theta - v)^2 + u^2 t_1^2 \sin^2\theta}}{t_1\gamma\left(1 - \frac{uv}{c^2}\cos\theta\right)}$$

$$u' = \frac{\sqrt{(u\cos\theta - v)^2 + u^2\left(1 - \frac{v^2}{c^2}\right)\sin^2\theta}}{\left(1 - \frac{uv}{c^2}\cos\theta\right)}$$

4.33

The inclination angle of the velocity vector in the primed system can be calculated as follows:

$$\tan\theta = \frac{z_1}{x_1} = \frac{ut_1\sin\theta}{ut_1\cos\theta}$$

$$\tan\theta' = \frac{z_1'}{x_1'} = \frac{ut_1\sin\theta}{\gamma(ut_1\cos\theta - vt_1)}$$

$$\tan\theta' = \frac{u\sin\theta}{\gamma(u\cos\theta - v)}$$

4.34

This example demonstrates the power of the Lorentz transformation. Further, if $u = c$ is substituted into equation (4.33), it reduces to $u' = c$. This is expected because the speed of light is the same in all inertial frames. If $u = c$ is substituted into the equation for (4.34), the result is:

$$\tan \theta' = \frac{\sin \theta}{\gamma \left( \cos \theta - \dfrac{v}{c} \right)}$$

4.35

Although the speed of light is the same in all inertial frames, the angle along which a given photon travels is relative to inertial frames. A consequence of this is that objects look different from their shapes. An object traveling by an observer contracts in the direction of its motion, but the observer will see it as rotated. Someone on a starship traveling through a uniformly distributed star field at a large fraction of the speed of light will observe the stars clustering toward the center of the forward view. Finally, consider a light source traveling through space, emitting photons equally in all directions in its rest frame. In any other inertial frame, the photons are preferentially emitted in the direction of motion of the source.

Events are described by vectors, $(x, y, z, t)$. But to understand the motion of an object along a path in space we must consider more than one or two events. Let us say that a spacecraft travels through space on a particular path in one inertial frame, $X(t) = (x(t), y(t), z(t), t)$. This path is characterized by an infinite number of events. A natural question arises: what is the path in a different inertial frame, $X'(t') = (x'(t'), y'(t'), z'(t'), t')$? One way to calculate this is to break up the path into a finite number of events and transform each event through the Lorentz transformation. Such a numerical procedure will yield an approximate broken line solution. In some situations it is possible to find an algebraic solution to $X'(t')$. The three-step method given below will work if it is possible to find the algebraic inverse to a certain equation:

*Step One.* Apply a Lorentz transformation to the path $X(t)$ to get:

$$\overline{X'}(t) = \begin{bmatrix} x'(t) \\ y'(t) \\ z'(t) \\ t'(t) \end{bmatrix} = L \begin{bmatrix} x(t) \\ y(t) \\ z(t) \\ t \end{bmatrix} = \begin{bmatrix} \gamma(x(t) - vt) \\ y(t) \\ z(t) \\ \gamma\left(t - x(t)v/c^2\right) \end{bmatrix}$$

4.36

This yields the new path, in the primed inertial frame, as a function of time in the unprimed inertial frame. The time coordinate function has the equation we want to invert.

$$t'(t) = \gamma \left( t - \frac{x(t)v}{c^2} \right) = g(t)$$

4.37

The equation $t' = g(t)$ is some function of $t$. If this function can be inverted, then the second step is to invert it.

*Step Two.* Find the inverse:

$$t = g^{-1}(t')$$

4.38

*Step Three.* Substitute equation (4.38) into the equations in (4.36), giving the final result:

$$\overline{X}'(t') = \begin{bmatrix} x'(g^{-1}(t')) \\ y'(g^{-1}(t')) \\ z'(g^{-1}(t')) \\ t' \end{bmatrix}$$

4.39

Thus the path in the primed inertial frame is $\boldsymbol{X}'(t') = (x'(t'), y'(t'), z'(t'), t')$. For an example of this procedure, consider an object traveling on the path given in (4.40), where the two $k$'s are constants. Suppose that the path in (4.40) applies only as long as the speed is less than the speed of light.

$$\overline{X}(t) = \begin{bmatrix} 0 \\ k_1\sqrt{t/t_0} \\ k_2(t/t_0)^2 \\ t \end{bmatrix}$$

4.40

To calculate the path of the object in another inertial frame traveling with constant speed $v$, first apply the Lorentz transformation to the path:

$$\overline{X}'(t) = \begin{bmatrix} \gamma(0-vt) \\ k_1\sqrt{t/t_0} \\ k_2(t/t_0)^2 \\ \gamma(t-0) \end{bmatrix} = \begin{bmatrix} -\gamma vt \\ k_1\sqrt{t/t_0} \\ k_2(t/t_0)^2 \\ \gamma t \end{bmatrix} = \begin{bmatrix} x'(t) \\ y'(t) \\ z'(t) \\ t'(t) \end{bmatrix}$$

4.41

The time coordinates are related by $t' = \gamma t$, and this equation can be inverted $t = t'/\gamma$. Next, substitute this value for $t$ into (4.41) to get the answer:

$$\overline{X}'(t') = \begin{bmatrix} -\gamma vt'/\gamma \\ k_1\sqrt{t'/\gamma t_0} \\ k_2(t'/\gamma t_0)^2 \\ t' \end{bmatrix} = \begin{bmatrix} -vt' \\ k_1\sqrt{(t'/t_0)}\sqrt{(1-v^2/c^2)} \\ k_2(t'/t_0)^2(1-v^2/c^2) \\ t' \end{bmatrix}$$

## Exercises

1.  Two starships depart from a space station and travel at forty percent of the speed of light in opposite directions. How fast are the starships moving relative to each other and to the space station?

2.  A spaceship traveling away from earth at sixty percent of the speed of light emits a projectile that travels toward the earth at forty percent of the speed of light, relative to the spaceship. How fast does the projectile move relative to the earth?

3.  Two rockets travel in opposite directions away from the earth at speeds very near that of light: $c-\delta_1$ and $c-\delta_2$. Each rocket is traveling at the speed $c-\delta_{12}$ relative to the other. Find $\delta_{12}$ as approximate functions of $\delta_1$ and $\delta_2$.

4.  For Problem Three, each rocket has a gamma factor of $\gamma_1$ and $\gamma_2$ relative to the earth. If each rocket has a gamma factor of $\gamma_{12}$ relative to the other, what is the approximate relationship between $\gamma_{12}$ and $\gamma_1$ and $\gamma_2$?

5.  Light travels at a speed of $c/n$ in a medium, where $n$ is the index of refraction of

the medium. Fizeau found experimentally that if a tank filled with a medium is moving at a speed $v \ll c$, that light inside the medium (traveling in the same direction as the medium) moves with a speed given by the equation below. Derive this equation using special relativity:

$$\frac{c}{n} + v\left(1 - \frac{1}{n^2}\right)$$

6. In one inertial frame an object has speed $u$ in the $y$-direction only. Relative to another inertial frame traveling at speed $v$ along the $x$-axis of the first, what is the speed of the object?

7. Show that $L(v)L(-v) = I$

8. Show that:

$$L(v)L(w) = L\left[\begin{array}{c} v + w \\ \hline 1 + \dfrac{vw}{c^2} \end{array}\right]$$

9. In an inertial frame, the path of a meteor through space is given by the equation below. Find the path of the meteor in another inertial frame and calculate its velocity in that frame.

$$\overline{X}(t) = (u_x t + x_0, u_y t + y_0, u_z t + z_0)$$

10. The path of a particle in an inertial frame is given by the equation below. Calculate its path in another inertial frame and then calculate the speed in both inertial frames if $v_0 = c$. Explain your answer.

$$\overline{X}(t) = [0, r_0 \sin(v_0 t / r_0), r_0 \cos(v_0 t / r_0), t]$$

# CHAPTER 5

# *The Relativistic Doppler Effect and the Twin Paradox*

THE WAVES EMITTED BY OBJECTS such as water, sound, or light waves, are subject to the Doppler effect. If the source of the waves is moving relative to the receiver, the waves undergo a Doppler shift for the receiver: a stretching or shrinking of wavelengths due to the relative motion between source and receiver.

## *The Classical Doppler Effect*

Using Galilean transformations, with source speed $v$, wave speed $c$, and angle $\theta$, it is a straightforward process to calculate changes in wavelengths. Consider a wave source located at the origin of a Galilean inertial frame and a receiver stationed at an arbitrary fixed point. Wave crests hit the receiver at a frequency $\omega$, where $\omega$ is the frequency of the wave source, because the receiver and the source are both stationary in the same inertial frame. The wave crests travel at speed $c$. Now suppose the receiver travels directly toward the source with a speed $v$. In this case wave crests hit the receiver with a higher frequency because the receiver is moving toward the source and running headlong into the oncoming wave crests. Each wave crest now hits the receiver with a speed of $c+v$, and to the receiver their frequency is

$$\omega' = \omega\left(1+\frac{v}{c}\right)$$

5.1

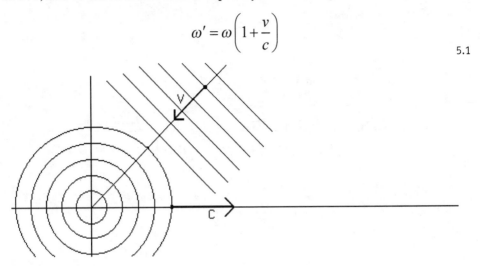

where $\omega$ is the frequency of the wave source in the rest frame of the source. If the receiver moves with speed $v$ directly away from the source, it travels in the same direction as the waves and is struck by wave fronts at the frequency of:

$$\omega' = \omega\left(1-\frac{v}{c}\right)$$

5.2

This gives us two special cases of the Doppler effect: directly toward or directly away from a wave source. What if the receiver is traveling obliquely to the source? Consider the case where the receiver travels at a constant speed $v$ parallel to the $x$-axis, in the negative $x$-direction, at an angle $\theta$ to the source.

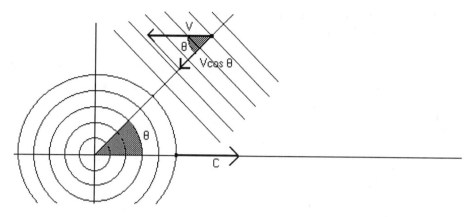

Now the receiver has a component velocity, $v\cos\theta$, headed directly toward the wave source, and it will be struck by the oncoming wave crests with the same frequency as if it were traveling directly to the wave source with a speed $v'$, where $v' = v\cos\theta$. We can substitute this for $v$ in equation (5.1), to get:

$$\omega' = \omega\left(1 + \frac{v}{c}\cos\theta\right)$$

5.3

In this equation the velocity sign is reversed because speed $v$ is in the negative $x$-direction. To align the signs with convention, replace $v$ with $-v$ and absorb the proper sign when $\cos\theta$ changes. (The diagram above demonstrates that this is consistent with the geometry of the situation.)

$$\omega' = \omega\left(1 - \frac{v}{c}\cos\theta\right)$$

5.4

This gives the correct classical definition of the Doppler effect for waves that obey the Galilean transformation. To calculate wavelength changes from the Doppler effect, recall that $\omega\lambda = c$, and substitute $c'/\lambda'$ for $\omega'$ and $c/\lambda$ for $\omega$.

## The Relativistic Doppler Effect

What re-considerations do we need for the relativistic equivalent of this equation? Let $c$ be the speed of light. One way to find the relativistic Doppler

shift formula is to transform wave crests by means of the Lorentz transformations. However, their formal rigor is not always necessary, and general
"thought experiments" will also work. If we assume that the wave source emits
waves of light in the vacuum of space, then special relativistic inertial frames,
not Galilean ones, apply. Relative to the inertial frame in which the wave source
is stationary, wave crests hit the moving receiver with the same frequency as
in the classical case, because of the geometry of the situation. Equation (5.4)
holds. But in the rest frame of the wave source, the receiver's time has slowed
down by a factor of $1/\gamma$. Relative to the receiver, then, the wave crests should
be striking $\gamma$ times more frequently, or:

$$\omega' = \omega\gamma\left(1 - \frac{v}{c}\cos\theta\right) = \frac{\omega\left(1 - \frac{v}{c}\cos\theta\right)}{\sqrt{1 - v^2/c^2}}$$

5.5

In the rest frame of the receiver, the wave source moves with a speed $v$, and
this equation allows calculation of its frequency $\omega'$ and wavelength $c/\omega'$ for an
angle $\theta$. But this is the angle between wave source and receiver in the rest frame
of the wave source. For the angle between the same two objects in the rest
frame of the receiver, $\theta'$, we need the angle of the light ray in the primed inertial
frame. That was calculated in equation (4.35) of Chapter Four, where the
relationship between the angles was found to be:

$$\tan\theta' = \frac{\sin\theta}{\gamma\left(\cos\theta - \frac{v}{c}\right)}$$

5.6

From basic trigonometry the identity can be used to find the cosine of the
primed angle:

$$\cos\theta' = \frac{1}{\sqrt{\tan^2\theta' + 1}}$$

5.7

Substituting equation (5.6) into (5.7) and simplifying gives us:

$$\cos\theta' = \frac{\cos\theta - \dfrac{v}{c}}{1 - \dfrac{v}{c}\cos\theta}$$

5.8

While equation (5.5) is expressed in terms of $\cos\theta$, we need to express it in terms of $\cos\theta'$. Solving equation (5.8) for $\cos\theta$ we get:

$$\cos\theta = \frac{\cos\theta' + \dfrac{v}{c}}{1 + \dfrac{v}{c}\cos\theta'}$$

5.9

Substituting this into equation (5.5) and simplifying gives the final result:

$$\omega' = \frac{\omega}{\gamma\left(1 + \dfrac{v}{c}\cos\theta'\right)} = \frac{\omega\sqrt{1 - v^2/c^2}}{\left(1 + \dfrac{v}{c}\cos\theta'\right)}$$

5.10

As before, let $c/\lambda' = \omega'$ and $c/\lambda = \omega$ and solve for $\lambda'$:

$$\lambda' = \lambda\gamma\left(1 + \frac{v}{c}\cos\theta'\right) = \lambda\frac{\left(1 + \dfrac{v}{c}\cos\theta'\right)}{\sqrt{1 - v^2/c^2}}$$

5.11

These, then, are the special relativistic equations for the Doppler effect on light waves. Of course, for many applications in astronomy where the speed of an object is small in comparison to light, $v \ll c$, the formula $\lambda' = \lambda[1 + (v/c)\cos\theta']$ is good enough. Further, note that sometimes equation (5.11) is not appropriate in general relativity, as in the case of the red shift for the expansion of the universe, which is not strictly a Doppler shift. Because the expansion of space itself creates that red shift, these equations discussed above should not be used.

For the case of Doppler shifting directly ahead of and behind a moving wave source, it is easy to calculate $\lambda_{min}$ and $\lambda_{max}$.

$$\lambda_{max} = \lambda\sqrt{\frac{c+v}{c-v}}$$

$$\lambda_{min} = \lambda\sqrt{\frac{c-v}{c+v}}$$

5.12

## The Twin Paradox

The *twin paradox* is often confusing to those newly acquainted with the theory of relativity. With regard to a given inertial frame, relativity requires that time run slower in all other inertial frames. But imagine twins, each in a different inertial frame. Each twin says the other is aging less. How can they both age less than each other? Each twin can age less than the other if no inertial forces act on them, in which case there is no contradiction. The apparent contradiction comes from forgetting that absolute simultaneity does not exist. Consider the following example: a rocket in the vicinity of the earth accelerates to a speed $v$ in a short time, and coasts at that speed all the way to Barnard's star. After arriving there, the rocket reverses direction and fires its engines, stopping at the Barnard star system. The sun and Barnard's star are in approximately the same inertial frame because their relative motion is small in comparison to the speed of light. If $x$ denotes the distance between the sun and Barnard's star in the inertial frame of the sun, then observers on earth or at Barnard's star age by the amount $t = x/v$ during the amount of time they perceive the rocket journey to take. Assuming clocks on earth and at Barnard's star are set to zero just before the trip starts, both clocks read $x/v$ just after the rocket arrives at Barnard's star. According to the Sol-Barnard inertial frame, time slows down for the rocket and when the rocket arrives at Barnard's star the rocket's clock should read $t'$:

$$t' = t\sqrt{1 - v^2/c^2}$$

5.13

Because the Sol-Barnard system is moving at speed $v$ relative to the rocket, time in the Sol-Barnard system should have slowed down relative to the rocket by the same factor. So why would observers in the rocket not see clocks at Barnard's star as reading $t$ in equation (5.14) after the trip?

$$t = t'\sqrt{1 - v^2/c^2}$$

5.14

In this equation $t'$ is the trip time from Sol to Barnard's star according to the rocket, and this problem is known as the *clock paradox* or *twin paradox*.

The solution is as follows: After the rocket stops in the Barnard star system, observers on the rocket see clocks already at Barnard's star as reading

$$\frac{t'}{\sqrt{1 - v^2/c^2}}$$

5.15

Here $t'$ is the trip time according to the rocket. Simultaneity is not absolute but relative. Remember the case of the moving box, where, relative to observers seeing the box in motion, time—and clocks—at the back of the box are ahead of time and clocks in the front. The "front" of the box is the part facing the direction of motion. In the rocket example, immediately after the rocket reaches its coasting speed $v$, but while it is still near earth, the sun defines the front of a large imaginary box from the rocket's perspective. Barnard's star defines the back of this imaginary box. The box is moving at speed $v$ relative to the rocket, with its length contracted as $x' = x\sqrt{1 - v^2/c^2}$ . Therefore, clocks at Barnard's star must be ahead of clocks in the solar system. Is the time difference enough to resolve the apparent contradiction of the clock paradox? It is exactly the right amount, and can be checked as follows: let $t'$ be the trip time from the solar system to Barnard's star according to the rocket. Equation (5.13) gives the size of $t'$. Relative to the rocket, clocks at Barnard's star should advance by the amount $t'\sqrt{1 - v^2/c^2}$ , as in equation (5.14), during the coasting phase of the trip. Upon arrival at Barnard's star, observers on the rocket will see clocks in the Barnard star system as reading the amount given in equation (5.15). Immediately after the rocket reaches speed $v$, then, but while it is still in the vicinity of the earth, clocks at Barnard's star would need to be ahead of clocks in the solar system by an amount equal to the difference between (5.15) and (5.14):

$$\frac{t'}{\sqrt{1 - v^2/c^2}} - t'\sqrt{1 - v^2/c^2} = \frac{t'v^2/c^2}{\sqrt{1 - v^2/c^2}} = \frac{x'v/c^2}{\sqrt{1 - v^2/c^2}}$$

5.16

Here $x' = vt'$, the distance between Sol and Barnard during the coasting phase of the journey, according to the rocket.

In the primed intertial frame, an event at $(x', 0,0,0)$ occurs at $(\gamma x', 0, 0, \gamma x'v/c^2)$ in the unprimed inertial frame. So, if observers in the primed frame could instantaneously see clocks in the unprimed frame (stationed at $x'$ at $t' = 0$ according to the primed frame) they would see those clocks as reading $\gamma x'v/c^2$, the same as equation (5.16). When the rocket reaches Barnard's star but is still coasting at speed $v$, earth time, relative to the rocket, is only the amount equal to the right hand side of equation (5.14). But when the rocket brakes to a stop at Barnard's star, earth time jumps from (5.14) to (5.15). Why, relative to the rocket, do Barnard's star's clocks race from $t=0$ to $\gamma x'v/c^2$ during the brief acceleration to $v$? And, relative to the rocket, why do clocks on earth jump from $t'/\gamma$ to $\gamma t'$ during the brief deceleration at Barnard's star? The answer is found in the *principle of equivalence,* the foundation of general relativity. The principle of equivalence says that, relative to accelerated systems, the acceleration is a true gravitational field. Time itself runs faster at the top of a gravitational field, relative to the bottom of that field. During the rocket accelerations considered here, the rocket, relative to itself, is at the base of a large gravity field. In the first case, Barnard's star is at a very high altitude in a large gravity field, and in the second case, the earth is at the top of a large gravity field. This accounts for the rapid advance of time in those cases.

In this thought-experiment the question posed in previous chapters recurs. Which set of observers is correct? Does time on the rocket run slower, or does time at Barnard's star and the earth undergo these rapid gravitational time advances? Special relativity answers this question, which once again is bogus, because it presupposes that time is absolute. All observers are equally right, and this thought-experiment provides yet another example of the relativity of time. Relative to the rocket, time advances very rapidly first at Barnard's star, and then in the solar system, because they are each at the top of a large gravitational potential. Relative to the earth and the Barnard system, time on the rocket is running slowly because of time dilation. Taking the accelerating rocket as the stationary frame, the distance between the sun and Barnard's star shrinks from $x$ to $x/\gamma$ via length contraction during the interval of acceleration. Thus, during the rocket's initial acceleration to Barnard's star, the star "moves" closer to the rocket and the earth by an amount easily greater than light speed: $x - x/\gamma$ divided by the acceleration time. This is an example in general relativity of the expansion or contraction of space at speeds greater than light. From the perspective of general relativity, in line with the principle of equivalence, the rocket is at rest in a gravitational field and that gravitational field causes space to contract in the direction of the rocket's motion.

## Exercises

1. Calculate the gamma factor, $\gamma$, as a function of red-shifted or blue-shifted wavelength. Assume that the light source emits light directly toward or away from its direction of motion.

2. Calculate the speed of an object as a function of its red-shifted or blue-shifted wavelength. Assume that the light source emits light directly toward or away from its direction of motion.

3. An object emits light waves in all directions. Relative to an inertial frame in which the object is moving, at what angle will the Doppler-shifted wavelength equal the wavelength in the rest frame of the radiation source?

4. A radiation source travels by the earth with a speed $v$ and emits radiation perpendicular to its direction of motion. What is the relativistic Doppler shift for this special case and how should it be interpreted?

5. A wave source emits photon pairs. In the rest frame of the wave source, the photon pairs travel in opposite directions, but their frequency is the same. In the rest frame of the source, the total energy of the photons is $E=\Sigma 2hc/\lambda_i$ because $E_i = h\nu_i$ for each photon. Expressed as a function of $E$, what is the total energy of all the photons in another inertial frame?

6. How much time passes for a photon traveling at the speed of light?

7. Consider an object moving in a circle with a constant speed $v$. Relative to the inertial frame in which the center of the circle is at rest, which clocks will run slow: those on the object or those in the inertial frame? Explain the answer.

8. For a spacecraft traveling with a varying speed, what equation relates ship-time to its starting inertial frame? Explain the answer.

# CHAPTER 6

## *Space-Time*

IN EUCLIDEAN SPACE IT IS EASY to show that the distance between two points is independent of the orientation of the co-ordinate axes. A re-orientation of the axes leaves the distance $\Delta x^2 + \Delta y^2 + \Delta z^2 = \Delta x'^2 + \Delta y'^2 + \Delta z'^2$ invariant. But the lack of absolute simultaneity, together with the full equivalence of all inertial frames, requires that space is not the three-dimensional space of classical thought. Rather, it requires that space and time be considered together. Time itself is a dimension that, together with the three familiar spatial dimensions, forms a four-dimensional *space-time*. This was the discovery of Hermann Minkowski, who realized that special relativity required it, and noted in a famous lecture: "Henceforth space by itself, and time by itself, are doomed to fade away into mere shadows, and only a kind of union of the two will preserve an independent reality."[1] By multiplying the time dimension by the speed of light, we put time into the same units as the other three dimensions: $w=ct$. In

---

[1] Albert Einstein, *The Principle of Relativity* (New York: Dover Publications, 1952), p. 75.

this case the distance between events can be calculated. Unlike the invariant three-dimensional distance of Euclidean space, however, the quantity $\Delta w^2 + \Delta x^2 + \Delta y^2 + \Delta z^2$ is not the same in all inertial frames. The quantity $\Delta w^2 - \Delta x^2 - \Delta y^2 - \Delta z^2$, however, *is* the same in all frames. Using $w$ in place of $ct$, the Lorentz transformation becomes:

$$x' = \gamma\left( x - w\frac{v}{c} \right)$$

$$y' = y$$

$$z' = z$$

$$w' = \gamma\left( w - x\frac{v}{c} \right)$$

6.1

The invariance of the interval $\Delta w^2 - \Delta x^2 - \Delta y^2 - \Delta z^2$ can easily be established. Consider two events in the unprimed inertial frame, both of which are transformed to the primed inertial frame, and form the interval $\Delta w'^2 - \Delta x'^2 - \Delta y'^2 - \Delta z'^2$. This interval reduces to its unprimed equivalent, which demonstrates its invariance. (The reader may perform this calculation on his or her own.) The invariant interval, $\Delta s$, is the proper distance between the two events:

$$\Delta s^2 = \Delta w^2 - \Delta x^2 - \Delta y^2 - \Delta z^2$$

6.2

A particle moving in space traces out a *world line* in space-time: a set of events constituting each place and time of the particle. For any two arbitrarily close events on the world line, the proper distance is expressed in differential form:

$$ds^2 = dw^2 - dx^2 - dy^2 - dz^2$$

6.3

The proper distance of a world line can be found by integrating equation (6.3) to find $s$, and dividing the proper distance by the speed of light $\tau = s/c$ gives us the proper time. For any inertial frame, $cdt$ can be substituted for $dw$ and both sides of equation (6.3) can be divided by $c^2 dt^2$, yielding:

$$\frac{1}{c^2}\left( \frac{ds}{dt} \right)^2 = 1 - \frac{1}{c^2}\left[ \left( \frac{dx}{dt} \right)^2 + \left( \frac{dy}{dt} \right)^2 + \left( \frac{dz}{dt} \right)^2 \right]$$

6.4

The square of the particle's speed is equal to the rightmost parenthesized expression in (6.4). Substituting $v^2$ for this expression and taking the square roots of both sides of (6.4) gives us:

$$\frac{1}{c}\frac{ds}{dt} = \sqrt{1 - \frac{v^2}{c^2}}$$

After integrating, we have:

$$\tau = s/c = \int_{t_1}^{t_2} \sqrt{1 - v^2/c^2}\, dt$$

6.5

This equation allows the calculation of proper time for a particle with speed $v(t)$, between any two times, specified in (6.5) as the limits of integration, in any inertial frame. In fact equation (6.3) yields a flat space-time metric:

$$g^{uv} = \begin{bmatrix} 1 & 0 & 0 & 0 \\ 0 & -1 & 0 & 0 \\ 0 & 0 & -1 & 0 \\ 0 & 0 & 0 & -1 \end{bmatrix}$$

6.6

(Readers who find this discussion difficult should simply concentrate at this point on its larger principles. An overview of metric tensors will be provided later in the book.)

Minkowski saw that special relativity required that the world be a four-dimensional space-time continuum. Because the metric (6.6) must be the same in each inertial frame, this metric tensor is isometric with respect to inertial frames. Minkowski also discovered an equivalent way of expressing special relativity, a space-time formulation which can be stated as follows:

---

The four-dimensional space described by this isometric line element is the world of space and time:     $ds^2 = c^2 dt^2 - dx^2 - dy^2 - dz^2$ .

---

This is a correct formulation of special relativity, as long as it is understood that physical laws must be the same in each inertial frame. For general relativity, however, it must be updated. In general relativity the metric does not have the constant values of (6.6). Rather, the metric components are functions of the coordinates. This provides a hint about the transition from Minkowski's four-dimensonial space to general relativity.

The flat-space metric in (6.6) is called the Minkowski metric. It meets the definition of an inner product, with the exception that $< \overline{X}, \overline{X} >$ can be less than zero. All other properties of an inner product hold, and the angle can be an imaginary number rather than a real number. The major mathematical properties of the Minkowski metric space are as follows:

1.   Each event has a space-time vector $\overline{X} = (x, y, z, w)$.

2.   The inner product of two events is $< \overline{X}_1, \overline{X}_2 >= w_1 w_2 - x_1 x_2 - y_1 y_2 - z_1 z_2$.

3.   The proper length of a space-time vector is $\left\| \overline{X} \right\| = \sqrt{< \overline{X}, \overline{X} >}$.

4.   The proper distance between two events is $d(\overline{X}_2, \overline{X}_1) = \left\| \overline{X}_2 - \overline{X}_1 \right\|$.

5.   The angle in space-time between two events is given by:

$$\cos \theta = \frac{< \overline{X}_2, \overline{X}_1 >}{\left\| \overline{X}_2 \right\| \left\| \overline{X}_1 \right\|}$$

For any inertial frame, events have the same proper distance in space-time. To show that the angle is the same for any inertial frame, all we must do is demonstrate that the "Minkowski inner product" of two events is invariant. To achieve this, substitute the Lorentz transformations of two events into the inner product and show that it simplifies to the inner product for the events without a Lorentz transformation. Substitute

$$x_2' x_1' = \gamma (x_2 - v t_2) \gamma (x_1 - v t_1)$$
$$y_2' y_1' = y_2 y_1$$
$$z_2' z_1' = z_2 z_1$$
$$c^2 t_2' t_1' = c^2 \gamma (t_2 - x_2 v / c^2) \gamma (t_1 - x_1 v / c^2)$$

6.7

into the definition of the Minkowski inner product (as above) and simplify. The result is:

$$c^2 t_2' t_1' - x_2' x_1' - y_2' y_1' - z_2' z_1' = c^2 t_2 t_1 - x_2 x_1 - y_2 y_1 - z_2 z_1 \qquad 6.8$$

Thus the angle between any two events is the same in all inertial frames.

Because neither angles between, nor lengths of, space-time vectors change from one inertial frame to another, we can view all events and their angles as a rigid structure. This means that a Lorentz transformation is really simply a rotation in space-time. To determine how much rotation occurs for a given Lorentz transformation of speed $v$, two events are needed, each confined to the $x$-$w$ plane. Consider an event $X$ in one inertial frame and the same event in another inertial frame $X'$. Then treat the two representations of this event as though they were two different events in the same inertial frame. The angle between the two events equals the angle between the two inertial frames.

$$\overline{X} = (\quad x_0, \qquad 0, \qquad 0, \qquad 0 \quad )$$
$$\overline{X'} = (\quad \gamma x_0, \qquad 0, \qquad 0, \qquad -\gamma x_0 v/c^2 \quad )$$
$$\cos\theta = \frac{<\overline{X}, \overline{X'}>}{\|\overline{X}\|\|\overline{X'}\|} = \frac{1}{\sqrt{1 - v^2/c^2}} = \gamma$$

Although the event occurs here at time zero, the same result holds for an event at any time $t$. The reader is encouraged to check this.

An alternative way to get this result is to consider two events $(x_0, 0, 0, 0)$ and $(x_0, 0, 0, t_0)$ with $\cos\theta = 1/\sqrt{1 - c^2 t_0^2/x_0^2}$. We can find an inertial frame where the second event is simultaneous with the event $(0, 0, 0, 0)$. This occurs when $t_0 = \gamma x' v/c^2$ and $x' = x_0/\gamma$ by the Lorentz transformation such that $v/c = ct_0/x_0$. Substituting this into $\cos\theta = 1/\sqrt{1 - c^2 t_0^2/x_0^2}$ gives the desired result. Since the cosine of the rotation angle is greater than 1, the angle must be an imaginary number. Both the sine and cosine of the angle are tabulated in (6.9):

$$\cos\theta = \gamma$$

$$\sin\theta = \sqrt{1 - \cos^2\theta} = \sqrt{1 - \gamma^2} = i\gamma\frac{v}{c}$$

$$6.9$$

If we substitute (6.9) into (6.1), the Lorentz transformation equations become:

$$w' = w\cos\theta + ix\sin\theta$$
$$x' = x\cos\theta + iw\sin\theta$$
$$y' = y$$
$$z' = z \qquad\qquad 6.10$$

Because the angle has to be an imaginary number, we can write it as a real number times the square root of minus one $\theta = i\hat{\theta}$. Using the mathematical identities

$$\cos(i\hat{\theta}) = \cosh(\hat{\theta})$$
$$\sin(i\hat{\theta}) = i\sinh(\hat{\theta})$$

we can express (6.10) in another way, as:

$$w' = w\cosh(\hat{\theta}) - x\sinh(\hat{\theta})$$
$$x' = x\cosh(\hat{\theta}) - w\sinh(\hat{\theta})$$
$$y' = y$$
$$z' = z \qquad\qquad 6.11$$

(Some readers may want to skip this next section and return to it after reviewing tensors.) To show that the Minkowski formulation of special relativity gives the Lorentz transformation, it is necessary only to derive the Lorentz transformation from (6.6). This is analogous to slicing space-time with three space-planes at different angles to find different eras of inertial frames. Substituting $dw = cdt$, the Minkowski metric takes the form given in (6.6) and transforms as a second-order tensor:

$$g'^{kl} = g^{st}\frac{\partial x'^k}{\partial x^s}\frac{\partial x'^l}{\partial x^t} \qquad\qquad 6.12$$

But in this case $g'^{kl}$ and $g^{st}$ equal each other. That is, they equal the values in (6.6), because of the isometric character of space. Assuming that the transformation takes place only along the $x$ and $w$ axes, transformations between the primed and unprimed coordinates should be of the form:

$$x' = Px + Qw$$
$$y' = y$$
$$z' = z$$
$$w' = Rx + Sw$$

6.13

The only non-zero terms are the diagonal elements of the metric. We can view equation (6.12) as constraints on the values of $P, Q, R,$ and $S$ because $g'^{kl}$ and $g^{st}$ both equal the matrix in (6.6). Taking partial derivatives of (6.13) with respect to $x, y, z,$ and $w$ and substituting those into (6.12) leaves three equations in four unknowns:

$$-1 = Q^2 - P^2$$
$$+1 = S^2 - R^2$$
$$0 = SQ - RP$$

6.14

To solve these one more equation is needed: one that relates the relative speed between the two inertial frames in terms of at least one of the variables $P, Q,$ $R,$ and $S.$ The speed is calculated as follows: transforming the two events $(0,0,$ $0,0)$ and $(0,0,0,w)$ to a new inertial frame yields $(0,0,0,0)$ and $(Qw,0,0,Sw).$ This allows the calculation of the speed of the primed inertial frame relative to the unprimed frame. That is, because the distance $Qw$ is traversed over time $Sw, Qw/Sw = Q/S = -v/c.$ This, together with the three equations in (6.14) above, gives four equations in four unknowns with solutions as in (6.15):

$$P = S = \gamma$$
$$Q = R = -\gamma \frac{v}{c}$$

6.15

Substituting these into (6.13) gives (6.1).

## *Exercises*

1. Calculate the real factor of the rotation angle in space-time as a function of relative speed $v$ between two inertial frames.

2. What is the proper distance in space-time between the two events below? Use $c = 3.00 \times 10^8$m/sec.

   Event 1 = $(10$m$, 100$m$, 0, 2.00 \times 10^{-7}$sec$)$
   Event 2 = $(30$m$, 200$m$, 0, 1.00 \times 10^{-6}$sec$)$

3. A rocket, starting near the earth with speed zero, travels at a constant acceleration relative to itself. Calculate the amount of time that elapses on the rocket as a function of the amount of time that elapses on the earth. Relate this answer to the travel distance of the rocket, relative to the earth.

4. What is the proper distance, in the time dimension only, for one second?

5. World lines are curves in space-time describing the paths of objects. What is the proper distance of world lines for photons? Why?

6. By methods used in this chapter, show that any event $(x_0, 0, 0, t_0)$ yields $\gamma = \cos\theta$.

7. If the proper time of a particle is given as a function of time in one inertial frame, calculate $v(t)$ for the object.

8. For the scenario in Problem Seven, if proper time $t'$ is related by the equation below, what is $v(t)$? Assume that $k$ is a constant.

$$t' = t_0 \log_e (t/k)$$

# PART 3

## *Mechanics and Electromagnetism*

# CHAPTER 7

# *Relativistic Mass and Momentum*

IN CLASSICAL MECHANICS, velocity in one direction adds according to the formula $u=w+v$, where $v$ is the speed of the first object relative, for example, to the earth, and $w$ is the speed of the second object relative to the first. The velocity of the second object relative to the earth is $w+v$. Consider a rocket with $n$ stages, each of which accelerates all remaining stages by some fixed velocity $v$ in the same direction of motion, relative to the last stage. That is, stage one accelerates stages two through $n$ to a speed $v$ relative to the earth. Stage one then detaches and stage two accelerates stages three through $n$ to a speed of $v$ relative to the first stage. When stage two detaches, stage three accelerates stages four through $n$ to a speed of $v$ relative to the second stage. Continuing in this fashion, how fast will the last stage travel relative to the earth? In classical mechanics the answer is simply $nv$, a repeated addition of speeds.

But in relativity the answer is different, because speeds in one direction add in a different manner, according to equation (7.1):

$$u = \frac{w+v}{1+\dfrac{wv}{c^2}}$$

7.1

The correct relativistic answer for the $n$-stage rocket problem is given by the formula:

$$u(v,n) = \left[ \frac{\left(\dfrac{c+v}{c-v}\right)^n - 1}{\left(\dfrac{c+v}{c-v}\right)^n + 1} \right] c$$

7.2

Because $u(v,n)$ cannot equal $c$ unless $n$ equals infinity, the rocket's engines can never accelerate their payload to the speed of light. Another way to consider the problem is as follows: remembering that the speed of light is the same in all inertial frames, consider a rocket, in the vicinity of the earth, that emits a photon in the direction it is going to travel. The rocket then accelerates to some speed, chasing the photon, and coasts at that speed for a short time. Relative to the rocket, as well as to the earth, the photon still recedes at the speed of light. The rocket then emits another photon in the same direction and chases the photons by accelerating again, say by the same amount of speed relative to its previous inertial frame. Relative to the rocket, the photons are still moving away at the speed of light. Because this holds true for all of the rocket's accelerations, it never catches up to the photons it emits in the forward direction.

What is the nature of this situation relative to the earth? Because the photons always travel at the same speed, $c$, and are always ahead of the rocket, it must be the case that the rocket creeps ever closer to the speed of light but never quite reaches it. The rocket's mass—its resistance to acceleration—increases relative to the earth. However, the principle of special relativity requires that, relative to the rocket, the rocket's mass does not change at all (other than the loss of stages and fuel). From the rocket's perspective, the earth moves at a speed approaching that of light, and the earth's resistance to acceleration—

its mass—increases. This is because the earth's speed is equal to the negative of the rocket's speed; it, too, can never reach the speed of light.

The effect of this mass increase is that the rocket will need much more fuel to reach speeds closer to the speed of light than in classical physics. The reverse is also true: the rocket will need much more fuel to slow down than in classical physics. To reach the speed of light, the rocket would need an infinite amount of fuel. Relative to the earth, the rocket's inertia (that is, its mass) has increased. To the rocket, its own mass has remained constant, but the earth's mass has increased. Now, our recurring question: which mass has actually increased? The principle of special relativity requires that neither situation is correct in an absolute sense. Each is true relative to its inertial frame because mass, like time and distance, is relative. Relative mass is often called *relativistic mass*.

Calculation of relativistic mass is intimately connected with relativistic momentum, relativistic force, and momentum conservation. The reasoning outlined below assumes that relativistic force is the rate of change of relativistic momentum and that Newton's first and third laws are true in special relativity without modification. Consider a box in the rest frame of the earth. Inside the box, two balls, stationed in the center of the box, travel in opposite directions along the $y$-axis. Each ball has a rest mass, $m$. As each ball accelerates to the same speed, they move away from the center of the box in opposite directions. Assuming that the speed they move in the $y$-direction is much less than the speed of light, the classical value for the momentum of each ball holds. Imagine that the balls always bounce up and back symmetrically and, when they meet in the center of the box, bounce off each other, repeating the previous $y$-motion. The $y$-momentum for each ball is:

$$p_y = F_y \Delta t = ma_y \Delta t$$

7.3

By Newton's third law, if the box is accelerated in the $x$-direction to a large percentage of the speed of light, no impulse change occurs in the $y$-direction and the balls will have the same $y$-momentum after acceleration as before. Because in reality this could not happen without disturbing the up and down motion of the balls, think of it in a different way. The box remains stationary and a rocket from earth accelerates in the $x$-direction to some very fast speed.

Now, as the y-speed of the balls is much less than the speed of light both in the rest frame of the box and in the rocket's rest frame, the y-momentum impulses can be approximated using classical principles. Now, in the rocket's rest frame imagine that a force $m'a'_y$ is applied in the y-direction over a time interval $\Delta t'$ to bring the y-momentum of one of the balls to zero. In the rest frame of the box, the ball is subjected to acceleration $a_y$ over time $\Delta t$. The y-acceleration of the ball transforms according to (4.26):

$$a'_y = a_y\left(1 - \frac{v^2}{c^2}\right)$$

7.4

And the time interval over which the ball decelerates is given by the equation (7.5):

$$\Delta t' = \frac{\Delta t}{\sqrt{1 - v^2/c^2}}$$

7.5

Because the y-component of momentum is the same in both the rest frames, the impulses must be equal:

$$F'_y \Delta t' = F_y \Delta t$$
$$m'a'_y \Delta t' = ma_y \Delta t$$

7.6

Hence, by substitution of (7.4) and (7.5) into (7.6) we get:

$$m'a_y\left(1 - v^2/c^2\right)\frac{\Delta t}{\sqrt{1 - v^2/c^2}} = ma_y \Delta t$$

7.7

On simplifying, the relativistic mass must be:

$$m' = \frac{m}{\sqrt{1 - v^2/c^2}}$$

7.8

This is the equation relating how mass increases in relation to inertial frames with speed $v$. The variable $m$ is called the rest mass, and $m'$ is called the relativistic mass or sometimes just mass. Notice that as $v$ approaches $c$, $m'$

approaches infinity. This explains why no material object can ever travel at or beyond the speed of light. If an object of finite rest mass could travel at the speed of light, its relativistic mass would be infinite. As an object accelerates, its mass increases and acceleration becomes more difficult. Objects moving at speeds close to that of light are extremely hard to push. In fact, it would take an infinite amount of work to accelerate an object of finite rest mass to the speed of light.

Because the balls have a tiny $y$-momentum, their masses would actually be slightly greater than we have determined here. But in the limiting case, as the $y$-velocity approaches zero, equation (7.8) gives the exact relativistic mass of the balls. Equation (7.8) also holds for accelerations in the $x$-direction, as will be shown below. This seems right, as a tiny change in $x$-momentum should be equal to the mass times the change in velocity plus the momentum of the mass increase traveling at that velocity: $\Delta p = m\Delta v + v\Delta m$.

Suppose that a rocket is traveling past the earth at eighty percent of the speed of light. To observers in the rocket, the earth's mass is two-thirds greater than what observers stationed on the earth observe it to be. And, to observers on the earth, the rocket's mass is two-thirds greater than what observers inside the rocket observe it to be. What is the true mass of the earth or the rocket? The question is invalid because it presupposes that mass is absolute. Mass is relative, there is no correct answer as to how much mass the earth or the rocket has.

### Relativistic Momentum

In classical physics, if an object moves in an unimpeded fashion, its change in momentum equals the impulse starting the motion. To calculate the classical value for the momentum of an object, it is easy to show that the impulse given to an object is $mv$, where $m$ is the mass of the object and $v$ is its final speed. This calculation assumes that the Galilean transformations are true. What, then, is the impulse under the Lorentz transformations? Because the relativistic version of $F = ma$ has not yet been discussed in this book, we cannot integrate that over time to get the relativistic impulse. We cannot get $F = dp/dt$ because the relativistic version of $p$ is the very thing being sought. Therefore an alternate method of calculating the impulse—hence, the momentum—must be used here.

In this context, it is useful to consider relativistic acceleration and the manner in which a linear force will transform between two inertial and accelerated systems. Imagine riding on an accelerating rocket. The rocket accelerates along the $x$-axis of its starting inertial frame, with acceleration equal to any function of time. For simplicity, assume that the rocket undergoes a constant acceleration relative to observers on the rocket. That is, relative to each inertial frame through which the rocket passes, it undergoes the same instantaneous acceleration there. How would an observer in an inertial frame, say the starting rest frame of the rocket, view the acceleration of the rocket? To the initial rest frame, the rocket of rest mass $m$ accelerates to some final speed $v$. In this starting frame, the object moves with speed $u_x(t)$ and accelerates with acceleration $a_x(t)$. Relative to the rocket, it undergoes a constant acceleration $a'_x$. This acceleration is related by the calculations shown previously:

$$a'_x = a_x \frac{\left(1 - \dfrac{v^2}{c^2}\right)^{3/2}}{\left(1 - \dfrac{u_x v}{c^2}\right)^3}$$

7.9

Assume that an external agent pushes the rocket, so that it neither expends fuel nor suffers a change in rest mass. Because the rocket always has speed $u_x$, relative to the initial rest frame of the rocket, $u_x = v$ at all times. Therefore equation (7.9) reduces to:

$$a'_x = \frac{a_x}{\left(1 - \dfrac{v^2}{c^2}\right)^{3/2}}$$

7.10

To clarify, the accelerated frame of reference of the rocket always travels at the same velocity as the rocket. The same equation results if the inverse transformation is used:

$$a_x = a_x' \frac{\left(1 - \dfrac{v^2}{c^2}\right)^{3/2}}{\left(1 + \dfrac{u_x' v}{c^2}\right)^3}$$

7.11

But in this case $u_x' = 0$ rather than $v$, because the rocket is always at speed zero in its instantaneous inertial frame. The same relation between $a_x'$ and $a_x$ is obtained. Note that if the primed frame of reference were the starting frame $u_x' = -v$, the same relation is also obtained, except that the primed and unprimed variables are switched because the speed is in the opposite direction. Now $a_x = dv/dt$ and $a_x' = a_0$ because observers on the rocket undergo a constant acceleration on board. Substituting these into equation (7.10) gives us:

$$a_0 dt = \frac{dv}{\left(1 - \dfrac{v^2}{c^2}\right)^{3/2}}$$

7.12

An observer riding in the accelerating rocket observes the rest mass of the rocket to be constant. This is because an external agent pushes the rocket; *i.e.* the rocket is not losing fuel or stages. So observers on board the rocket say its mass is constant and that it undergoes a constant acceleration $a_0$ relative to the rocket. Therefore to observers on the rocket, a constant force acts upon it at all times during the acceleration. That constant force should equal the rest mass of the rocket multiplied by its acceleration $F_0 = ma_0$. This is allowable because Newton's second law holds true in the ever-changing instantaneous inertial frame of the rocket.

It turns out that this force has the same constant value in all inertial frames at all times, including the rocket's starting inertial frame, for the following reason: imagine two springs of equal rest mass, traveling toward each other along the $x$-axis with a relative speed of $v$. An observer, stationary in the rest frame of either spring, will see the two collide and will see the other spring transfer all of its momentum to the spring "at rest." For observers in the rest frame of either spring, the change of momentum will be equal and will occur over the same time interval. This is true because of the symmetry of the situation and is also required by the principle of special relativity. Here, because the relative speed between the springs is arbitrary, for any force transmitted along the x-axis, $F'_x = F_x$ holds true if there is no y or z motion. When y or z motion is present, the x-component of force transforms by a more complicated expression. In the rocket's frame of reference, the force exerted at all times during acceleration equals the force exerted in the starting inertial frame. This does not necessarily follow from Newton's third law because the force on the rocket is being considered in two different inertial frames. However, it holds true in this special case. Therefore, when we multiply equation (7.12) by m, the rest mass of the rocket, all that remains is to integrate the resulting equation over time to find the relativistic impulse:

$$I = \int_{t=0}^{t=t} ma_0 dt = \int_{v=0}^{v=v} \frac{mdv}{\left(1-v^2/c^2\right)^{3/2}} = \left.\frac{mv}{\sqrt{1-v^2/c^2}}\right|_{v=0}^{v=v} = \frac{mv}{\sqrt{1-v^2/c^2}}$$

7.13

Because change in momentum equals impulse, $p = I$. Therefore, the equation for momentum in special relativity is $m'v$, where $m'$ is the relativistic mass. In this calculation the force was along the x-axis, but it could easily have been along any straight line, and so equation (7.13) can be put into vector form with no loss of generality. The relativistic momentum of an object with rest mass $m$, with $v^2 = \bar{v} \bullet \bar{v}$, is given by:

$$\bar{p} = \frac{m\bar{v}}{\sqrt{1-v^2/c^2}} = \gamma m\bar{v} = m'\bar{v}$$

7.14

In relativity, as in classical physics, the force is the rate of change of momentum of an object. However relativity requires a modification of Newton's second law of motion because of equation (7.14). The relativistic version of Newton's three fundamental laws of motion can then be stated:

(1)    The velocity of an object, $\bar{v} = d\bar{x}/dt$, remains constant unless acted upon by a net external force.

(2)    A net external force, $F$, exerted on an object of constant rest mass $m$, with $v^2 = \bar{v} \bullet \bar{v}$, is given by:

$$\overline{F} = \frac{d}{dt}\left[\frac{m\overline{v}}{\sqrt{1-v^2/c^2}}\right]$$

(3)   If object one exerts a force, $F$, on object two, then object two exerts an equal and opposite force, $-F$, on object one.

The relativistic version of Newton's three laws of motion makes relativistic mechanics possible. However, the calculations performed above are not the most general. They also hold true if the acceleration for observers on the rocket is not constant. In that case, equation $F'_x = F_x$ is a function of time, as, for example, in the rocket's starting inertial frame $F'_x(t) = F_x(t)$. In the rocket's starting inertial frame, the impulse becomes a general integral but still equals $m'v$. The variable $a_0$ in equation (7.13) becomes an arbitrary function of time. Relativistic momentum and force are approximately the same as their classical counterparts when speeds are small in comparison to the speed of light. However, as speeds approach that of light, the momentum of any object approaches infinity. If an object with a finite rest mass were to travel at exactly the speed of light, its momentum would be infinite. No matter how great an impulse an object receives, it can never accelerate up to or beyond the speed of light.

## Exercises

1.   For an $n$-stage rocket as described in this chapter, use induction to prove equation (7.2).

2.   Show that for $v \ll c$ equation (7.2) is approximated by $u(v,n) = nv$.

3.   Relative to the earth, a sphere with a rest mass of 150 kilograms travels at ninety-five percent of the speed of light. For observers stationed on the earth, what is the relativistic mass and relativistic momentum of the sphere?

4.   Suppose that the planet Jupiter were traveling at one-half the speed of light through the solar system. In order to have the same momentum as Jupiter, at what speed would the earth have relative to the solar system?

5. Consider an inertial frame with five planets, each with the rest mass of the earth, traveling at speeds $1/10\ c$, $1/3\ c$, $2/3\ c$, $8/9\ c$, and $100/101\ c$. What are their masses in this inertial frame?

6. What is the average force required to accelerate a spacecraft with a rest mass of $2.07 \times 10^9$ kg to 99.99 percent of the speed of light in ten seconds?

7. Show that the average density of an object is given by $\rho' = \rho \left(1 - v^2/c^2\right)^{-1}$ where $\rho$ is the average density of the object in its rest frame.

8. Suppose that the momentum of a charged particle increases linearly with time. Also suppose that the charged particle is traveling in a straight line. How does the speed of the particle vary with time? How does the position of the particle vary as a function of time?

9. Show that an object traveling in circular motion is kept at a constant radial distance, $r$, by a centripetal force with magnitude:

$$F_r = \frac{m'v^2}{r}$$

10. A spacecraft of rest mass $m$ travels in an inertial frame with speed $v$ along the $x$-axis. In another inertial frame that travels with speed $w$ relative to the first, what is the momentum of the spacecraft as expressed in terms of $m$, $v$, and $w$?

# CHAPTER 8

# *Relativistic Energy and its Transformations*

THE WORK DONE ON AN OBJECT, moving along a curve in space is defined as the line integral $\int \vec{F} \bullet d\vec{s}$ . For the special case of force acting upon an object along the *x*-axis only, where the object moves along the *x*-axis only, the line integral becomes:

$$W = \int_{x_1}^{x_2} F dx$$

8.1

Consider work done on an object of mass *m* in the vacuum of space, with no gravitational fields or other impediments present. In this idealized case, force acting on the object, integrated over the distance the force acts, is defined as being equal to the change in the object's kinetic energy. The work required to accelerate an object of mass *m* from speed zero to speed *v* is easily shown to be ½*mv²*, if the Galilean transformations are used. If we employ the Lorentz transformations instead, the relativistic work done will be equal to the change in relativistic kinetic energy of the object relative to its starting inertial frame. With the definition in (8.1) the relativistic force, found in the previous chapter, can be used to calculate the work done. The work done can be expressed in terms of momentum:

$$W = \int F dx = \int \frac{dp}{dt} dx = \int v \, dp$$

For an object starting at rest in the inertial frame, the total work done on $m$ can be found by equation (8.2):

$$E_K = \int_0^p v \, dp$$

8.2

To evaluate the integral, the velocity $v$ must be expressed as a function of momentum. Solving $p = m'v$ for $v$ gives us:

$$v = \frac{p}{\sqrt{m^2 + p^2/c^2}}$$

8.3

And substituting (8.3) into (8.2) gives:

$$E_K = \int_0^p \frac{p}{\sqrt{m^2 + p^2/c^2}} dp = c^2 \sqrt{m^2 + p^2/c^2} \Big|_0^p = \frac{mc^2}{\sqrt{1 - v^2/c^2}} \Big|_0^v = m'c^2 - mc^2$$

8.4

Now force is a vector quantity, and this calculation for kinetic energy was performed along one dimension only. But because energy is a scalar quantity, there is no loss in generality here. Therefore the line integral of a force over a curve can be reduced to the special case solved above.

$$\int \vec{F} \bullet d\vec{s} = \int \frac{d}{dt}(m'\vec{v}) \bullet d\vec{s} = \int \vec{v} \bullet d(m'\vec{v}) = \int \vec{v} \bullet (\vec{v}dm' + m'd\vec{v})$$

$$= \int (\vec{v} \bullet \vec{v}dm' + m'\vec{v} \bullet d\vec{v}) = \int (v^2 dm' + m'v dv) = \int vd(m'v) = \int v \, dp$$

The equation $\vec{v} \bullet d\vec{v} = v \, dv$ can be shown to be true by using the Pythagorean expression for $v$ as a function of its components, and differentiating. This shows the generality of equation (8.4). Finally, the equation for relativistic kinetic energy is $E_K = m'c^2 - mc^2$ , which reduces to the classical equation at speeds that are small in comparison to the speed of light.

$$E_K = \frac{mc^2}{\sqrt{1-v^2/c^2}} - mc^2 = \frac{mv^2}{(1-v^2/c^2)+\sqrt{1-v^2/c^2}} \approx \frac{mv^2}{2}$$

8.5

It is not surprising that, as an object approaches the speed of light, its kinetic energy increases without limit, just as its momentum does. As an object accelerates it constantly gains energy. At near-light speeds, relative to the inertial frame measuring kinetic energy, the speed of an object hardly changes at all, yet its kinetic energy can increase constantly. Kinetic energy, like other forms of energy, is relative rather than absolute. Relative to the earth, a rocket traveling at a large fraction of the speed of light has a great deal of kinetic energy. Relative to the rocket, on the other hand, it has no kinetic energy at all. The relativity of motion requires the relativity of energy. Special relativity also demands that matter and energy be inter-convertible.

The equation for relativistic kinetic energy bears a close resemblance to the matter-energy conversion formula, given below as equation (8.19). Equation (8.4), however, is not a derivation of (8.19). To understand why matter and energy can change into one another, we must examine various conservation laws. In classical physics, various quantities such as mass, momentum, energy, and angular momentum are conserved. But in relativity, because the mass of an object increases relative to inertial frames, mass by itself is not conserved. Neither is the classical equation for kinetic energy. Einstein solved this problem by showing that in relativity the conservation laws for mass and for energy are combined into a single law, called the *conservation of mass-energy*. In fact, special relativity requires the conservation of momentum, mass-energy, and angular momentum in the most general sense, because of symmetries in time, translation, and rotation.

The relativistic forms of Newton's laws, like their classical counterparts, also imply conservation of momentum. Consider a head-on elastic collision between two objects. By momentum conservation, this collision can be expressed in terms of rest masses and initial and final speeds:

$$\frac{m_1 v_1}{\sqrt{1-\dfrac{v_1^2}{c^2}}} + \frac{m_2 v_2}{\sqrt{1-\dfrac{v_2^2}{c^2}}} = \frac{m_1 v_1'}{\sqrt{1-\dfrac{v_1'^2}{c^2}}} + \frac{m_2 v_2'}{\sqrt{1-\dfrac{v_2'^2}{c^2}}}$$

8.6

From a different inertial frame moving along the x-axis at speed $w$ relative to the first, the elastic collision still obeys equation (8.6), but each speed $v$ is replaced by $(v+w)/(1+vw/c^2)$. Using the relations in (8.7) below, it is possible to simplify the momentum conservation in this second inertial frame:

$$\frac{1}{\sqrt{1-\dfrac{1}{c^2}\cdot\left(\dfrac{v-w}{1-vw/c^2}\right)^2}} = \frac{\left(1-\dfrac{vw}{c^2}\right)}{\sqrt{1-\dfrac{v^2}{c^2}}\sqrt{1-\dfrac{w^2}{c^2}}}$$

$$\frac{1}{\sqrt{1-\dfrac{1}{c^2}\cdot\left(\dfrac{v+w}{1+vw/c^2}\right)^2}} = \frac{\left(1+\dfrac{vw}{c^2}\right)}{\sqrt{1-\dfrac{v^2}{c^2}}\sqrt{1-\dfrac{w^2}{c^2}}}$$

8.7

For each term in equation (8.6), after substituting an equivalent expression of (8.7), simplifying, and subtracting equation (8.6) from the result, the following equation is left over:

$$\frac{m_1}{\sqrt{1-\dfrac{v_1^2}{c^2}}} + \frac{m_2}{\sqrt{1-\dfrac{v_2^2}{c^2}}} = \frac{m_1}{\sqrt{1-\dfrac{v_1'^2}{c^2}}} + \frac{m_2}{\sqrt{1-\dfrac{v_2'^2}{c^2}}}$$

8.8

This is the conservation of relativistic mass—or of kinetic energy—in an elastic collision. To see the kinetic part, multiply equation (8.8) by the square of the speed of light and subtract the term $(m_1 c^2 + m_2 c^2)$ from both sides. Thus momentum, specified in equation (8.6), is conserved in every inertial frame only if kinetic energy (or, in this case, relativistic mass) is conserved in the initial inertial frame. The same procedure can be carried out for the conservation of kinetic energy. The kinetic energy of the system is:

$$m_1c^2(\gamma_1-1)+m_2c^2(\gamma_2-1)=m_1c^2(\gamma_1'-1)+m_2c^2(\gamma_2'-1) \qquad 8.9$$

Or:

$$m_1\gamma_1+m_2\gamma_2=m_1\gamma_1'+m_2\gamma_2' \qquad 8.10$$

If we replace each velocity term by an equivalent expression from (8.7) and subtract a copy of equation (8.10) from the result, we get back equation (8.6), the original conservation of momentum. That is why, for a head-on elastic collision, momentum is conserved in every inertial frame only if kinetic energy is conserved in every inertial frame and vice versa. In relativity, the conservation of energy and of momentum are linked: one cannot be conserved without the other, as seen here. Likewise, the conservation of angular momentum is linked to the conservation of energy and momentum.

Now consider an inelastic collision. Here momentum and total energy are conserved, but kinetic energy is not. Thus one object may be hotter than the other, or some of its original kinetic energy is now stored as potential energy. A head-on inelastic collision, where two objects collide and stick together, is given by equation (8.11):

$$\frac{m_1v_1}{\sqrt{1-v_1^2/c^2}}+\frac{m_2v_2}{\sqrt{1-v_2^2/c^2}}=\frac{M_{tot}w}{\sqrt{1-w^2/c^2}} \qquad 8.11$$

This follows from momentum conservation. By transforming this equation to another inertial frame, using velocity substitutions like those in (8.7), we find that the sum of relativistic mass is also conserved. Once again this demonstrates that momentum conservation in all inertial frames requires conservation of relativistic mass in all inertial frames. For a head-on inelastic collision, the momentum and relativistic mass conservation are written together as:

$$\gamma_1m_1v_1+\gamma_2m_2v_2=\gamma_wM_{tot}w$$
$$\gamma_1m_1c^2+\gamma_2m_2c^2=\gamma_wM_{tot}c^2 \qquad 8.12$$

These two equations describe the head-on inelastic collision we have just discussed. The left sides of the equations are given as initial values before the collision. Because the right sides have the unknowns $M_{tot}$ and $w$, there are two equations in two unknowns. If the total mass were simply the sum of the rest masses before collision, then there would be two different equations specifying different values for $w$, and if that were the case, the equations would be over-determined. Consequently, the value of the rest mass $M_{tot}$, created after the two masses collide and stick together, will be different from the sum of the two rest masses before collision. Because total energy, not kinetic energy, is conserved, some of the extra kinetic energy appears as part of the mass of $M_{tot}$.

This leads to consideration of the inter-convertibility between matter and energy. Consider the following scenario: a spring of rest mass $m_S$ is compressed. In its compressed state it stores a potential energy of $E_S$. At each end of the spring are two objects of equal rest mass $m_L$. When the spring decompresses itself, it gives half its potential energy to each of the two objects, in the form of kinetic energy. Each object receives $E_S/2$ amount of energy, as kinetic energy, and each object moves away from the spring at speed $\pm u$.

Total momentum is conserved here, as expressed in the following equation:

$$\frac{-m_L u}{\sqrt{1-u^2/c^2}} + \frac{m_L u}{\sqrt{1-u^2/c^2}} = 0$$

8.13

The speed $u$ of each object is related to $E_S$ via equation (8.14):

$$\frac{E_S}{2} = \left( \frac{m_L c^2}{\sqrt{1 - u^2/c^2}} - m_L c^2 \right)$$

8.14

This spring example is itself an inelastic collision reversed in time. In keeping with our discussion of inelastic collisions, then, the equations must allow for the possibility of change in the rest mass of the spring. After decompression, the rest mass of the spring is $\overline{m_S}$ .

Now consider this interaction in an inertial frame different from the rest frame of the spring. Because total momentum must be conserved, we must consider momentum before and after the spring decompresses:

$$p'_{Before} = \frac{(m_S + 2m_L)v}{\sqrt{1 - \frac{v^2}{c^2}}}$$

$$p'_{After} = \frac{\overline{m_S} v}{\sqrt{1 - \frac{v^2}{c^2}}} + \frac{m_L \left( \frac{v + u}{1 + vu/c^2} \right)}{\sqrt{1 - \frac{1}{c^2} \cdot \left( \frac{v + u}{1 + vu/c^2} \right)^2}} + \frac{m_L \left( \frac{v - u}{1 - vu/c^2} \right)}{\sqrt{1 - \frac{1}{c^2} \cdot \left( \frac{v - u}{1 - vu/c^2} \right)^2}}$$

$$p'_{After} = \frac{\overline{m_S} v}{\sqrt{1 - \frac{v^2}{c^2}}} + \frac{2m_L v}{\sqrt{1 - \frac{v^2}{c^2}} \sqrt{1 - \frac{u^2}{c^2}}}$$

$$p'_{After} - p'_{Before} = \frac{(\overline{m_S} - m_S)v}{\sqrt{1 - \frac{v^2}{c^2}}} + \frac{2m_L v}{\sqrt{1 - \frac{v^2}{c^2}}} \left[ \frac{1}{\sqrt{1 - \frac{u^2}{c^2}}} - 1 \right] = 0$$

This last expression gives the change in momentum, which, by conservation of momentum, must be zero. Substituting equation (8.14) into this last equation gives us:

$$p'_{After} - p'_{Before} = \frac{(\overline{m_S} - m_S)v}{\sqrt{1 - v^2/c^2}} + \frac{vE_S/c^2}{\sqrt{1 - v^2/c^2}} = 0$$

8.15

To conserve momentum in every inertial frame, the rest mass of the spring must change. That is, when the spring is compressed it has rest mass $m_S$ and stores a potential energy of $E_S$ After the spring expands and releases potential energy, its rest mass is $\overline{m_S}$ . Call the change in the rest mass of the spring $\Delta m_S = m_S - \overline{m_S}$ . If $\Delta m_S$ were equal to zero, the change in momentum would not be zero. We can use this to calculate the relationship between $\Delta m_S$ and the total energy of the spring before decompression. Substituting $\Delta m_S$ into (8.15) gives:

$$-\gamma \Delta m_S v + \gamma v E_S/c^2 = 0$$

After dividing by the product $v\gamma$, we get:

$$\Delta m_S = E_S/c^2$$

8.16

Because $m_S = \overline{m_S} + \Delta m_S$ , the $\Delta m_S$ part of the compressed spring's mass was the weight of the potential energy originally stored there. Although for inelastic interactions kinetic energy is not conserved, total energy is. Because the mass of an object increases with relative speed by a known amount, a mass difference of $\Delta m_S$ in the original frame must be a mass difference of $\Delta m_S / \sqrt{1 - v^2/c^2}$ to the observer traveling at speed $v$. And, if matter and energy are interchangeable via the formula above, then an observer traveling at speed $v$ must see an energy difference of $\Delta m_S c^2 / \sqrt{1 - v^2/c^2}$ . The total energy of the system, before and after spring decompression, remains the same. Before decompression, it is expressed as a function of the uncompressed spring's rest mass, the potential energy of the spring, and the kinetic energy of the two objects. Thus we can calculate the equation for total energy: the kinetic energy of the uncompressed spring's relativistic mass plus the energy stored in the spring:

$$E'_{Before} = \frac{(\overline{m_S} + 2m_L)c^2}{\sqrt{1 - \dfrac{v^2}{c^2}}} - (\overline{m_S} + 2m_L)c^2 + \frac{\Delta m_S c^2}{\sqrt{1 - \dfrac{v^2}{c^2}}}$$

$$E'_{After} = \frac{\overline{m_S}c^2}{\sqrt{1 - \dfrac{v^2}{c^2}}} - \overline{m_S}c^2 + \frac{m_L c^2}{\sqrt{1 - \dfrac{1}{c^2} \cdot \left(\dfrac{v+u}{1 + vu/c^2}\right)^2}} - m_L c^2$$

$$+ \frac{m_L c^2}{\sqrt{1 - \dfrac{1}{c^2} \cdot \left(\dfrac{v-u}{1 - vu/c^2}\right)^2}} - m_L c^2$$

$$E'_{After} = \frac{\overline{m_S}c^2}{\sqrt{1 - \dfrac{v^2}{c^2}}} - \overline{m_S}c^2 + \frac{2m_L c^2}{\sqrt{1 - \dfrac{v^2}{c^2}}\sqrt{1 - \dfrac{u^2}{c^2}}} - 2m_L c^2$$

The energy before the collision has to equal the energy after, so their differences should be zero:

$$E'_{After} - E'_{Before} = \frac{-\Delta m_S c^2}{\sqrt{1 - \dfrac{v^2}{c^2}}} + \frac{2m_L c^2}{\sqrt{1 - \dfrac{v^2}{c^2}}}\left[\frac{1}{\sqrt{1 - \dfrac{u^2}{c^2}}} - 1\right] = 0$$

$$E'_{After} - E'_{Before} = \frac{-\Delta m_S c^2}{\sqrt{1 - \dfrac{v^2}{c^2}}} + \frac{E_S}{\sqrt{1 - \dfrac{v^2}{c^2}}} = 0$$

8.17

Because total energy conservation requires that the energy difference be zero, $E_S = \Delta m_S c^2$.

In another example of the inter-convertibility of matter and energy, some elements of elementary quantum theory are used. An object of rest mass $m_S$ emits two photons, each of frequency $f$, in opposite directions. The total energy emitted is then $E = 2hf$, where $h$ is Planck's constant. The quanta have momentum of $+hf/c$ and $-hf/c$. As before, we must allow for the possibility that the rest mass of $m_S$ changes to $\overline{m}_S$ after emission of the quanta. Another inertial frame travels at speed $v$ in a direction parallel to that of the two photons. In accordance with the principle of special relativity, momentum must be conserved. Taking into account Doppler shifts for each photon, the momentum before emission of the photons must equal the momentum of the photons plus the momentum of $\overline{m}_S$ :

$$p'_{Before} = \gamma m_S v$$

$$p'_{After} = \frac{hf}{c}\gamma(1+v/c) - \frac{hf}{c}\gamma(1-v/c) + \overline{m}_S v\gamma$$

$$p'_{After} - p'_{Before} = \frac{2hf}{c^2}v\gamma + \overline{m}_S v\gamma - \gamma m_S v = 0$$

8.18

If we divide both sides of the last equation of (8.18) by $v\gamma$, substitute the mass difference $\Delta m_S = m_S - \overline{m}_S$ , and substitute $E=2hf$, the result is the same as before: equation (8.16).

In general, matter and energy are inter-convertible. A small amount of matter can be converted into a large amount of energy, and a large amount of energy can be converted into a small amount of mass, according to the well-known formula:

$$E = mc^2$$

8.19

## Mass-Energy

Mass and energy are not separately conserved in special relativity. Rather, their classical conservation laws are combined in special relativity as the single law of the conservation of mass-energy. The conservation law of mass-energy can be simply stated: mass-energy cannot and can never be created or destroyed, it can only change forms. To state it in mathematical terms: let the total mass of any closed system be $m$ and let the total energy in that system be $E$. Then $T$ is defined to be the total mass-energy:

$$T = m + \frac{E}{c^2}$$

8.20

The conservation of mass-energy, then, can be expressed simply:

$$\frac{dT}{dt} = 0$$

8.21

This is the new conservation law. Substituting (8.20) into (8.21) and differentiating gives:

$$\frac{1}{c^2}\frac{dE}{dt} = -\frac{dm}{dt}$$

Therefore, the rate of mass loss equals the rate of energy increase divided by the square of the speed of light. Like time and space, mass-energy is not an absolute quantity, but relative. Each inertial frame will disagree on the amount of mass-energy in a certain system, but each will observe that amount as conserved.[1]

One can get a feel for how much mass-energy is needed, for example, to accelerate objects to given speeds. The relativistic mass of an object traveling at about eighty-seven percent of the speed of light is about double its rest mass. From the equation for relativistic kinetic energy given above, it is clear that the amount of mass-energy needed to boost an object to eighty-seven percent of the speed of light is very nearly equal to the rest energy of the object. To accelerate a brick to this speed requires the conversion of an identical brick entirely into energy, to be given to the first brick in the form of kinetic energy. Actually it would take more than this—a minimum of nearly 2.8 bricks—because increasing the original brick's momentum requires mass energy

---

[1] While some discussions of relativity, including this one, express mass-energy in terms of mass units, and others express it in terms of energy, either description works.

moving in the opposite direction as counter momentum. At 99.5 percent the speed of light, to take another example, objects have a relativistic mass about ten times their rest mass. To accelerate a brick to approximately 99.5 percent of the speed of light requires converting nine other identical bricks entirely into energy, and giving all that energy to the accelerating brick in the form of kinetic energy. Again, it would actually take a minimum of almost nineteen bricks, because momentum conservation requires that some of the mass energy fly off in the opposite direction to counterbalance the momentum of the accelerated brick.

While it is clearly difficult for bulky objects to reach relativistic speeds, subatomic particles such as cosmic rays are so light that they can be accelerated to many trillions of times their rest mass. Matter can be converted into energy by a variety of processes, of which the best known are fission and fusion in nuclear weapons, where a small fraction of the mass converts into energy. However, nature has provided a way in which matter can be converted entirely into energy: *antimatter*, a form of matter identical to ordinary matter except that all its subatomic particles have opposite electrical charges. An anti-electron, for example, is just like the familiar electron except for its positive electrical charge. Likewise, an antiproton is just like a proton except for its negative electrical charge: that is, all its quarks have opposite electrical charges. Even the electrically neutral neutron has an antiparticle: the antineutron, whose quarks have electrical charges opposite to those of the neutron. But for some particles, such as the photon, there are no antiparticles. When a particle of matter collides with an identical particle of antimatter, both are converted entirely into energy in, for example, the form of gamma ray photons. The most efficient type of nuclear engine, say for interstellar travel, is in fact an antimatter engine with photons for exhaust. A nuclear rocket with both matter and antimatter for propellant and gamma ray photons for exhaust will accelerate to the fastest speed for the amount of propellant it has. The most efficient type of nuclear rocket can be thought of as a gamma ray flashlight.

Suppose a rocket emits only electromagnetic radiation as its exhaust. Any process—fission, fusion, or matter-antimatter collisions—can produce this radiation. To find the relationships among the total initial mass of the rocket, $M_T$, the final rest mass of the rocket after exhausting its fuel, $m_f$, and the final speed of the rocket relative to its starting inertial frame $v_f$, consider momentum and energy conservation in the starting inertial frame of the rocket. Because light, or electromagnetic waves, has no rest mass, the energy of a light wave or a photon can be calculated from the equation $E = \sqrt{p^2 c^2 + m^2 c^4}$, which will be derived later in this chapter. The momentum of a photon is $p = E/c$ because the rest mass of photons is zero. The net momentum of all exhaust radiation to the momentum of the rocket should be zero. The total energy of all photons plus the total energy of the moving rocket should equal the total rest energy of the rocket before it expends any fuel:

$$\sum E_i + m_f \gamma_f c^2 = M_T c^2$$
$$-\sum E_i / c + m_f \gamma_f v_f = 0$$

The terms $\sum E_i$ and $\sum E_i / c$ are the total energy and momentum of exhaust photons. Solving these equations gives:

$$\frac{M_T}{m_f} = \sqrt{\frac{c + v_f}{c - v_f}}$$

8.22

## *Transformation of Energy between Inertial Frames*

Using the relations given below in (8.23), it is possible to compare the total momentum and total energy of moving objects in one inertial frame with these quantities in another inertial frame. An object's total energy is simply its relativistic mass multiplied by the square of the speed of light. Consider an inertial frame where the total momentum and total energy of a particle traveling at a relative velocity $\bar{u} = (u_x, u_y, u_z)$, with speed $u = \sqrt{u_x^2 + u_y^2 + u_z^2}$, are:

$$\bar{p} = \frac{m}{\sqrt{1 - u^2/c^2}} (u_x, u_y, u_z)$$

$$E = \frac{mc^2}{\sqrt{1 - u^2/c^2}}$$

8.23

In another rest frame traveling at speed $v$ along the $x$-axis relative to the first, a particle's total momentum and total energy can be computed only after taking into account its velocity vector in the new inertial frame:

$$u'_x = \frac{u_x - v}{1 - \dfrac{u_x v}{c^2}}$$

$$u'_y = \frac{u_y \sqrt{1 - \dfrac{v^2}{c^2}}}{1 - \dfrac{u_x v}{c^2}}$$

$$u'_z = \frac{u_z \sqrt{1 - \dfrac{v^2}{c^2}}}{1 - \dfrac{u_x v}{c^2}}$$

8.24

By direct calculation we have:

$$\frac{1}{\sqrt{1 - (u'^2_x + u'^2_y + u'^2_z)/c^2}} = \frac{1 - u_x v / c^2}{\sqrt{1 - v^2/c^2} \sqrt{1 - u^2/c^2}}$$

8.25

Thus total momentum in the new inertial frame is found by substituting (8.25) into (8.23):

$$\vec{p'} = \frac{m}{\sqrt{1 - u'^2/c^2}} (u'_x, u'_y, u'_z)$$

$$= \frac{m}{\sqrt{1 - u^2/c^2}} \left[ \frac{1 - u_x v / c^2}{\sqrt{1 - v^2/c^2}} \right] (u'_x, u'_y, u'_z)$$

$$= m\gamma_u \left[ \frac{u_x - v}{\sqrt{1 - v^2/c^2}}, u_y, u_z \right]$$

8.26

Tabulation of these results makes it clear that the transformations of total energy and total momentum are similar to the Lorentz transformation:

$$\overline{p'} = \left[ \frac{p_x - vE/c^2}{\sqrt{1-v^2/c^2}}, p_y, p_z \right]$$

$$E' = \frac{mc^2}{\sqrt{1-u'^2/c^2}} = \frac{mc^2(1-u_x v/c^2)}{\sqrt{1-u^2/c^2}\sqrt{1-v^2/c^2}} = \frac{E - p_x v}{\sqrt{1-v^2/c^2}}$$

8.27

These equations can be written in a cleaner form as:

$$p'_x = \gamma(p_x - vE/c^2)$$
$$p'_y = p_y$$
$$p'_z = p_z$$
$$E' = \gamma(E - vp_x)$$

8.28

Their inverses are found by inverting the equations above, which gives the same results as substituting $-v$ for $v$ and swapping the primed and unprimed quantities. Because these equations have the same form as the Lorentz transformation, we should find an invariant quantity analogous to proper distance in the Lorentz transformation. Further, total energy and total momentum can be put into the same units by defining $p'_w = E'/c$ and $p_w = E/c$, so that the expressions in (8.28) become:

$$p'_x = \gamma\left( p_x - p_w \frac{v}{c} \right)$$
$$p'_y = p_y$$
$$p'_z = p_z$$
$$p'_w = \gamma\left( p_w - p_x \frac{v}{c} \right)$$

8.29

These four $p$ components are components of a space-time "momentum" four vector. Like the space-time invariant, $s$, the invariance of (8.30) is found by means of simple substitution:

$$p_w'^2 - p_x'^2 - p_y'^2 - p_z'^2 = p_w^2 - p_x^2 - p_y^2 - p_z^2$$

8.30

The invariant is easily calculated to be:

$$\left(\frac{E}{c}\right)^2 - \bar{p} \bullet \bar{p} = \left(\frac{E}{c}\right)^2 - p^2 = (\gamma mc)^2 - (\gamma mv)^2 = m^2 c^2$$

8.31

Here the invariant is the square of the rest mass of the particle multiplied by the speed of light squared. This gives a new relation between the total energy of a particle and its momentum $E^2/c^2 - p^2 = m^2 c^2$. Solving for $E$, the total energy, gives:

$$E = \sqrt{m^2 c^4 + (pc)^2}$$

8.32

Because particles that can move at the speed of light—such as photons—have zero rest mass, their energy is equal to their momentum multiplied by the speed of light. For an object with a rest mass greater than zero, with no momentum, total energy is simply rest energy, or rest mass multiplied by the square of the speed of light.

## Exercises

1. Prove that equation (8.5) holds true for small speeds.

2. The energy of nuclear explosions is measured in terms of tons. One ton = $4.186 \times 10^9$ Joules, one kiloton = $4.186 \times 10^{12}$ Joules, one megaton = $4.186 \times 10^{15}$ Joules, and so on. How many kilograms of hydrogen are needed to create a 2.9-megaton explosion, assuming that all atoms of hydrogen fuse into helium? The masses of hydrogen and helium atoms are:

   Mass of 1 Hydrogen Atom = $1.673534 \times 10^{-27}$ Kg
   Mass of 1 Helium Atom = $6.646483 \times 10^{-27}$ Kg

3. Carry out the relativistic equivalent of the classical problem where the power on an accelerating object in free space is given by:

$$dE/dt = d[mv^2/2]/dt = mva$$

4. Calculate the relativistic rotational kinetic energy of a rotating stick, using the method given below, which corresponds to the classical case. Then calculate the rotational kinetic energy if the tip of the rod is moving at exactly the speed of light.

> A thin rod has one end anchored at a location around which the rest of the rod rotates. The speed of the other end of the rod—its tangential speed—is $v_0$. Let $r_0$ be the length of the rod and $\rho$ be the mass of the rod per unit length. Each portion of the rod rotates at a speed given by $v = v_0(r/r_0)$ and each small segment of the rod has mass $\rho dr = dm$. Integrating this last equation gives the rest mass of the rod as $m = \rho r_0$. The total rotational energy is given by:

$$\int v^2/2 \, dm = \int_0^{r_0} \rho v_0^2 r^2 / 2r_0^2 \, dr = m v_0^2 / 6$$

5. Carry out the relativistic equivalent of this classical problem:

> A bullet of rest mass $m_b$ leaves the barrel of a gun with speed $v_b$. The rest mass of the gun is $m_g$. Calculate the energy $E$ of the explosion in the chamber of the gun and the recoil speed of the gun $v_g$ in terms of $v_b$ and the masses. Solving this according to classical physics, we get two equations in two unknowns $E$ and $v_g$. Solving these equations for $v_g$ and substituting into the other one gives the result:

$$E = \frac{1}{2}m_b v_b^2 + \frac{1}{2}m_g v_g^2$$
$$0 = m_b v_b + m_g v_g$$
$$E = \frac{1}{2}m_b v_b^2 + \frac{1}{2}\left(\frac{m_b}{m_g}\right)^2 v_b^2$$

6. For a classical problem similar to number five above, the energy $E$ is given. An explosion of energy $E$ delivers all of its energy, in the form of kinetic energy, to two objects with rest masses as given below. For the classical case, there are two equations in two unknowns, $v_1$ and $v_2$, and solving the final speeds gives:

$$\frac{1}{2}m_1 v_1^2 + \frac{1}{2}m_2 v_2^2 = E$$

$$m_1 v_1 + m_2 v_2 = 0$$

$$v_1 = \sqrt{\frac{2E/m_1}{1 + m_1/m_2}}$$

$$v_2 = -\frac{m_1}{m_2}v_1$$

What are the final relativistic speeds of the two masses?

7. Show that for a relativistic rocket, emitting only photons for its exhaust, the rest energy of the rocket and fuel is approximately $2\gamma$, where $\gamma$ is the gamma factor for its final speed relative to its starting inertial frame. This is true only when its final speed is very close to that of light.

8. Consider a space ship with a mirror, or solar sail, that reflects incoming photons to gain speed.

    a. Calculate the speed of the space ship as a function of the total energy of incident photons.

    b. Assuming that the total energy of incoming photons is proportional to time, calculate the proper time for the solar mirror during acceleration.

9. Redo the derivation of equation (8.19), for a spring that is perpendicular to the direction of relative motion.

10. Calculate the relativistic rotational kinetic energy of a rotating pie-shaped wedge using the method below. Then calculate the rotational kinetic energy if the perimeter of the pie shaped wedge is moving at exactly the speed of light. The classical rotational kinetic energy is calculated as follows: let $\theta$ be the angle of the pie-shaped wedge and let $r_0$ be the radius. The point of the wedge is anchored and

its edge travels with speed $v_0$. The mass of a thin arc at radius $r$ is given by $dm=\theta\rho r dr$, and $\rho$ is the (constant) density per unit area. The total rest mass of the wedge is $m = \rho\theta r_0^2/2$ and its rotational kinetic energy is expressed as a function of rest mass and tangential speed at the edge:

$$\int_0^m v^2/2\,dm = \int_0^{r_0} (v_0^2 r^2/r_0^2)(\theta\rho r/2)\,dr = mv_0^2/4$$

# CHAPTER 9

# *Relativistic Angular Momentum and Force*

NEWTON'S LAWS IMPLY one further mechanical conservation law: angular momentum. Consider a swarm of particles in which each particle exerts forces on other particles, and assume that the force exerted by two particles on each other is in the direction of a straight line connecting the two. In particular, consider two particles, $A$ and $B$, at positions $\overline{X_A}$ and $\overline{X_B}$ respectively. Particle $A$ exerts a force $\boldsymbol{F}$ on particle $B$. By Newton's third law, particle $B$ exerts an opposite force, $-\boldsymbol{F}$, on particle $A$. This force acts over a small time, $\Delta t$. The change in angular momentum of the two particles is given by the equations:

$$\overline{\tau_A}\Delta t = \overline{X_A} \times \overline{F}\Delta t$$
$$\overline{\tau_B}\Delta t = -\overline{X_B} \times \overline{F}\Delta t$$

9.1

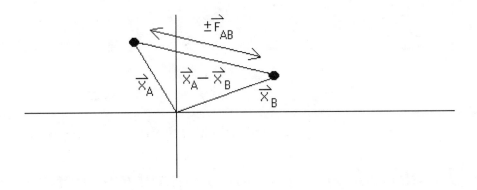

The total change in angular momentum between the two particles is zero, the sum of these two terms:

$$\Delta \vec{l} = (\overline{X_A} - \overline{X_B}) \times \vec{F}\Delta t = 0$$

9.2

The vector $(\overline{X_A} - \overline{X_B})$ is parallel to $\boldsymbol{F}$, as can be readily seen from the diagram, and the cross product of two parallel vectors is always zero. For all other combinations of particles in the swarm, this argument holds true. Therefore angular momentum is conserved under the assumption that the forces exerted by particles upon each other are along their mutual line of sight.

For relativistic rather than Newtonian force, the geometry of this situation is not changed. In relativity, however, when a particle $A$ exerts a force on another particle $B$, particle $B$ feels the force from $A$ at what is called $A$'s *retarded position* (assuming that particle $A$ is moving relative to particle $B$). That is, $B$ feels a force pulling toward $A$'s location at a previous time, at a time interval equal to the distance between $B$'s location and $A$'s previous location divided by the speed of light. This is true for electromagnetic influences because of the wave character of Maxwell's equations. In special relativity influences cannot propagate at speeds faster than light. Therefore the reasoning that demonstrates angular momentum conservation for the swarm of particles applies only in local regions of space-time where particles are very close together. For particles separated by large distances, angular momentum, along with energy and momentum, is propagated between objects at speeds no greater than the speed of light. The total angular momentum of a system can be found by integration of angular momentum density, over a given volume. (The flow of energy, momentum, and angular momentum through electromagnetic fields will be explored in later chapters.)

Of the four known forces in nature, only the two long-range forces, gravity and electromagnetism, transfer angular momentum across long distances (the strong and weak nuclear forces transfer it only over very small distances). In spite of these complications, the total angular momentum of a closed system is conserved in relativity, as it is in classical mechanics. The relativistic angular momentum and torque, for a point mass with rest mass $m$ traveling at speed $v$ relative to the origin of an inertial frame, is:

$$\bar{\tau} = \bar{r} \times \frac{d}{dt}\left(\frac{m\bar{v}}{\sqrt{1-v^2/c^2}}\right) = \bar{r} \times \frac{d}{dt}\,\bar{p}$$

$$\bar{l} = \bar{r} \times \left(\frac{m\bar{v}}{\sqrt{1-v^2/c^2}}\right) = \bar{r} \times \bar{p}$$

9.3

The classical relationship between torque and angular momentum also holds in special relativity:

$$\bar{\tau} = \frac{d\bar{l}}{dt} = \bar{v} \times (\gamma m\bar{v}) + \bar{r} \times \frac{d}{dt}(\gamma m\bar{v}) = \bar{r} \times \frac{d}{dt}(\gamma m\bar{v})$$

The same units apply as well. Torque, for example, is still measured in Joules per radian. What relationships do relativistic torque and angular momentum have to relativistic work and momentum? Because the only difference is the use of relativistic force rather than Newtonian force, the classical relations hold. From the equations in (9.3) above, it is apparent that $\bar{r} \times d\bar{p} = \bar{\tau}dt = d\bar{l}$. Therefore, work done on mass $m$ by an applied torque can be calculated by the methods of classical physics. Equation (9.4) relates the line integral of torque through an angle, or the line integral of angular momentum over angular velocity:

$$W = \int \bar{F} \bullet d\bar{s} = \int \frac{d\bar{p}}{dt} \bullet d\bar{s} = \int \bar{v} \bullet d\bar{p}$$

$$= \int (\bar{\omega} \times \bar{r}) \bullet d\bar{p} = \int \bar{\omega} \bullet (\bar{r} \times d\bar{p}) = \int \bar{\omega} \bullet \bar{\tau} dt$$

9.4

The last term in (9.4) can be written in two ways:

$$W = \int \bar{\tau} \bullet \bar{\omega} dt = \int \bar{\tau} \bullet d\bar{\beta}$$

$$W = \int \bar{\tau} \bullet \bar{\omega} dt = \int \bar{\omega} \bullet d\bar{l}$$

9.5

In space-time, angular momentum is generalized to a second order tensor, $l^{ij} = x^i p^j - x^j p^i$ , where the $p$'s are the 4-momentum vector. (Four-momentum vectors and tensors are covered in later chapters.)

## Relativistic Force Transformations

To study electromagnetic forces it is important to understand how forces transform between Lorentz inertial frames. With the definition of relativistic momentum in hand, this is comparatively easy. To study relativistic force transformation, however, power comes into the equations. In relativity, power has the same definition as in classical physics: the rate at which energy changes. Differential change in work done on a particle is equal to the force vector dot product of the differential change in the displacement vector:

$$dE = \bar{F} \bullet d\bar{s}$$

Here **F** is the relativistic force. Divide both sides of this equation by the differential $dt$:

$$\frac{dE}{dt} = \bar{F} \bullet \frac{d\bar{s}}{dt} = \bar{F} \bullet \bar{u}$$

9.6

Two methods can be used to calculate how forces transform between inertial frames. The first method uses Newton's second law and substitutes transformations for variables involved in that law. The second relies on the ways momentum and energy transform between inertial frames.

*Method One.* Consider a particle with rest mass $m$ and velocity vector $\bar{u}$ changing over time. In two different inertial frames, the forces acting on a particle can be calculated by the relativistic version of Newton's third law:

$$\bar{F} = \frac{d}{dt}\left( \frac{m\bar{u}}{\sqrt{1-u^2/c^2}} \right)$$

$$\bar{F}' = \frac{d}{dt'}\left( \frac{m\bar{u}'}{\sqrt{1-u'^2/c^2}} \right)$$

9.7

The equations in (9.7) can be used to calculate the transformation of forces. To transform the last equation of (9.7) into the unprimed terms of the first equation, we need only transform time and speed $u$. Using the equations $dt'=\gamma (dt - vdx/c^2)$ and $dx = u_x dt$, and substituting these for the primed values into the last equation of (9.7), gives the primed components of the primed force vector expressed in terms of its unprimed counterpart:

$$\bar{F}' = \frac{1}{\gamma\left(1-\frac{u_x v}{c^2}\right)} \frac{d}{dt}\left[ \frac{m\left(1-\frac{u_x v}{c^2}\right)}{\sqrt{1-\frac{v^2}{c^2}}\sqrt{1-\frac{u^2}{c^2}}}\left[ \frac{u_x - v}{\left(1-\frac{u_x v}{c^2}\right)}, \frac{u_y}{\gamma\left(1-\frac{u_x v}{c^2}\right)}, \frac{u_z}{\gamma\left(1-\frac{u_x v}{c^2}\right)} \right] \right]$$

9.8

After some simplification we have:

$$\bar{F}' = \frac{1}{(1-u_x v/c^2)}\cdot\left[ f_x - v\frac{d}{dt}(m\gamma_u), \frac{f_y}{\gamma}, \frac{f_z}{\gamma} \right]$$

9.9

To complete the force transformations, use the equation $d(m\gamma_u)/dt = (1/c^2)(dE/dt)$ and substitute $dE/dt = \bar{F}\bullet\bar{u} = f_x u_x + f_y u_y + f_z u_z$ to re-express equation (9.9) totally in terms of forces. The end result of this calculation is summarized in (9.13) below.

*Method Two.* Another way to calculate transformation of force between inertial frames is to differentiate equations (9.10), which relate how momentum and energy transform with respect to time:

$$p'_x = \gamma(p_x - Ev/c^2)$$
$$p'_y = p_y$$
$$p'_z = p_z$$
$$E' = \gamma(E - vp_x)$$

9.10

Apply the operator in (9.11) to the equations in (9.10):

$$\frac{d}{dt'} = \frac{1}{\gamma(1 - u_x v/c^2)} \cdot \frac{d}{dt}$$

9.11

We now have:

$$\frac{dp'_x}{dt'} = \frac{\dfrac{dp_x}{dt} - \dfrac{v}{c^2}\dfrac{dE}{dt}}{1 - \dfrac{u_x v}{c^2}}$$

$$\frac{dp'_y}{dt'} = \frac{dp_y/dt}{\gamma\left(1 - \dfrac{u_x v}{c^2}\right)}$$

$$\frac{dp'_z}{dt'} = \frac{dp_z/dt}{\gamma\left(1 - \dfrac{u_x v}{c^2}\right)}$$

9.12

The equation $dE'/dt' = (dE/dt - vf_x)/(1 - u_x v/c^2)$ can be ignored because here only forces are being considered. Substituting $dE/dt = \vec{F} \bullet \vec{u} = f_x u_x + f_y u_y + f_z u_z$, $f_i = dp_i/dt$ and $f'_i = dp'_i/dt'$ into (9.12), the force transformation are then:

$$f'_x = f_x - \frac{vu_y/c^2}{(1-u_xv/c^2)}f_y - \frac{vu_z/c^2}{(1-u_xv/c^2)}f_z$$

$$f'_y = f_y \frac{\sqrt{1-v^2/c^2}}{(1-u_xv/c^2)}$$

$$f'_z = f_z \frac{\sqrt{1-v^2/c^2}}{(1-u_xv/c^2)}$$

9.13

For the inverse transformations, these calculations can be performed using the inverse relations for all quantities or, as usual, by changing all primed quantities to unprimed quantities and substituting $v$ for $-v$:

$$f_x = f'_x + \frac{vu'_y/c^2}{(1+u'_xv/c^2)}f'_y + \frac{vu'_z/c^2}{(1+u'_xv/c^2)}f'_z$$

$$f_y = f'_y \frac{\sqrt{1-v^2/c^2}}{(1+u'_xv/c^2)}$$

$$f_z = f'_z \frac{\sqrt{1-v^2/c^2}}{(1+u'_xv/c^2)}$$

9.14

These equations explain the transformation of forces from one inertial frame to another. An object in one inertial frame, traveling with velocity $u$ and exerting a force $F$, travels with speed $u'$ and exerts a force $F'$ in the other inertial frame. In Newtonian and relativistic physics forces cause objects to change velocity. If a vector field of forces is being transformed, the primed quantities of (9.13) will be functions of the unprimed coordinates. Therefore, the inverse Lorentz transformations must be substituted to get the primed force quantities in terms of the primed inertial frame's coordinates. As electromagnetic forces cause objects to change speeds, the equations given above will be essential to understanding the electromagnetic force.

## Exercises

1. For the special cases where $\bar{a} \bullet \bar{v} = 0$, show that $\overline{F} = m'\bar{a}$ where $m' = \gamma m$ as usual.

2. Carry out the relativistic equivalent of this classical problem. An object of mass $m$ is divided into two equal parts separated by a thin rod at distance $2r_1$ and rotating about the center of mass. The radial distance from the center of mass changes from $r_1$ to $r_2$. By the conservation of angular momentum we know that $m_1 v_1 r_1 = m_2 v_2 r_2$ and the new speed of the masses is calculated to be $v_2 = v_1 r_1 / r_2$.

3. Calculate the relativistic torque at the origin for an object traveling in a circle centered on the origin. Only the tangential speed of the object changes.

4. In one inertial frame a particle travels with velocity $u = (0, c/3, 0)$ and is subject to a force $F = (0, 10N, 15N)$. What force and velocity does the particle have in another inertial frame traveling at four-fifths of the speed of light? Assume that the motion between inertial frames is along the $x$ axes as usual.

5. Write the magnitude of relativistic angular momentum in terms of the magnitudes of position and velocity vectors for a point mass. Assume that the angular momentum is relative to the origin of a coordinate system.

6. If a force vector is finite in one inertial frame, can it be infinite in any other inertial frames with relative velocity less than the speed of light?

7. Show that equations (9.13) and (9.14) are inverses of each other.

# CHAPTER 10

# *Relativistic Electrodynamics*

IN STUDYING ELECTROMAGNETIC PHENOMENA, it is customary to start with *Gauss's law,* which states that the surface integral of the electric field, over a surface enclosing a charge $q$, is proportional to the electric charge:

$$\iint_S \vec{E} \cdot d\vec{A} = q/\varepsilon_0$$

10.1

The constant $\varepsilon_o$ is $8.85418781762 \times 10^{-12}$ $C^2sec^2/Kg\text{-}m^3$. Using spherical symmetry for a point charge, Gauss's law simplifies in such a way that we can find Coulomb's law, which gives the force of an electric field on a point charge $q$. Gauss's law for a charge $q$ inside a sphere is $(E)(4\pi r^2) = q/\varepsilon_o$. This, together with the equation $F = qE$, allows calculation of the force between two charges, $F = q_2 E = q_1 q_2/4\pi\varepsilon_o r^2$. Gauss's law is written above in integral form. To write it in differential form requires only that we use the divergence theorem on the surface integral and write the electric charge as a volume integral of charge density. Then, by the methods explained in chapter one, Gauss's law can be written in differential form:

$$div\overline{E} = \rho/\varepsilon_0$$

10.2

Both the electric field and the charge density are functions of space and time. From the study of electrostatics comes the *potential,* an important electrostatic quantity that can be calculated by dividing the electrostatic potential energy of a given charge by the charge itself. For a point charge the potential is:

$$\phi = \frac{1}{4\pi\varepsilon_0}\frac{q}{r}$$

10.3

To find the Coulomb potential, we can use equation (10.4), which holds true by direct substitution. Let $r = \sqrt{x^2 + y^2 + z^2}$ , we get:

$$\overline{E} = -grad\phi = -\left(\frac{\partial\phi}{\partial x},\frac{\partial\phi}{\partial y},\frac{\partial\phi}{\partial z}\right) = \frac{q}{4\pi\varepsilon_0 r^3}(x,y,z)$$

10.4

The equation $\mathbf{E} = -grad\phi$ only holds true for electrostatic cases. By the fundamental theorem of line integrals, the line integral of the gradient of the potential is merely the negative of the change in potential. Because the electric field is a conservative field, the line integral of the gradient of the potential is not dependent upon the path between any two end points. The electrostatic potential energy at any location for a charge $q$ can be found by $q\phi$. Equation (10.2) can be written in terms of the potential by substituting $\mathbf{E} = -grad\phi$ into (10.2):

$$Lap(\phi) = -\rho/\varepsilon_0$$

10.5

Next let us consider the modifications demanded by special relativity for electromagnetic theory. In relativity, the mass of an object increases relative to an inertial frame by the amount $\gamma m$. We might expect the electric charge of a particle to increase similarly as $\gamma q$. But ordinary experience, experiments in electric charge, and the principles of basic atomic theory show that it does not. If electric charge increased with speed, then each atom would possess excess negative charge because of the motion of its electrons about its positively charged nucleus. Moreover, if charge increased with speed, then dropping a charged object in a gravitational field would increase the charge as the speed of fall increased. Electric charge would therefore not be a conserved quantity, and Gauss's law would have to be modified so that the charge inside a closed volume was a function of its speed.

Experiments clearly demonstrate that electric charge is a conserved quantity. Because of this, the electric charge of an object is independent of its speed and Gauss's law is true. As shown above, if charge increased with speed, matter could not maintain its basic structure. To illustrate, consider the effect of an electric charge that increased with speed upon an atom with atomic number $N$. The nucleus has electrical charge $+Ne$. Surrounding this would be a swarm of electrons with total charge greater than $-Ne$, because each electron travels with some speed. The excess negative charge on atoms would add up for large collections of matter. Two one-gram samples of matter separated by about one meter, for example, would mutually repel each other with forces at least tens to hundreds of billions of Newtons. The fact that matter is electrically neutral—with one electron for each proton in the nucleus—combined with the fact that electrons move at a continuum of different speeds inside matter, shows that electric charge does not change with speed. Thus if an object has charge $q$ in one inertial frame, then it has that same charge in every other inertial frame, and the charge of an object is independent of the inertial frame in which it is stationed.

It has been shown in experiments that the charge to mass ratio of subatomic particles changes with speed in proportion to a constant charge divided by relativistic mass. Now, the mass of an object increases by the inverse of the amount its volume shrinks due to length contraction in the direction of motion. These two factors require that the mass density change by $\gamma^2$ multiplied by rest mass density. But since electric charge is invariant, the charge density should change according to the equation $\gamma\rho$, because charge divided by volume is inversely proportional to the contraction ratio. Current density then must change by the amount $\bar{j} = \gamma\rho\bar{u}$, and charge density by the amount $\gamma\rho$, where $\rho$ is the charge density in the inertial frame in which the charges are stationary. But this is an exact analogy to the ways in which momentum ($\bar{p} = \gamma m\bar{u}$) and energy ($E = \gamma mc^2$) change with speed. The transformation laws for energy and momentum are already known. Because charge density and current density are of the same mathematical form, they transform in the same fashion:

$$j'_x = \gamma\,(j_x - \rho v)$$
$$j'_y = j_y$$
$$j'_z = j_z$$
$$\rho' = \gamma\,(\rho - v j_x / c^2)$$

10.6

Like the inverses of momentum and energy, the inverses of charge density and current are found by swapping the primed and unprimed quantities and changing $-v$ to $+v$.

Some unusual consequences come from these transformations. Consider a wire with positive and negative electrical charges equally spaced, so that the total charge density is zero. In the inertial frame in which the wire is stationary, if either the positive or the negative set of charges is moving, then we have two different charge densities and two different current densities. If the negative charges are moving, they have a non-zero current density, while the stationary positive charges have a zero current density. Now assume that the negative charge density plus the positive charge density equals zero. If these transformations are applied to both the charge and current densities of the positive and negative charges, then in another inertial frame the total charge density of the wire is not zero. Therefore a charged particle at rest in different inertial frame must feel an electric force and move accordingly, say on a curved path. However, because in the original inertial frame there is no net electric charge, the curving path of this particle must result from some new force. From this we can posit another electric-like force, called the *magnetic force,* which is a function of electric current. Thus special relativity requires the existence of the magnetic force. We will see shortly that the properties of the magnetic force as required by relativity exactly match those of the magnetic force discovered empirically in the nineteenth century.

To explore the nature of the magnetic force, begin by considering two inertial frames which coincide at time $t = t' = 0$:

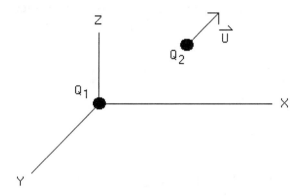

In one frame the charge $q_1$ is at rest at the origin and $q_2$ is moving at a velocity $\overline{u}$. In the other frame (for the most general case), both charges are moving, $q_1$ at velocity $(-v, 0, 0)$ and $q_2$ at velocity $\overline{u'}$. In the original inertial frame Coulomb's law gives the electric force on $q_2$:

$$\overline{F} = \frac{q_1 q_2}{4\pi\varepsilon_0 r^3}(x, y, z)$$

10.7

To calculate the force in another frame, we must employ force transformation equations, Lorentz transformations, and velocity transformations. Substitution of the Coulomb equation (10.7) into the force transformation equations from Chapter Nine gives:

$$F'_x = \frac{q_1 q_2 x}{4\pi\varepsilon_0 r^3} - \frac{u_y v/c^2}{(1 - u_x v/c^2)}\frac{q_1 q_2 y}{4\pi\varepsilon_0 r^3} - \frac{u_z v/c^2}{(1 - u_x v/c^2)}\frac{q_1 q_2 z}{4\pi\varepsilon_0 r^3}$$

$$F'_y = \frac{q_1 q_2 y}{4\pi\varepsilon_0 r^3}\frac{1}{\gamma(1 - u_x v/c^2)}$$

$$F'_z = \frac{q_1 q_2 z}{4\pi\varepsilon_0 r^3}\frac{1}{\gamma(1 - u_x v/c^2)}$$

10.8

Notice that the primed force components are expressed in terms of the unprimed $(u_x, u_y, u_z)$ and unprimed $(x, y, z)$. In order to see the force components expressed in terms of their corresponding primed quantities, substitute the inverse Lorentz transformations (4.11) and velocity transformations (4.24) into the equations in (10.8):

$$F'_x = \frac{q_1 q_2 \gamma}{4\pi\varepsilon_0 r'^3}\left( x' - \frac{v}{c^2}u'_y y' - \frac{v}{c^2}u'_z z' \right)$$

$$F'_y = \frac{q_1 q_2 \gamma}{4\pi\varepsilon_0 r'^3}\left( 1 + \frac{u'_x v}{c^2} \right) y'$$

$$F'_z = \frac{q_1 q_2 \gamma}{4\pi\varepsilon_0 r'^3}\left( 1 + \frac{u'_x v}{c^2} \right) z'$$

10.9

Because $t$ was set to zero here, $x'$ is merely $\gamma x$. This gives the force on $q_2$, in the primed inertial frame, at time zero. In the primed inertial frame $r'=r$, which is the retarded distance of $q_1$ from $q_2$. These equations can be put in vector form and partitioned as a Coulomb charge plus another term. Equation (10.9) then becomes:

$$\overline{F'} = \frac{q_1 q_2 \gamma}{4\pi\varepsilon_0 r'^3}(x', y', z') + \frac{v q_1 q_2 \gamma}{4\pi\varepsilon_0 c^2 r'^3}(-u'_z z' - u'_y y', u'_x y', u'_x z')$$

10.10

The vector part of the non-Coulomb term can be written as the cross product of two vectors:

$$(-u'_z z' - u'_y y', u'_x y', u'_x z') = (0, -z', y') \times (u'_x, u'_y, u'_z)$$

10.11

In this way force in the primed inertial fame is expressed solely as a function of primed quantities. Splitting up the terms into an electric field $E$ and a new field $B$ can further parse the terms of equation (10.10):

$$\overline{E}' = \frac{q_1\gamma}{4\pi\varepsilon_0 r'^3}(x', y', z')$$

$$\overline{B}' = \frac{-vq_1\gamma\mu_0}{4\pi r'^3}(0, -z', y') = -\frac{\mu_0}{4\pi}\frac{vq_1\gamma}{r'^3}(0, -z', y')$$

$$\mu_0 = \frac{1}{\varepsilon_0 c^2}$$

10.12

Then if we apply (10.11) and (10.12) to (10.10), equation (10.10) can be written as:

$$\overline{F}' = q_2(\overline{E}' + \overline{u}' \times \overline{B}')$$

10.13

Equation (10.13) is called the *Lorentz force equation*. Electromagnetic force is simply the sum of electric force and magnetic force. Notice that a field that is purely electric in one inertial frame is both electric and magnetic in another inertial frame. So, just as time and mass are not absolute, electromagnetic fields arc not absolute. No field is purely electric in any absolute sense.

A charged particle moving in an electromagnetic field does so in accordance with the equation $d\left(\gamma m\overline{v}\right)/dt = q\left(\overline{E} + \overline{v} \times \overline{B}\right)$. To calculate the transformation of electric and magnetic fields between different inertial frames, use the Lorentz force equation. From the principle of special relativity, the laws of physics are the same in every inertial frame. Equation (10.13) can be transformed into its unprimed counterpart $\overline{F} = q_2(\overline{E} + \overline{u} \times \overline{B})$ by substituting the unprimed component values of $\overline{F} = q_2(\overline{E} + \overline{u} \times \overline{B})$ into the force transformation equations, (9.13), and equating them with the components of (10.13). Also substitute in the velocities $u$ and $u'$, recalling their transformations as given in (4.17), (4.18) and (4.19). By equating all terms with the coefficients $(u_x, u_y, u_z)$ it is easy to find the transformations of the primed and unprimed values of $E$ and $B$. This is because the only unprimed quantities in the equations are primed and unprimed $E$'s and $B$'s. While this method does not provide us with the transformations for $E'_y$ and $E'_z$, they are easily calculated from the others. The transformations of electromagnetic fields between inertial frames are now tabulated:

$$E'_x = E_x$$
$$E'_y = \gamma(E_y - vB_z)$$
$$E'_z = \gamma(E_z + vB_y)$$
$$B'_x = B_x$$
$$B'_y = \gamma(B_y + vE_z/c^2)$$
$$B'_z = \gamma(B_z - vE_y/c^2)$$

10.14

These are the transformation equations for electric and magnetic fields. Their inverses are given by:

$$E_x = E'_x$$
$$E_y = \gamma(E'_y + vB'_z)$$
$$E_z = \gamma(E'_z - vB'_y)$$
$$B_x = B'_x$$
$$B_y = \gamma(B'_y - vE'_z/c^2)$$
$$B_z = \gamma(B'_z + vE'_y/c^2)$$

## Maxwell's Equations and Magnetic Monopoles

Now we can investigate how electric and magnetic fields change as functions of space and time. We know from calculus that when $G$ is a function of $x, y, z$ and $w$ and each of these are functions of $x', y', z',$ and $w'$, the partial derivatives of $G$, with respect to a primed variable, can be calculated by the chain rule. Take the partial derivative of $G$ with respect to $h'$, where $h'$ is any of the variables $x', y', z',$ or $w'$, to get:

$$\frac{\partial G}{\partial h'} = \frac{\partial x}{\partial h'}\frac{\partial G}{\partial x} + \frac{\partial y}{\partial h'}\frac{\partial G}{\partial y} + \frac{\partial z}{\partial h'}\frac{\partial G}{\partial z} + \frac{\partial w}{\partial h'}\frac{\partial G}{\partial w}$$

And from this we get an operator:

$$\frac{\partial}{\partial h'} = \frac{\partial x}{\partial h'}\frac{\partial}{\partial x} + \frac{\partial y}{\partial h'}\frac{\partial}{\partial y} + \frac{\partial z}{\partial h'}\frac{\partial}{\partial z} + \frac{\partial w}{\partial h'}\frac{\partial}{\partial w}$$

Applying this kind of analysis to Lorentz transformations, we can examine how changes in $E$ and $B$ in one inertial frame correspond to changes in $E'$ and $B'$ in another frame. To do this, it is useful to use operators. Because partial derivatives exist with respect to the primed space-time co-ordinates, we must use inverse Lorentz transformations to derive operators for the Lorentz transformations. This leaves us with the operators in (10.15):

$$\frac{\partial}{\partial x'} = \gamma\frac{\partial}{\partial x} + \gamma\frac{v}{c^2}\frac{\partial}{\partial t}$$

$$\frac{\partial}{\partial y'} = \frac{\partial}{\partial y}$$

$$\frac{\partial}{\partial z'} = \frac{\partial}{\partial z}$$

$$\frac{\partial}{\partial t'} = \gamma\frac{\partial}{\partial t} + \gamma v\frac{\partial}{\partial x}$$

10.15

Gauss's law tells us that the divergence of an electric field equals charge density divided by a constant. To study the relationship between current density and the strength of electric and magnetic fields, we must use on the electric field the operators given above. Because by special relativity the laws of physics are the same in all inertial frames, we must analyze Gauss's law in two different inertial frames, $div\overline{E'} = \rho'/\varepsilon_0$ and $div\overline{E} = \rho/\varepsilon_0$, to see what this requires for current density. Applying the above operators (10.15) to the electric components of (10.14) gives:

$$\frac{\partial E'_x}{\partial x'} = \gamma \left( \frac{\partial E_x}{\partial x} + \frac{v}{c^2} \frac{\partial E_x}{\partial t} \right)$$

$$\frac{\partial E'_y}{\partial y'} = \gamma \left( \frac{\partial E_y}{\partial y} - v \frac{\partial B_z}{\partial y} \right)$$

$$\frac{\partial E'_z}{\partial z'} = \gamma \left( \frac{\partial E_z}{\partial z} + v \frac{\partial B_y}{\partial z} \right)$$

10.16

Adding these three equations together and substituting Gauss's law for the divergence of $E$, in both the primed and unprimed quantities, gives:

$$\frac{\rho'}{\varepsilon_0} = \gamma \left[ \frac{\rho}{\varepsilon_0} - \frac{v}{c^2} \left( \left( \frac{\partial B_z}{\partial y} - \frac{\partial B_y}{\partial z} \right) c^2 - \frac{\partial E_x}{\partial t} \right) \right]$$

10.17

As seen previously, charge density transforms between inertial frames by the last equation in (10.6). Dividing this equation by $\varepsilon_o$ gives:

$$\frac{\rho'}{\varepsilon_0} = \gamma \left( \frac{\rho}{\varepsilon_0} - \frac{v}{c^2} \frac{j_x}{\varepsilon_0} \right)$$

10.18

Comparing equation (10.17) to equation (10.18) gives the relation:

$$\frac{j_x}{\varepsilon_0} = \left( \frac{\partial B_z}{\partial y} - \frac{\partial B_y}{\partial z} \right) c^2 - \frac{\partial E_x}{\partial t}$$

10.19

This equation shows how the $x$-component of current density is related to electric and magnetic fields. To study the relationships of the remaining components of current density to electric and magnetic fields, note that the first term of (10.19) is the $x$-component of *Curl B*, and the last term the $x$-component of the partial derivative of $E$ with respect to time. It is reasonable, then, to state that electric and magnetic fields are related to current densities by:

$$\frac{\overline{j}}{\varepsilon_0 c^2} = curl\,\overline{B} - \frac{1}{c^2}\frac{\partial \overline{E}}{\partial t}$$

10.20

This equation, immediately recognizable as *Ampère's law,* can be tested to ensure that all of its components are compatible with the transformation equations of current and charge densities. The primed version of the equation (10.20), $\overline{j}'/\varepsilon_0 c^2 = curl\,\overline{B}' - (1/c^2)\partial\overline{E}'/\partial t'$, is transformed to its unprimed twin by using the transformation operators in (10.15) on the transformation equations for electric and magnetic fields, (10.14). First, the *x*-component of current density is transformed from the primed inertial frame to the unprimed inertial frame:

$$\frac{j'_x}{\varepsilon_0 c^2} = \frac{\partial B'_z}{\partial y'} - \frac{\partial B'_y}{\partial z'} - \frac{1}{c^2}\frac{\partial E'_x}{\partial t'}$$

$$= \gamma\left(\left(\frac{\partial B_z}{\partial y} - \frac{\partial B_y}{\partial z} - \frac{1}{c^2}\frac{\partial E_x}{\partial t}\right) - \frac{v}{c^2}\left(\frac{\partial E_x}{\partial x} + \frac{\partial E_y}{\partial y} + \frac{\partial E_z}{\partial z}\right)\right)$$

$$= \gamma\left(\frac{j_x}{\varepsilon_0 c^2} - \frac{v}{c^2}div\,\overline{E}\right)$$

$$= \frac{\gamma}{\varepsilon_0 c^2}(j_x - v\rho)$$

10.21

This satisfies the first equation of (10.6). The *y* and *z* components of charge density are handled in the same manner and, after some manipulation, transform as:

$$\frac{j'_y}{\varepsilon_0 c^2} = \left(\frac{\partial B'_x}{\partial z'} - \frac{\partial B'_z}{\partial x'} - \frac{1}{c^2}\frac{\partial E'_y}{\partial t'}\right) = \left(\frac{\partial B_x}{\partial z} - \frac{\partial B_z}{\partial x} - \frac{1}{c^2}\frac{\partial E_y}{\partial t}\right) = \frac{j_y}{\varepsilon_0 c^2}$$

$$\frac{j'_z}{\varepsilon_0 c^2} = \left(\frac{\partial B'_y}{\partial x'} - \frac{\partial B'_x}{\partial y'} - \frac{1}{c^2}\frac{\partial E'_z}{\partial t'}\right) = \left(\frac{\partial B_y}{\partial x} - \frac{\partial B_x}{\partial y} - \frac{1}{c^2}\frac{\partial E_z}{\partial t}\right) = \frac{j_z}{\varepsilon_0 c^2}$$

10.22

These satisfy the transformations for the $y$ and $z$ components of (10.6). The considerations above, taken together, leave us with two equations, Gauss's law and Ampère's law:

$$div\overline{E} = \frac{\rho}{\varepsilon_0}$$

$$curl\overline{B} = \frac{\overline{j}}{\varepsilon_0 c^2} + \frac{1}{c^2}\frac{\partial \overline{E}}{\partial t}$$

10.23

Examination of this approach to Ampère's law suggests that the magnetic field can be approached in a similar way by studying the divergence of $\boldsymbol{B}$. Using the same operators in (10.15) and applying them to the magnetic components of (10.14) gives three equations:

$$\frac{\partial B'_x}{\partial x'} = \gamma \left( \frac{\partial B_x}{\partial x} + \frac{v}{c^2}\frac{\partial B_x}{\partial t} \right)$$

$$\frac{\partial B'_y}{\partial y'} = \gamma \left( \frac{\partial B_y}{\partial y} + \frac{v}{c^2}\frac{\partial E_z}{\partial y} \right)$$

$$\frac{\partial B'_z}{\partial z'} = \gamma \left( \frac{\partial B_z}{\partial z} - \frac{v}{c^2}\frac{\partial E_y}{\partial z} \right)$$

10.24

Adding these three equations together gives:

$$div\overline{B'} = \gamma \left( div\overline{B} + \frac{v}{c^2}\left( \frac{\partial B_x}{\partial t} + \frac{\partial E_z}{\partial y} - \frac{\partial E_y}{\partial z} \right) \right)$$

10.25

Clearly, the rightmost parenthesized term in (10.25) is the $x$-component of $\partial \overline{B}/\partial t + curl\overline{E}$. Its transformation can be calculated by applying the operators of (10.15) to the equations in (10.14):

$$\frac{\partial B'_x}{\partial t'} + \frac{\partial E'_z}{\partial y'} - \frac{\partial E'_y}{\partial z'} = \gamma \left( \left( \frac{\partial B_x}{\partial t} + \frac{\partial E_z}{\partial y} - \frac{\partial E_y}{\partial z} \right) + v div\overline{B} \right)$$

10.26

Transformations of the $y$ and $z$ components of $\partial \overline{B}/\partial t + curl\,\overline{E}$ result from applying (10.15) to (10.14) again. The final results are:

$$\frac{\partial B'_y}{\partial t'} + \frac{\partial E'_x}{\partial z'} - \frac{\partial E'_z}{\partial x'} = \frac{\partial B_y}{\partial t} + \frac{\partial E_x}{\partial z} - \frac{\partial E_z}{\partial x}$$

$$\frac{\partial B'_z}{\partial t'} + \frac{\partial E'_y}{\partial x'} - \frac{\partial E'_x}{\partial y'} = \frac{\partial B_z}{\partial t} + \frac{\partial E_y}{\partial x} - \frac{\partial E_x}{\partial y}$$

10.27

We make the definitions:

$$div\,\overline{B} = \frac{\rho_m}{\varepsilon_0 c^2}$$

$$-\frac{\partial \overline{B}}{\partial t} - curl\,\overline{E} = \frac{\overline{j_m}}{\varepsilon_0 c^2}$$

10.28

Now equation (10.25), (10.26), and (10.27) become the equations in (10.29) which are transformations similar to those of charge and current density for the electric field:

$$j'_{mx} = \gamma\,(j_{mx} - v\rho_m)$$

$$j'_{my} = j_{my}$$

$$j'_{mz} = j_{mz}$$

$$\rho'_m = \gamma\,(\rho_m - j_{mx}v/c^2)$$

10.29

Here $\rho_m$ is called the *magnetic charge density* and $\overline{j_m} = \rho_m\overline{u}$ is called the *magnetic current density*. The equations in (10.28) relate magnetic charge and current densities to electric and magnetic field strengths. Combining these with Gauss's law and Ampère's law, we get Maxwell's equations with magnetic monopoles (10.30):

$$div\,\overline{E} = \frac{\rho}{\varepsilon_0}$$

$$c^2 curl\,\overline{B} - \frac{\partial \overline{E}}{\partial t} = \frac{\overline{j}}{\varepsilon_0}$$

$$c^2 div\,\overline{B} = \frac{\rho_m}{\varepsilon_0}$$

$$-c^2 curl\,\overline{E} - c^2 \frac{\partial \overline{B}}{\partial t} = \frac{\overline{j_m}}{\varepsilon_0}$$

10.30

The constant $\varepsilon_0 c^2$ is used to set the quantity and units of magnetic monopole charges and their currents. A different constant could have been used in the equations of (10.28).

What are magnetic monopoles? Subatomic particles have both positive and negative electrical charges: electrons negative, protons positive. Magnetic fields are always observed to have both positive and negative "charges," a north pole is always associated with a south pole. If a bar magnet is chopped in half, in an attempt to make two magnets (one with a north magnetic pole and one with a south magnetic pole), we get two magnets each with a north and south magnetic pole. Subatomic particles, apparently, cannot have just a north magnetic pole or south magnetic pole. Magnetic monopoles are subatomic particles that have only a north or south magnetic pole. If such particles existed, the equations given in (10.28) would characterize its relationships to electric and magnetic fields. If such object do not exists, $\rho_m = 0$ and $\overline{j_m} = 0$ , then the equations in (10.30) reduce to the standard Maxwell equations for electromagnetism. So far there is no experimental evidence for magnetic monopoles. Some grand unified theories predict the existence of magnetic monopoles, however it is not known if magnetic monopoles exist or can exist. The so far undiscovered grand unified field theory may or may not allow for the existence of magnetic monopoles. This subject is one of the great remaining mysteries of physics.

## The Electromagnetic Vector Potential

Electric and magnetic fields can store potential energy. Under the assumption that magnetic monopoles do not exist, what are the equations for electromagnetic potential energy? For a static electric field with potential $\phi$, a charge $q$ has potential energy $q\phi$. Suppose that along the $y$-axis in an inertial frame there are two charges, each with a charge $q$, separated by the constant distance $r$. Assuming that each charge is of equal mass $m$, the total energy of this system is:

$$E = 2mc^2 + \frac{q^2}{4\pi\varepsilon_0 r}$$

10.31

In another inertial frame, moving in the $x$-direction at speed $v$ relative to the first, it may be assumed naïvely that the total energy is given by (10.32). This is because, although the mass has increased by the normal relativistic amount, $r$ does not change because it is perpendicular to the direction of relative motion.

$$E' = 2\gamma mc^2 + \frac{q^2}{4\pi\varepsilon_0 r}$$

10.32

Equation (10.32) is incorrect. If we apply the momentum and energy transformation laws to (10.31), we get:

$$p'_x = \gamma\left(p_x - \frac{vE}{c^2}\right) = \gamma\left[0 - \frac{v}{c^2}\left(2mc^2 + \frac{q^2}{4\pi\varepsilon_0 r}\right)\right]$$

$$p'_y = p_y$$

$$p'_z = p_z$$

$$E' = \gamma(E - vp_x) = \gamma\left[\left(2mc^2 + \frac{q^2}{4\pi\varepsilon_0 r}\right) - 0\right]$$

10.33

Clearly, total energy in the primed inertial frame is given not by equation (10.32), but by the last equation in (10.33), a difference of $(\gamma - 1)q^2/4\pi\varepsilon_0 r$. From the original inertial frame the total potential energy is made greater by the relative motions of the two charges. As in the example of spring potential energy in Chapter Eight, potential energy itself has momentum and that contributes to the $x$-momentum given in (10.33). From these facts, we can deduce that the magnetic field generated by the moving charges must be storing potential energy, just as the electric field can store potential energy.

In classical electromagnetism the electric field was calculated by taking first partial derivatives of the electric potential, so it is natural to say that the magnetic field should also be derivable from first partial derivatives of a potential. Electric and magnetic fields can transform into each other in different inertial frames, and it is reasonable to suggest that magnetic and electric fields can both be generated by taking first partial derivatives of a generalized common potential, a vector potential. Because space-time is a four-dimensional manifold, the vector potential should be a four-vector ($\phi$, $A_x$, $A_y$, $A_z$). This is called the *electromagnetic vector potential*. Any four-vector in special relativity is a first-order tensor and must transform according to the following formula, with the partial derivative terms corresponding to a Lorentz transformation:

$$A'^k = A^l \frac{\partial x'^k}{\partial x^l}$$

10.34

(These transformation laws will be reviewed later in the book.) The electromagnetic four-potential transforms as follows:

$$A'_x = \gamma \left( A_x - \frac{v}{c^2} \phi \right)$$
$$A'_y = A_y$$
$$A'_z = A_z$$
$$\phi' = \gamma \left( \phi - v A_x \right)$$

10.35

This transformation can be found by representing the four-vector as ($\varphi = \phi / c^2$, $A_x$, $A_y$, $A_z$) in equation (10.34). To see that the units work out correctly, think of the energy-momentum transformation equations as representing "electromagnetic energy," and divide both sides of all the equations in (10.33) by a charge $q$. The result is the same transformation as in (10.35). Inverses of these equations are found the usual way. To simplify the calculations, put all four components of the electromagnetic four-potential in the same units, as in the study of space-time discussed in earlier chapters. To study space-time, the time dimension was converted to units of distance by multiplying all time coordinates by the speed of light. Letting $A_w = \phi/c$ makes an analogous change, and (10.35) can be rewritten as:

$$A'_x = \gamma \left( A_x - \frac{v}{c} A_w \right)$$

$$A'_y = A_y$$

$$A'_z = A_z$$

$$A'_w = \gamma \left( A_w - \frac{v}{c} A_x \right)$$

10.36

To evaluate electric and magnetic fields as first partial derivatives of the potentials, we can use operators to see how changes in the potentials transform between inertial frames. Because all four components of the electromagnetic vector potential are in the same units, the operators must all be in the same units. This is easy to do in space-time. As in the chapter on space-time, the fourth dimension is expressed as $w = ct$. If we write the time dimension in terms of $w$, the operators in (10.15) become:

$$\frac{\partial}{\partial x'} = \gamma \frac{\partial}{\partial x} + \gamma \frac{v}{c} \frac{\partial}{\partial w}$$

$$\frac{\partial}{\partial y'} = \frac{\partial}{\partial y}$$

$$\frac{\partial}{\partial z'} = \frac{\partial}{\partial z}$$

$$\frac{\partial}{\partial w'} = \gamma \frac{\partial}{\partial w} + \gamma \frac{v}{c} \frac{\partial}{\partial x}$$

10.37

For static situations the electric field is found by means of the equation $E = -grad\phi$. The electric field strength is a function of the first partial derivatives of the potential. Assuming that magnetic monopoles do not exist, to find the set of partial derivatives of $(A_x, A_y, A_z)$ that would yield the magnetic field $\boldsymbol{B}$, note that the divergence of $\boldsymbol{B}$ is zero by the equations in (10.30). From calculus we know that $\boldsymbol{B}$ is the curl of some other vector field because the divergence of the curl of any vector field is always zero. On the basis of magnetic field properties as discussed so far, we can guess that the magnetic field is related to its potentials by the equation $\boldsymbol{B} = Curl\,\boldsymbol{A}$, where $\boldsymbol{A} = (A_x, A_y, A_z)$ and then check to see that this is consistent with the transformation properties of electric and magnetic fields. If $\boldsymbol{B} = Curl\,\boldsymbol{A}$ holds true in the unprimed inertial frame, then by the principle of special relativity, $\boldsymbol{B'} = Curl\,\boldsymbol{A'}$ must be true in the primed inertial frame. Using the vector potential transformation law in (10.36) and the Lorentz transformation operators in (10.37) we can check that the claim "$\boldsymbol{B'} = Curl\,\boldsymbol{A'}$ implies $\boldsymbol{B} = Curl\,\boldsymbol{A}$" satisfies the field transformations for $\boldsymbol{E}$ and $\boldsymbol{B}$. Applying the operators in (10.37) to the transformation law in (10.36) for $\boldsymbol{B} = Curl\,\boldsymbol{A}$ gives:

$$B'_x = \left( \frac{\partial A'_z}{\partial y'} - \frac{\partial A'_y}{\partial z'} \right) = \left( \frac{\partial A_z}{\partial y} - \frac{\partial A_y}{\partial z} \right)$$

$$B'_y = \left( \frac{\partial A'_x}{\partial z'} - \frac{\partial A'_z}{\partial x'} \right) = \gamma \left( \left( \frac{\partial A_x}{\partial z} - \frac{\partial A_z}{\partial x} \right) + \frac{v}{c}\left( -\frac{\partial A_w}{\partial z} - \frac{\partial A_z}{\partial w} \right) \right)$$

$$B'_z = \left( \frac{\partial A'_y}{\partial x'} - \frac{\partial A'_x}{\partial y'} \right) = \gamma \left( \left( \frac{\partial A_y}{\partial x} - \frac{\partial A_x}{\partial y} \right) - \frac{v}{c}\left( -\frac{\partial A_w}{\partial y} - \frac{\partial A_y}{\partial w} \right) \right)$$

10.38

Thus $B_x' = B_x$ satisfies the first $\boldsymbol{B}$ transformation of (10.14). However, the last two equations of (10.38) satisfy the other equations of (10.14) only if $E_z$ and $E_y$ are given by:

$$E_z = c\left( -\frac{\partial A_w}{\partial z} - \frac{\partial A_z}{\partial w} \right)$$

$$E_y = c\left( -\frac{\partial A_w}{\partial y} - \frac{\partial A_y}{\partial w} \right)$$

10.39

Substituting $cA_w = \phi$ and $t = w/c$, into (10.39) gives
$E_z = -\partial\phi/\partial z - \partial A_z/\partial t$, $E_y = -\partial\phi/\partial y - \partial A_y/\partial t$, which implies that

$E_x = -\partial\phi/\partial x - \partial A_x/\partial t$  or, in the previous notation for $E_y$ and $E_z$ in (10.39), $E_x$ is:

$$E_x = c\left(-\frac{\partial A_w}{\partial x} - \frac{\partial A_x}{\partial w}\right)$$

10.40

When written in vector notation, equation (10.39) and (10.40) are $\overline{E} = -grad\phi - \partial\overline{A}/\partial t$ . So the equation $\boldsymbol{B} = curl\,\boldsymbol{A}$ requires that $\boldsymbol{E}$ be given by the equation $\overline{E} = -grad\phi - \partial\overline{A}/\partial t$ . This value for the $\boldsymbol{E}$ field needs to have its transformation properties checked in addition to finishing up the test on $\boldsymbol{B} = Curl\,\boldsymbol{A}$.

The equation $\overline{E}' = -grad\phi' - \partial\overline{A}'/\partial t'$ must transform to $\overline{E} = -grad\phi - \partial\overline{A}/\partial t$ by applying the transformation operators of (10.37) to the vector potential (10.36). This gives the equations:

$$E'_x = \left(-\frac{\partial A'_w}{\partial x'} - \frac{\partial A'_x}{\partial w'}\right)c = \left(-\frac{\partial A_w}{\partial x} - \frac{\partial A_x}{\partial w}\right)c$$

$$E'_y = \left(-\frac{\partial A'_w}{\partial y'} - \frac{\partial A'_y}{\partial w'}\right)c = \gamma\left(\left(-\frac{\partial A_w}{\partial y} - \frac{\partial A_y}{\partial w}\right) - \frac{v}{c}\left(\frac{\partial A_y}{\partial x} - \frac{\partial A_x}{\partial y}\right)\right)c$$

$$E'_z = \left(-\frac{\partial A'_w}{\partial z'} - \frac{\partial A'_z}{\partial w'}\right)c = \gamma\left(\left(-\frac{\partial A_w}{\partial z} - \frac{\partial A_z}{\partial w}\right) + \frac{v}{c}\left(\frac{\partial A_x}{\partial z} - \frac{\partial A_z}{\partial x}\right)\right)c$$

10.41

The first equation of (10.14) is now satisfied for electric components. The other two, $E_y$ and $E_z$, are satisfied provided that $B_y = \partial A_x/\partial z - \partial A_z/\partial x$ and $B_z = \partial A_y/\partial x - \partial A_x/\partial y$ are both true, which they are. That finishes the test on $\boldsymbol{B} = Curl\,\boldsymbol{A}$. Also $E_y$ and $E_z$ match the correct values for the test on the equation $\overline{E} = -grad\phi - \partial\overline{A}/\partial t$ . The solutions for the electric and magnetic fields in terms of partial derivatives of the vector potential are:

$$\overline{E} = -grad\phi - \frac{\partial\overline{A}}{\partial t}$$

$$\overline{B} = curl\,\overline{A}$$

10.42

Taking the *curl* of the first equation and the divergence of the second equation of (10.42) gives:

$$curl\,\overline{E} = -\frac{\partial \overline{B}}{\partial t}$$

$$div\,\overline{B} = 0 \qquad\qquad 10.43$$

The *curl* of a gradient and the divergence of a *curl* are always zero. These two equations are immediately recognizable as *Gauss's law for the magnetic field* and *Faraday's law*. Further, (10.43) is simply (10.28) without magnetic monopoles. The results of these calculations show that relativistic electrodynamics requires no changes to the classical equations of electromagnetism. Maxwell's equations are given in (10.44).

$$div\,\overline{E} = \frac{\rho}{\varepsilon_0}$$

$$div\,\overline{B} = 0$$

$$curl\,\overline{E} = -\frac{\partial \overline{B}}{\partial t}$$

$$curl\,\overline{B} = \frac{\overline{j}}{c^2 \varepsilon_0} + \frac{1}{c^2}\frac{\partial \overline{E}}{\partial t} \qquad\qquad 10.44$$

### The Lorentz Gauge

Because previous calculations assumed that charge is invariant and conserved, this assumption also comes out of the equations. Taking the divergence of both sides of Ampère's law and substituting Gauss's law for the electric field gives the result:

$$0 = div\,\overline{j} + \frac{\partial \rho}{\partial t} \qquad\qquad 10.45$$

This is the *continuity equation for the conservation of electric charge.* The relationships between electromagnetic potentials and current and charge densities, have an infinite number of solutions because, for an arbitrary function $\lambda(x, y, z, t)$, the substitutions $\overline{A}' = \overline{A} + grad\,\lambda$ and $\phi' = \phi - \partial\lambda/\partial t$ leave the values of $E$ and $B$ unchanged. With this degree of freedom, called *gauge freedom,* it is possible to make the equations simpler. We can write the electromagnetic potentials as functions of charge and current densities by specifying the *Lorentz gauge:*

$$div\,\overline{A} = -\frac{1}{c^2}\frac{\partial\phi}{\partial t}$$

10.46

Then, taking the divergence of the first equation in (10.42) and substituting Gauss's law, we have:

$$\frac{\rho}{\varepsilon_0} = \frac{1}{c^2}\frac{\partial^2\phi}{\partial t^2} - lap\,\phi$$

10.47

Taking the curl of both sides of Ampère's law and substituting the Lorentz gauge, (10.46), gives:

$$\frac{\overline{j}}{\varepsilon_0 c^2} = \frac{1}{c^2}\frac{\partial^2\overline{A}}{\partial t^2} - lap\,\overline{A}$$

10.48

Using the *D'Alembrian operator,* $\Box = \left(1/c^2\right)\partial^2/\partial t^2 - lap$ , equation (10.47) and (10.48) can be written in the following way:

$$\Box\phi = \rho/\varepsilon_0$$
$$\Box\overline{A} = \overline{j}/\varepsilon_0 c^2$$

10.49

Equation (10.49) can be simplified in a notational sense by defining $A_v = \left(\overline{A}, \phi/c^2\right)$ and $j_v = \left(\overline{j}, \rho\right)$ . With these defintions, Maxwell's equations can be expressed in terms of the electromagnetic vector potential and four-current densities:

$$\Box A_v = \mu_0 j_v$$

## Generalizing The Biot-Savart Law

For electrostatics and magnetostatics the equations relating electromagnetic potentials to charge and current densities become:

$$lap\phi = -\rho/\varepsilon_0$$
$$lap\overline{A} = -\overline{j}/\varepsilon_0 c^2$$

10.50

The equations in (10.50) are just (10.47) and (10.48) when the potentials don't vary as a function of time. It is possible to find the solution for $\phi$ in terms of $\rho$ by seeing the potential at a point $\overline{X}_1$, for a small charge $q_2$, in a small region $dx_2 dy_2 dz_2$, where $q_2 = \rho\, dx_2 dy_2 dz_2$:

$$d^3\phi\,(x_1, y_1, z_1) = \frac{1}{4\pi\varepsilon_0 r_{12}}\,\rho\,(x_2, y_2, z_2)dx_2 dy_2 dz_2$$

$$r_{12} = \sqrt{(x_1 - x_2)^2 + (y_1 - y_2)^2 + (z_1 - z_2)^2}$$

This solution follows from the fact that electric potential, at any point, is inversely proportional to the distance from that point to the source. To solve for $\phi$, we need only take the volume integral over all of space:

$$\phi\,(x_1, y_1, z_1) = \iiint\limits_{all-space} \frac{\rho\,(x_2, y_2, z_2)}{4\pi\varepsilon_0 r_{12}}dx_2 dy_2 dz_2$$

10.51

Here $r_{12}$ is the distance between a charged particle with charge $q_1$, and the charge $q_2$. This solves the first equation of (10.50). Breaking the second equation of (10.50) into its three components, each component of $A$ has the same form as the first equation in (10.50). Because the second equation of (10.50) must have the same mathematical solution as in (10.51), solving it is easy:

$$\overline{A}\,(x_1, y_1, z_1) = \iiint\limits_{all-space} \frac{\overline{j}\,(x_2, y_2, z_2)}{4\pi\varepsilon_0 c^2 r_{12}}dx_2 dy_2 dz_2$$

10.52

The formal study of partial differential equations shows that these equations solve the Maxwell equations. It is now possible to calculate $B = Curl\,A$, by taking partial derivatives with respect to $(x_1, y_1, z_1)$, rather than $(x_2, y_2, z_2)$, and bringing the partial derivatives through the integrals. The one variable in the integrand that is a function of $(x_1, y_1, z_1)$ only is $r_{12}$. After differentiating and collecting the results in vector form, we get:

$$\overline{B}(x_1, y_1, z_1) = \iiint_{all-space} \frac{\overline{j}(x_2, y_2, z_2) \times \overline{r_{12}}}{4\pi\varepsilon_0 c^2 r_{12}^3} dx_2 dy_2 dz_2$$

10.53

Here, as before, $\overline{r_{12}} = (x_1 - x_2, y_1 - y_2, z_1 - z_2)$ and $r_{12}$ is the magnitude of $\overline{r_{12}}$. Using $j\Delta V = jAds = ids$, for steady currents in a thin long wire, the volume integral in (10.53) can be very nearly approximated by the integral:

$$\overline{B} = \frac{\mu_0}{4\pi} \int \frac{id\overline{s} \times \overline{r_{12}}}{r_{12}^3}$$

10.54

This is the Biot-Savart law of steady currents. Equations (10.51) and (10.52) are solutions to (10.50). The general solutions to (10.47) and (10.48) are stated here without proof:

$$\phi(x_1, y_1, z_1, t) = \iiint_{all-space} \frac{\rho(x_2, y_2, z_2, t - r_{12}/c)}{4\pi\varepsilon_0 r_{12}} dx_2 dy_2 dz_2$$

$$\overline{A}(x_1, y_1, z_1, t) = \iiint_{all-space} \frac{\overline{j}(x_2, y_2, z_2, t - r_{12}/c)}{4\pi\varepsilon_0 c^2 r_{12}} dx_2 dy_2 dz_2$$

10.55

The physical significance of these equations is as follows: the potentials $(\phi, \overline{A})$ at a point in space-time $(x_1, y_1, z_1, t_1)$ cannot be influenced instantaneously by events from other regions of space-time. The farther electromagnetic influences are from a point $(x_1, y_1, z_1, t_1)$, the more time must pass before the influences are felt at that point. That amount of time is $t - r_{12}/c$.

## Electromagnetic Potential Energy

Work done on a particle, $\int \overline{F} \bullet d\overline{s} = \int \overline{F} \bullet \overline{v} dt$, can be evaluated if the power $\overline{F} \bullet \overline{v}$ function is known. An electromagnetic field can do work on a charged particle, with charge $q$, and the rate at which work is done is:

$$Power = \overline{F} \bullet \vec{v} = q \, (\overline{E} + \vec{v} \times \overline{B}) \bullet \vec{v} = q \vec{v} \bullet \overline{E}$$

Thus the work done on a charged particle, $q$, is $\int q \vec{v} \bullet \overline{E} dt$. The *power density*, or power per unit volume, is $\rho \vec{v} \bullet \overline{E}$. Substituting $\rho \vec{v} = \vec{j}$, into the power density it becomes $\vec{j} \bullet \overline{E}$. Let $u$ be the energy density of the potential energy stored in an electromagnetic field. Over a closed surface let $S$ be the flux of electromagnetic energy through that surface. Then $u$ will decrease, due to dissipation of $S$ and dissipation caused by work done by the electromagnetic field on particles inside the volume. With the help of the conservation of energy, a continuity equation for this case can be written:

$$\frac{\partial u}{\partial t} = -div\overline{S} - \vec{j} \bullet \overline{E}$$

10.56

Solving Ampere's law for $j$ and taking the dot product of that with $E$ gives:

$$\overline{E} \bullet \vec{j} = \overline{E} \bullet curl \left( \frac{\overline{B}}{\mu_0} \right) - \varepsilon_0 \overline{E} \bullet \frac{\partial \overline{E}}{\partial t}$$

10.57

This equation can be manipulated into the same form as the continuity equation (10.56). Using the vector relation $div(\overline{P} \times \overline{Q}) + \overline{P} \bullet curl\overline{Q} = \overline{Q} \bullet curl\overline{P}$ and substituting $div(\overline{B}/\mu_0 \times \overline{E}) + \overline{B}/\mu_0 \bullet curl\overline{E} = \overline{E} \bullet curl \, (\overline{B}/\mu_0)$ into (10.57) yields:

$$\overline{E} \bullet \vec{j} = div \left( \frac{\overline{B}}{\mu_0} \times \overline{E} \right) + \frac{\overline{B}}{\mu_0} \bullet curl\overline{E} - \varepsilon_0 \overline{E} \bullet \frac{\partial \overline{E}}{\partial t}$$

Substituting Faraday's law into this equation and writing $(\overline{B}/\mu_0) \bullet (\partial \overline{B}/\partial t)$ and $\varepsilon_0 \overline{E} \bullet \partial \overline{E}/\partial t$ as $\partial/\partial t \, (\overline{B} \bullet \overline{B}/2\mu_0)$ and $\varepsilon_0 \, \partial/\partial t \, (\overline{E} \bullet \overline{E}/2)$ gives:

$$\overline{E} \bullet \vec{j} = -div \left( \overline{E} \times \frac{\overline{B}}{\mu_0} \right) - \frac{\partial}{\partial t} \left( \frac{\overline{B} \bullet \overline{B}}{2} \varepsilon_0 c^2 + \frac{\overline{E} \bullet \overline{E}}{2} \varepsilon_0 \right) = -div\overline{S} - \frac{\partial u}{\partial t}$$

If we view this equation as one equation in the two unknowns, $S$ and $u$, it is apparent that one solution is:

$$u = \varepsilon_0 \frac{\overline{E} \bullet \overline{E}}{2} + \varepsilon_0 c^2 \frac{\overline{B} \bullet \overline{B}}{2}$$

$$\overline{S} = \frac{1}{\mu_0} \overline{E} \times \overline{B}$$

10.58

This is in agreement with experiment. *S* is the *Poynting's vector* that gives the flow of electromagnetic energy. The term *u* is the power density of electromagnetic energy and *S*/*c*² gives the momentum density of electromagnetic energy.

## Electromagnetic Waves

Taking the curl of both sides of Ampère's equation and substituting Faraday's law gives the equation:

$$-lap\,\overline{B} = \frac{1}{\varepsilon_0 c^2} curl\,\overline{j} - \frac{1}{c^2} \frac{\partial^2 \overline{B}}{\partial t^2}$$

10.59

Then, taking the curl of Faraday's law and substituting Ampère's law and Gauss's law gives:

$$grad\left(\frac{\rho}{\varepsilon_0}\right) + \frac{1}{\varepsilon_0 c^2} \frac{\partial \overline{j}}{\partial t} = lap\,\overline{E} - \frac{1}{c^2} \frac{\partial^2 \overline{E}}{\partial t^2}$$

10.60

These equations, (10.59) and (10.60), can be rewritten as:

$$\Box \overline{B} = \frac{1}{\varepsilon_0 c^2} curl\,\overline{j}$$

$$\Box \overline{E} = -\frac{1}{\varepsilon_0} grad\,\rho - \frac{1}{\varepsilon_0 c^2} \frac{\partial \overline{j}}{\partial t}$$

10.61

For empty space, $\rho = 0$ and $J = 0$, these wave equations reduce to $\Box \overline{B} = 0$ and $\Box \overline{E} = 0$. Thus the electromagnetic fields propagate through empty space in accordance with wave equations. This aspect of electromagnetic theory is unaltered by relativity.

## Exercises

1.  Calculate the integral form of Maxwell's equations with magnetic monopole charges and currents.

2.  Let a point charge $q$ be stationary at the origin of an inertial frame. The four-potential for this charge is $A_x = A_y = A_z = 0$ and $\phi = q/4\pi\varepsilon_o r$. Calculate electromagnetic field strengths in both this inertial frame and another inertial frame.

3.  Imagine a space where all points in space have the same charge density $\rho_o$. What are the charge and current densities in another inertial frame?

4.  Show that $\overline{B} \bullet \overline{E}$ is Lorentz invariant.

5.  Show that $\overline{B} \bullet \overline{B} - \overline{E} \bullet \overline{E}/c^2$ is Lorentz invariant.

6.  Assume that an electrically neutral wire runs along the $x$-axis of an inertial frame. Some of the negatively charged particles in the wire move in the same direction, generating a current. Prove that the wire is charged in another inertial frame and calculate the amount of charge it has there.

7.  A charged particle $q$ with rest mass $m$ moves in a uniform magnetic field, $B$, on a circular path with radius $r$. At what speed does the charged particle travel?

8.  Consider a region of space with a constant magnetic field $\overline{B} = (0, B_0, 0)$ and constant electric field $\overline{E} = (0,0,0)$. What is the electric and magnetic field in another inertial frame? As usual, assume that the other inertial frame travels parallel to the $x$-axis of the first.

9.  Prove that the gauge transformation given by $\overline{A}' = \overline{A} + grad\lambda$ and $\phi' = \phi - \partial\lambda/\partial t$ leaves the electromagnetic field intensities unaltered.

10. Considering the constant fields given in problem eight, calculate the energy density and Poynting vector in this inertial frame and another inertial frame.

11. Recalculate the equations in (10.61) for Maxwell's equations with magnetic monopoles.

12. Derive the equations in (10.14) and their inverses.

13. For problem two, calculate the energy density $u$ and the Poynting vector $S$

# PART 4

# *Curved Spaces*

# CHAPTER 11

## *Overview of Tensor Algebra*

THE TOOLS USED TO STUDY physical theories include everything from group theory or topology to differential equations. In the study of general relativity, mathematical objects called tensors are used to formulate the equations. While this chapter provides an overview of the notation and mathematical formulas of tensors and the next two chapters are concerned with tensor calculus, they are not meant to substitute for books devoted solely to tensor algebra and tensor calculus.

Most of mathematics uses subscripts as labels to distinguish among variables, and superscripts usually to refer to powers. With tensors, superscripts serve as labels rather than powers. Monomials, then, can have subscripts or superscripts. According to the *summation convention,* introduced by Albert Einstein, if the same index appears only once as a subscript and only once as a superscript, it implies a sum over those indices. For example, the monomial $a_u T^{uv} b_u$ has no summation on the index $u$ because $u$ appears twice as a subscript. Because general relativity involves four-dimensional space, these sums range through (0, 1, 2, and 3) or (1, 2, 3 and 4), depending on the convention for labeling dimensions. Different writers also assign different index symbols to the time dimension: some use 0 or 1, others 4. Many writers also use Greek symbols to imply sums over four terms and Latin symbols for sums over three terms. This is not the convention used in this book, all sums occur over four terms unless otherwise stated. In an $n$-dimensional space, however, the sum ranges from 1 to $n$ or 0 to $n-1$, covering the dimensions of the space. Some examples of the summation convention are given in (11.1):

$$T^{ij}x_j = T^{i1}x_1 + T^{i2}x_2 + T^{i3}x_3 + T^{i4}x_4$$

$$u_m \frac{\partial f^m}{\partial x^n} = u_0 \frac{\partial f^0}{\partial x^n} + u_1 \frac{\partial f^1}{\partial x^n} + u_2 \frac{\partial f^2}{\partial x^n} + u_3 \frac{\partial f^3}{\partial x^n}$$

11.1

Each of these examples represents four sums because the index not summed over can take on four different values. In an $n$-dimensional space, each term would represent $n$ sums. Thus the summation convention allows for an elegant notational brevity. According to another labeling convention in tensor math, superscripts of variables correspond to contravariant and subscripts to covariant. (These distinctions will be reviewed later in this chapter.) A series of sums can also be implied through the summation convention. For example, the monomial $u^i_j v^j_k w^k_i$ is really the triple sum:

$$\sum_{i=1}^{4}\sum_{j=1}^{4}\sum_{k=1}^{4} u^i_j v^j_k w^k_i$$

Consider the equation in (11.2):

$$\frac{\partial P^{ij}}{\partial x^k}\frac{\partial Q^{kl}}{\partial x^i} = 2R^{jl} - S^{jm}T^l_m$$

11.2

Here there are actually sixteen equations, each with a double sum on the left side and a single sum on the right. The indices summed on range from one to four. In an $n$-dimensional space there are $n$ squared equations. An alternative notation for partial differentiation with respect to a coordinate variable is the comma. Equation (11.2) then would be:

$$P_{,k}^{ij}Q_{,i}^{kl} = 2R^{jl} - S^{jm}T_m^l$$

The summation convention makes possible compact notation of complex systems of equations, as well as quick manipulation of the equations. Combining the comma for partial differentiation with the summation convention, the four equations in (11.1) can be written very briefly as $u_m f^m{}_{,n}$. While none of these equations is necessarily a tensor, these notational conventions apply to tensors and non-tensors alike.

The *Kronecker delta* is defined as follows:

$$\delta_{ij} = \begin{cases} 1 \, if \, i = j \\ 0 \, if \, i \neq j \end{cases}$$

11.3

Indices of the Kronecker delta can also be notated as superscripts or as a combination of subscripts and superscripts:

$$\delta_i^j z_j = \delta_i^1 z_1 + \delta_i^2 z_2 + \delta_i^3 z_3 + \delta_i^4 z_4$$

If $i = 2$, then $\delta_2^j z_j = z_2$ because $\delta_2^2$ will be the only non-zero term. Because this holds true for other values of $i$, only when $i=j$ will there be a nonzero term:

$$\delta_i^j z_j = z_i$$

In an $n$-dimensional Euclidean space, coordinates can mark a location $(x_*^1,...,x_*^n)$. A curvilinear coordinate system maps each such coordinate to a new coordinate $(x^1,...,x^n)$ by a set of continuous and differentiable functions:

$$x^j = x^j (x_*^1,...,x_*^n)$$

And their inverses are given by:

$$x_*^i = x_*^i (x^1,...,x^n)$$

Because general relativity requires a four-dimensional space, $n = 4$. All the results considered here hold true, however, in $n$-dimensional spaces generally.

Restricting the transformations to four-dimensional spaces, the curvilinear coordinate transformations and their inverses are given by:

$$x^j = x^j \left( x_*^1, x_*^2, x_*^3, x_*^4 \right)$$

$$x_*^i = x_*^i \left( x^1, x^2, x^3, x^4 \right)$$

11.4

The chain rule identities of vector calculus, as summarized in Chapter One, can be applied to these curvilinear coordinate transformations and written using the summation convention:

$$\delta^i_j = \frac{\partial x_*^i}{\partial x_*^j} = \frac{\partial x_*^i}{\partial x^k} \frac{\partial x^k}{\partial x_*^j}$$

$$\delta^k_i = \frac{\partial x^k}{\partial x^i} = \frac{\partial x'^l}{\partial x^i} \frac{\partial x^k}{\partial x'^l}$$

$$\frac{\partial x'^i}{\partial x^j} = \frac{\partial x'^i}{\partial x_*^l} \frac{\partial x_*^l}{\partial x^j}$$

$$\frac{dx'^m}{dt} = \frac{\partial x'^m}{\partial x^n} \frac{dx^n}{dt}$$

11.5

From linear algebra, we know that any point in euclidean four-space can be written as a linear combination of basis vectors for any point $p$:

$$\overline{p} = x_*^k \overline{i}_k$$

11.6

Here $\overline{i}_1 = (1,0,0,0), \overline{i}_2 = (0,1,0,0), \overline{i}_3 = (0,0,1,0)$ and $\overline{i}_4 = (0,0,0,1)$, with curvilinear coordinates $x^k$ and, via (11.4), Cartesian coordinates $x^k_*$. This is a mapping from four-dimensional Euclidean space to a new space or coordinate system through the curvilinear coordinate transformation. Viewing this position vector as a function of the curvilinear coordinate system, the covariant basis vectors at each point in the curvilinear coordinate system are defined as:

$$\overline{g}_l = \frac{\partial \overline{p}}{\partial x^l} = \frac{\partial x_*^k}{\partial x^l} \overline{i}_k$$

11.7

A *coordinate curve* is a curve defined in a curvilinear coordinate system when all coordinates are set to constant values except one. Because the four basis vectors $\overline{g}_l$ are tangent to the coordinate curves $x^l$, each point in space has its own associated set of basis vectors given by (11.7). A vector $\overline{v}$ can be written as a linear combination of the basis vectors, provided that the basis vectors $\overline{g}_l$ are linearly independent:

$$\overline{v} = v^l \overline{g}_l$$

11.8

The $v^l$ are defined as the components of the vector. The vector field in (11.8), is now written in the new space defined by the curvilinear coordinate transformation. Curvilinear coordinates define mappings from one space to another: a mapping from one curved space to another, for example, or one coordinate system to another. It is easy to visualize a curved two dimensional space residing in Euclidean three-space by the formula $z(x,y)$. A different way to describe a curved two dimensional space is by a curvilinear coordinate transformation from two space parameters $(u,v)$ to $(x,y)$ given by $x(u,v)$ and $y(u,v)$. Now, this curvilinear coordinate transformation can be described in yet another way. For any point $(x(u,v), y(u,v))$, the distance to an arbitrarily close point $(x(u+du,v+dv), y(u+du,v+dv))$ can be described by a set of metric equations which are functions of $u$ and $v$. These metric equations are an alternate way of describing the curved space characterized by a curvilinear coordinate transformation. A four-dimensional curved space can be described by the curvilinear coordinate transformation given in (11.4). But for a given space, described by a curvilinear coordinate transformation, how are the metric equations calculated?

The *covariant components of the metric tensor*, $g_{kl}$, are defined by the dot product of each basis vector with itself and all other basis vectors:

$$g_{kl} = \overline{g}_k \bullet \overline{g}_l$$

11.9

As will be seen below, the metric tensor relates the distance between two arbitraily close points as functions of the coordinates for those points. Because the dot product is commutative, the metric tensor is symmetric: $g_{kl} = g_{lk}$. Thus in a four-dimensional space the metric tensor has ten components, not sixteen, because six of them are duplicates. Substituting the definition of the covariant basis vectors into equation (11.9) gives an alternate description of the metric tensor:

$$g_{kl} = \frac{\partial x_*^m}{\partial x^k} \frac{\partial x_*^n}{\partial x^l} \delta_{mn}$$

A change in the vector $p$, by the chain rule, is:

$$d\overline{p} = \frac{\partial \overline{p}}{\partial x^l} dx^l$$

Substituting the definition of the covariant basis vectors (11.7) into this equation gives:

$$d\overline{p} = \overline{g}_l dx^l$$

The square of the length of $dp$ is found by taking the dot product of this equation with itself:

$$ds^2 = d\overline{p} \bullet d\overline{p} = \overline{g}_r dx^r \bullet \overline{g}_s dx^s = \overline{g}_r \bullet \overline{g}_s dx^r dx^s = g_{rs} dx^r dx^s \qquad 11.10$$

This equation relates the distance from a point to a nearby point in terms of the coordinate differences between those points. Consider a path coursing through a space described by a given metric. If that path is parameterized as a function of some dummy variable, $\tau$, then the length of the path is found by dividing both sides of (11.10) by $(d\tau)^2$ and integrating:

$$s = \int_{\tau_1}^{\tau_2} \sqrt{\left( g_{rs} \, (dx^r/d\tau)(dx^s/d\tau) \right)} d\tau \qquad 11.11$$

A metric tensor describes the shape of a given space expressed in a given coordinate system. For Euclidean space $g_{rs} = \overline{i}_r \bullet \overline{i}_s = \delta_{rs}$, so the Kronecker delta is the metric tensor for flat-Euclidean space. From linear algebra we know that angles and distances are defined for spaces by inner products, as, in the case of Euclidean three-space:

$$< d\overline{u}, d\overline{v} > = \delta^{ij} du_i dv_j$$

The Kronecker delta thus serves as coefficients of the product of two coordinate differentials. In linear algebra differential distances and angles are defined as:

$$ds = \sqrt{<d\bar{u},d\bar{u}>}$$

$$\cos\theta = \frac{<d\bar{u},d\bar{v}>}{\sqrt{<d\bar{u},d\bar{u}><d\bar{v},d\bar{v}>}}$$

Therefore the metric tensor has geometric significance in three ways. First, it provides a generalized description of curved spaces, for the purposes of this book superior to descriptions such as $z = z(x, y)$ for curved two-spaces, $w = w(x, y, z)$ for curved three-spaces, and so on. Second, it embodies a generalization of the inner product spaces studied in linear algebra. Third, it defines curved and flat spaces in terms of how differential distances between points are related to coordinates for those points. Thus, because the metric tensor gives descriptions at localized regions in a given space, it is ideal for studying local properties of spatial regions.

However, the same space can have different metric tensors for different coordinate systems. For example, two-dimensional Euclidean space can be described in either Cartesian or polar coordinates. The *contravariant* basis vectors $\overline{g^r}$ (orthogonally related to covariant basis vectors) are defined as:

$$\overline{g^r} \bullet \overline{g_s} = \delta_s^r$$

11.12

With this equation it is easy to solve for the contravariant basis vectors:

$$\overline{g^r} = \frac{\partial x^r}{\partial x_*^n} \overline{i^n}$$

11.13

This can easily be verified by substituting these solutions into the definition of the contravariant basis vectors and remembering that $\overline{i^n} \bullet \overline{i_m} = \delta_m^n$ :

$$\overline{g^r} \bullet \overline{g_s} = \frac{\partial x^r}{\partial x_*^n} \overline{i^n} \bullet \frac{\partial x_*^m}{\partial x^s} \overline{i_m} = \frac{\partial x^r}{\partial x_*^n} \frac{\partial x_*^m}{\partial x^s} \delta_m^n = \frac{\partial x^r}{\partial x_*^n} \frac{\partial x_*^n}{\partial x^s} = \frac{\partial x^r}{\partial x^s} = \delta_s^r$$

The definitions of the covariant and contravariant basis vectors make their interpretation clear. At any point in a curvilinear coordinate system, the contravariant basis vectors are tangent to coordinate curves going from one curvilinear coordinate system $X^*$ to another system $X$. The covariant basis vectors are tangent to coordinate curves at that point going through the inverse curvilinear coordinate transformation from $X$ to $X^*$. The covariant components of the metric tensor were given in (11.9), and the contravariant components are:

$$g^{ab} = \overline{g^a} \bullet \overline{g^b} \qquad\qquad 11.14$$

The metric tensor interchanges covariant and contravariant basis vectors $g^{ab}\overline{g_b} = \overline{g^a}$ and $g_{uv}\overline{g^v} = \overline{g_u}$, and the two versions of the metric tensor are inverses:

$$g_{ij}g^{jk} = \delta^k_i \qquad\qquad 11.15$$

The metric tensor describes a mathematical space. Rather than representing two different spaces, the contravariant $g^{uv}$ and covariant $g_{ij}$ are simply two different representations of the same mathematical object. The shape and structure of a space does not depend on which set of basis vectors is used to describe it. Every point in a curvilinear coordinate system has an associated a set of basis vectors and a metric tensor value. Any vector can be written as a function of the basis vectors at that point:

$$\overline{v} = v_k \overline{g^k} = v^l \overline{g_l} \qquad\qquad 11.16$$

The $v_k$ are the covariant components of $\overline{v}$, and the $v^l$ are the contravariant components of $\overline{v}$. The metric tensor can convert contravariant components of a vector to their covariant components and vice versa. To see this take the dot product of equation (11.16) with $g_m$ to get:

$$\overline{v} \bullet \overline{g_m} = v_m = v^l g_{lm} \qquad\qquad 11.17$$

Thus the metric can raise and lower indices, in this case on the components of a vector.

## Transitions Between Two Curvilinear Coordinate Systems

Now consider two curvilinear coordinate systems, the second one denoted by a prime. For the primed system, the coordinates, basis vectors, metric tensor, and vector components are denoted as $x'_t$, $\overline{g'_l}$, $g'^{mn}$, $v'_k$. To see how these quantities transform between the two systems, begin with the basis vectors for the primed and unprimed coordinate systems:

$$\overline{g_r} = \frac{\partial x^k_*}{\partial x^r}\overline{i_k} \qquad \overline{g'_s} = \frac{\partial x^k_*}{\partial x'^s}\overline{i_k}$$

Multiplying both sides of the unprimed basis vectors by $\partial x^r / \partial x'^s$ (from now on, this means to multiply and take appropriate sums according to the summation convention) gives:

$$\overline{g'_s} = \overline{g_r}\frac{\partial x^r}{\partial x'^s}$$

11.18

It is easy to show that $\overline{g'^s} = \overline{g^r}\,\partial x'^s/\partial x^r$. To find the relationship between metric tensors in the two coordinate systems, use the relationship between the basis vectors in (11.18) twice:

$$g'_{mn} = \overline{g'_m} \bullet \overline{g'_n} = \overline{g_p}\frac{\partial x^p}{\partial x'^m} \bullet \overline{g_q}\frac{\partial x^q}{\partial x'^n} = g_{pq}\frac{\partial x^p}{\partial x'^m}\frac{\partial x^q}{\partial x'^n}$$

$$g'_{mn} = g_{pq}\frac{\partial x^p}{\partial x'^m}\frac{\partial x^q}{\partial x'^n}$$

11.19

Contravariant components transform in a similar way:

$$g'^{mn} = g^{pq}\frac{\partial x'^m}{\partial x^p}\frac{\partial x'^n}{\partial x^q}$$

11.20

Between the coordinate systems, the relationship among components of an arbitrary vector $\overline{v}$ at $p$ can be found by writing the same vector $\overline{v}$ as a linear combination of the primed and unprimed basis vectors:

$$\bar{v} = v_k \overline{g^k} = v_l' \overline{g^{\prime l}} = v_l' \frac{\partial x^{\prime l}}{\partial x^k} \overline{g^k}$$

It follows that:

$$v_k = v_l' \frac{\partial x^{\prime l}}{\partial x^k}$$

11.21

Multiplying this equation by $\partial x^k / \partial x^{\prime m}$ gives the primed components $v_m' = v_k \, \partial x^k / \partial x^{\prime m}$ as functions of the unprimed components. Clearly, the contravariant components transform as:

$$v^{\prime t} = v^u \frac{\partial x^{\prime t}}{\partial x^u}$$

11.22

The vector $\bar{v}$ depends on a particular point $p$ in a given curvilinear coordinate system. The metric tensor and basis vectors also depend on the point $p$. A scalar quantity is also called a zero-order, or zero-rank, tensor. A vector is called a first-order, or first-rank tensor, and its contravariant components transform according to the following equation:

$$A^{\prime t} = A^u \frac{\partial x^{\prime t}}{\partial x^u}$$

11.23

The contravariant components of any second-order tensor transform as follows:

$$A^{\prime st} = A^{uv} \frac{\partial x^{\prime t}}{\partial x^u} \frac{\partial x^{\prime s}}{\partial x^v}$$

11.24

From the point of view of computation, carrying out the transformations of (11.24) give the primed tensor components in terms of the unprimed coordinates. Therefore, it is then necessary to substitute the inverse coordinate transformation to get the primed tensor components in terms of the primed coordinates. As shown previously, the metric tensor is a tensor because it transforms exactly as (11.24) does. An $n$th-order tensor transforms, in the contravariant case, as follows:

$$A'^{l_1 l_2 \ldots l_n} = A^{s_1 s_2 \ldots s_n} \frac{\partial x'^{l_1}}{\partial x^{s_1}} \frac{\partial x'^{l_2}}{\partial x^{s_2}} \cdots \frac{\partial x'^{l_n}}{\partial x^{s_n}}$$

11.25

Analogous laws hold for covariant transformations and can easily be generalized from (11.19). Any mathematical object that transforms in this manner is a tensor, and exists independently of coordinate systems. For example, although the same vector can have different components if the coordinate axes (in a flat space) change, the vector itself does not change. The length of a vector is the square root of this quantity:

$$v_k \overline{g^k} \bullet v^l \overline{g_l} = v_k v^l \delta_l^k = v_k v^k$$

And, because $v_k' v'^k = v_k v^k$ holds true, the length of the vector is invariant and does not depend upon the coordinate system. Angles between vectors are also invariant. Thus the transformation laws for tensors ensure that they represent coordinate-free objects; they are objective. To see why objectivity is embodied in the general case, consider a tensor whose components are composed of the product of three four-vectors $\overline{u}, \overline{v}, \overline{w}$ :

$$T^{ijk} = u^i v^j w^k$$

Because each vector transforms according to (11.23), $T^{ijk}$ must transform as a third-rank tensor and exist independently of a coordinate system. Note that tensors can be written in contravariant, covariant, or mixed forms. A mixed tensor has a mixture of contravariant and covariant indices. For example, the seventh-order tensor $B^{pq\ t\ v}_{rs\ u}$ is expressed in mixed components. It transforms as follows:

$$B'^{ab\ e\ g}_{cd\ f} = B^{pq\ t\ v}_{rs\ u} \frac{\partial x'^a}{\partial x^p} \frac{\partial x'^b}{\partial x^q} \frac{\partial x^r}{\partial x'^c} \frac{\partial x^s}{\partial x'^d} \frac{\partial x'^e}{\partial x^t} \frac{\partial x^u}{\partial x'^f} \frac{\partial x'^g}{\partial x^v}$$

Again, a vector is an objective mathematical object because it remains the same even when its coordinate axes (hence its coordinates) change. Consider two vectors each of a fixed length and at a fixed angle in relation to each other. If coordinate axes are changed arbitrarily, the lengths of the vectors and their relative angle remain the same. In fact, it is the linearity of vectors that preserves their lengths and angles.

So, the generalized definition of a tensor is as follows: an $n$th-order tensor $T$ is defined by the scalar function $r = H_T(\overline{u_1}, \overline{u_2}, ..., \overline{u_n})$ such that when any $\overline{u_i}$ is replaced by $\alpha \overline{p} + \beta \overline{q}$ (called $r_{\alpha \overline{p} + \beta \overline{q}}$), its value is given by:

$$r_{\alpha \overline{p} + \beta \overline{q}} = \alpha r_{\overline{p}} + \beta r_{\overline{q}}$$

11.26

Here $r_{\overline{p}}$ and $r_{\overline{q}}$ is the function $H_T$, replacing the slot $\overline{u_i}$ with $\overline{p}$ and $\overline{q}$ respectively. The components of the tensor $T$ are found by evaluating the function $H_T$ at the basis vectors at a given point. For example, the fourth-order tensor $C$, defined by the function $H_C$, the mixed components of $C$, $C^{lm\,o}_{\quad n}$, are as follows:

$$C^{lm\,o}_{\quad n} = H_C\left(\overline{g^l}, \overline{g^m}, \overline{g_n}, \overline{g^o}\right)$$

In another coordinate system, here primed, the components of $C$ are:

$$C'^{lm\,o}_{\quad n} = H_C\left(\overline{g'^l}, \overline{g'^m}, \overline{g'_n}, \overline{g'^o}\right)$$

If the transformation laws for the primed basis vectors are substituted into the expression above, and the partial derivative of their transformations terms to the unprimed coordinate system are factored out in accordance with (11.26), it will transform as a fourth-order tensor to the unprimed components. Every linear function $H$ satisfying the definition above generates tensors and is a coordinate-independent object.

As stated earlier, the metric tensor can be used to raise and lower indices on tensors. Using the general tensor definition, (11.26), together with the properties of the metric tensor and basis vectors, we can lower the contravariant index $l$ to a covariant index $s$ on the tensor $M$:

$$M^{kl}_{\ mn} = H_M\left(\overline{g^k}, \overline{g^l}, \overline{g_m}, \overline{g_n}\right) = H_M\left(\overline{g^k}, \overline{g_s}g^{sl}, \overline{g_m}, \overline{g_n}\right)$$

$$= g^{sl}H_M\left(\overline{g^k}, \overline{g_s}, \overline{g_m}, \overline{g_n}\right) = g^{sl}M^k_{\ smn}$$

Therefore:

$$M^{kl}_{\ \ mn} = g^{sl} M^{k}_{\ smn}$$

11.27

The transformation properties of tensors ensure that they can be added and subtracted:

$$U^{\gamma}_{\alpha\beta} + V^{\gamma}_{\alpha\beta} = W^{\gamma}_{\alpha\beta}$$
$$U^{\gamma}_{\alpha\beta} - V^{\gamma}_{\alpha\beta} = T^{\gamma}_{\alpha\beta}$$

11.28

They can also be multiplied:

$$R^{\alpha\beta\gamma} S_{\gamma\beta\delta} = Q^{\alpha}_{\ \delta}$$
$$A_{ijk} B_{lmn} = C_{ijklmn}$$

11.29

The equations in (11.28) and the last equation of (11.29) can be expressed in a manner free of coordinates:

$$\overline{\overline{U}} + \overline{\overline{V}} = \overline{\overline{W}}$$
$$\overline{\overline{U}} - \overline{\overline{V}} = \overline{\overline{T}}$$
$$\overline{\overline{A}} \otimes \overline{\overline{B}} = \overline{\overline{C}}$$

The multiplication of tensors, in the sense of this last equation, is called the *tensor product*. A tensor such as $A^{st}_{\ \ uvw}$ can be contracted with respect to any pair of indices to generate new tensors. For example, if we let the index $v$ equal the index $t$, we have a sum on those two indices:

$$D^{s}_{\ uw} = A^{st}_{\ \ utw}$$

Here the third-order tensor $\boldsymbol{D}$ is formed by contraction on the fifth-order tensor $\boldsymbol{A}$. The reader is encourage to verify all these statements by studying the transformation laws for tensors and the functions that obey the rules established for $H$ in (11.26). Multiplying two tensors can produce tensors of lower, higher, or the same rank, depending on whether an index is free or summed over with another index.

Consider the tensor product $R^{\alpha\beta\gamma} S_{\gamma\beta\delta}$. Here the tensor product is defined as inner with respect to the indices $\beta$ and $\gamma$ and outer with respect to $\alpha$ and $\delta$. The quotient theorem in tensor algebra says that for any vector $v^k$, if the sum $v^k B_{klm}$ is a tensor, then $B_{klm}$ is also a tensor.[1] Recall that the vector $\overline{v} = v_k \, \overline{g}^k = v'_l \, \overline{g}'^l$ is independent of any coordinate system. The generalization of this is straightforward: for an nth order tensor, here considered in covariant components, the full tensor is:

$$\overline{\overline{T}} = T_{l_1 l_2 \ldots l_n} \, \overline{g}^{l_1} \otimes \overline{g}^{l_2} \otimes \cdots \otimes \overline{g}^{l_n}$$

11.30

The tensor $T$ will be the same regardless of the coordinate system used. That is, if the right side of (11.30) is substituted with the primed counterparts for all its quantities, the left side remains the same. Of course, the equation in (11.30) can also be written in contravariant or mixed form.

## Exercises

1.  Let the Jacobian be the matrix of partial derivatives given by $\mathbb{J} = \left[ \partial x_*^p / \partial x^k \right]$. Also let $J = \det(\mathbb{J})$ and $g = \det(g_{kl})$. Prove that $g = J^2$.

2.  Consider the two-dimensional space of the Cartesian plane, with basis vectors $\overline{i}_1 = (1,0)$ and $\overline{i}_2 = (0,1)$ and metric tensor $\overline{i}_j \bullet \overline{i}_k = \delta_{jk}$. Calculate the basis vectors and metric tensor for this same space in polar coordinates $x = r\cos\theta$, $y = r\sin\theta$.

3.  For a four-dimensional space, show that $g_{ab} g^{ab} = 4$, and for an $n$-dimensional space show that $g_{ab} g^{ab} = n$.

4.  Prove that $g^{ab} \overline{g}_b = \overline{g}^a$ and $g_{uv} \overline{g}^v = \overline{g}_u$ are true.

[1] A proof can be found in Dirac's book on general relativity, listed in the bibliography.

5. Compute the basis vectors and metric tensor for Euclidean three-space in cylindrical coordinates. The transformations are $y^1 = x^1 \cos x^2$, $y^2 = x^1 \sin x^2$, $y^3 = x^3$.

6. Verify that $r = H_T(\overline{u}_1, \overline{u}_2) = \overline{u}_1 \bullet A\overline{u}_2$ is a second rank tensor, $T$, where $A$ is given below. Also, evaluate the covariant components of this tensor in Cartesian and polar coordinates.

$$A = \begin{bmatrix} 2 & 0 \\ 0 & 3 \end{bmatrix}$$

7. For the fourth-order tensor below, find the $T_{1132}$ component in Cartesian three-space and cylindrical coordinates. Use the transformations given in Problem Five.

$$r = H_T(\overline{u}_1, \overline{u}_2, \overline{u}_3, \overline{u}_4)$$
$$= ((-1,2,0) \bullet \overline{u}_1)((1,3,-1) \bullet \overline{u}_2)((1,1,4) \bullet \overline{u}_3)((-7,5,0) \bullet \overline{u}_4)$$

8. Suppose that the rectangular Cartesian coordinates are related to another curvilinear coordinate system by the transformation below. Find the covariant and contravariant basis vectors and the covariant and contravariant components of the vector $(v_{*1}, v_{*2}, v_{*3}) = (1,2,3)$.

$$x_*^1 = 2x^1$$
$$x_*^2 = x^1 + x^2$$
$$x_*^3 = x^2 - 2x^3$$

# CHAPTER 12

## *Overview of Geodesic Lines*

IN A CURVILINEAR COORDINATE SYSTEM, a scalar field $h(x_1,...,x_n)$ has different values at each point $(x_1,...,x_n)$, as do vector and tensor fields at each location $\bar{v}(x_1,...,x_n)$ and $T(x_1,...,x_n)$. The value of each component, then, is a function of the coordinates. As previously mentioned, partial differentiation with respect to a coordinate variable is denoted by a comma:

$$\frac{\partial T^{ijk}_{\ lmn}}{\partial x^r} = T^{ijk}_{\ lmn,r}$$

Repeated partial differentiation is also be denoted by commas, where each index following a comma represents further partial differentiation:

$$\frac{\partial^2 T^{ijk}_{\ lmn}}{\partial x^s \partial x^r} = T^{ijk}_{\ lmn,r,s} = T^{ijk}_{\ lmn,rs}$$

While partial differentiation of tensor fields does not generally produce new tensor fields, the partial derivative of a scalar field is always a vector field:

$$v_m = \frac{\partial h}{\partial x^m}$$

12.1

To see this, multiply both sides of (12.1) by , $\partial x^m / \partial x'^n$ to get:

$$v'_n = \frac{\partial h}{\partial x'^n}$$

Thus, when we differentiate a scalar field, a vector field is a guaranteed byproduct because vectors transform according to the law $v'_n = v_m \, \partial x^m / \partial x'^n$ . The partial derivatives of $h$ are the vector components of the gradient of the scalar function $h$, which is given by:

$$grad(h) = \bar{v} = \frac{\partial h}{\partial x^m} \overline{g^m} = h_{,m} \overline{g^m} = v_m \overline{g^m}$$

12.2

Later it will be shown that objects in free fall in a gravitational field (light rays and planets, for example) can travel on paths called *geodesics*. In a curved or flat space, a geodesic is the path with the minimum distance between two points. An *extremal path* has either the minimum or the maximum distance between two points on a surface or in a space. The extremal paths for two arbitrary points in a curved space are found by means of a branch of mathematics called the *calculus of variations*, which can also find extremal values for other physical quantities. In calculus, the minimum and maximum points on curves $y(x)$ are found by differentiating the function, setting the result equal to zero, and solving the resulting equation. This technique is utilized in the calculus of variations. To find the shortest distance between two points $(x_1, y_1, z(x_1, y_1))$ and $(x_2, y_2, z(x_2, y_2))$ on a surface $z(x, y)$, find the $y(x)$ where $(x, y(x), z(x, y(x)))$ is the path of minimum distance between the two points. If $y(x)$ and $z(x, y)$ are given, we can calculate the length of any line $(x, y(x), z(x, y(x)))$ in three-space:

$$s = \int_{x_1}^{x_2} \sqrt{1 + (dy/dx)^2 + (dz/dx)^2} \, dx$$

12.3

Here $(d/dx)[z(x, y(x))]$ is given by $(\partial z/\partial x) + (\partial z/\partial y)(dy/dx)$ from regular calculus. Although we want to find the $y(x)$ that minimizes $s$, it is useful to solve the slightly more general problem by minimizing the following equation:

$$s = \int_{x_1}^{x_2} f(x, y, z, y', z')dx$$

12.4

This problem is <u>not limited</u> to the special case of minimizing the length of a line where $f = \sqrt{1 + y'^2 + z'^2}$ . In equation (12.3) $z$ does not appear as an independent variable only its derivative does. The steps outlined below yield one equation in (12.8) but the most general case gives two equations in (12.8).

For the moment, however, it is simpler to minimize (12.3). An infinite number of curves $y(x)$ pass through the two points $(x_1, y_1)$ and $(x_2, y_2)$. We wish to find the curve(s) $y(x)$ that minimize the integral in (12.4). Assume there exists a unique function, $y(x)$, that minimizes $s$. To find it, note that any other function $\overline{y}(x) = y(x) + h\delta(x)$, where $\delta(x)$ is any function and $h$ is a real number, must have a larger $s$ value than $y(x)$. This function and its derivative, where the prime denotes differentiation with respect to $x$, are:

$$\overline{y}(x) = y(x) + h\delta(x)$$

$$\overline{y}'(x) = y'(x) + h\delta'(x)$$

12.5

The length of the line $s$ can be written as a function of $h$:

$$s(h) = \int_{x_1}^{x_2} f(x, \overline{y}, z, \overline{y}', z')dx$$

$$= \int_{x_1}^{x_2} f(x, y(x) + h\delta(x), z, y'(x) + h\delta'(x), z')dx$$

12.6

On the line $\overline{y}(x)$ we must impose the two conditions $\delta(x_1) = \delta(x_2) = 0$ so that $\overline{y}(x)$ and $y(x)$ both intersect at the points $(x_1, y_1)$ and $(x_2, y_2)$. When $h = 0, s(0)$ is the minimum distance between the two points, a graph of $s(h)$ must look like the following:

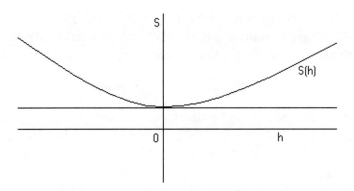

Because $s(0)$ is the minimum, ordinary calculus requires that the slope there be zero: $s'(0) = 0$. Taking the derivative with respect to $h$ gives:

$$\frac{d}{dh} s(h) = \int_{x_1}^{x_2} \frac{\partial}{\partial h} f\, (x, \bar{y}, z, \bar{y}', z')\, dx$$

For the integrand in (12.3), the partial derivative of $f$ with respect to $h$ evaluates to:

$$\frac{\partial f}{\partial h} = \frac{\partial f}{\partial x}\frac{\partial x}{\partial h} + \frac{\partial f}{\partial \bar{y}}\frac{\partial \bar{y}}{\partial h} + \frac{\partial f}{\partial z}\frac{\partial z}{\partial h} + \frac{\partial f}{\partial \bar{y}'}\frac{\partial \bar{y}'}{\partial h} + \frac{\partial f}{\partial z'}\frac{\partial z'}{\partial h}$$

$$= \frac{\partial f}{\partial \bar{y}}\delta(x) + \frac{\partial f}{\partial \bar{y}'}\delta'(x)$$

Substituting this gives equation (12.7):

$$\frac{d}{dh} s(h) = \int_{x_1}^{x_2} [\delta(x)\,\partial f/\partial \bar{y} + \delta'(x)\,\partial f/\partial \bar{y}']\, dx$$

12.7

If the derivatives $y'$ and $\delta'(x)$ are negative, the integral can vanish, satisfying $s'(0) = 0$, and we fail to find $y(x)$. But if we set $h = 0$ so that $\bar{y}$ and $\bar{y}'$ become $y$ and $y'$, then split up the integral, we will have:

$$0 = s'(0) = \int_{x_1}^{x_2} \delta(x)\,\partial f/\partial y\, dx + \int_{x_1}^{x_2} \delta'(x)\,\partial f/\partial y'\, dx$$

Integrating by parts on the second integral, this equation becomes:

$$0 = s'(0) = \int_{x_1}^{x_2} \delta(x) \, \partial f / \partial y \, dx + \delta(x) \, \partial f / \partial y' \big|_{x_1}^{x_2} - \int_{x_1}^{x_2} \delta(x) \frac{d}{dx} (\partial f / \partial y') dx$$

The term $\delta(x) \, \partial f / \partial y' \big|_{x_1}^{x_2}$ is zero because $\delta(x_1) = \delta(x_2) = 0$, and the remaining terms can be combined under one integral:

$$0 = s'(0) = \int_{x_1}^{x_2} \left[ \partial f / \partial y - d/dx \, (\partial f / \partial y') \right] \delta(x) dx$$

As $\delta(x)$ is an arbitrary non-zero function, and because the total integral is always zero, the integrand is always zero for the $y(x)$ and that minimizes the original problem:

$$\frac{\partial f}{\partial y} - \frac{d}{dx} \left( \frac{\partial f}{\partial y'} \right) = 0$$

12.8

Now it is clear how to compute $y(x)$. Equation (12.8) is called Euler's equation and it is useful for finding geodesics. To find geodesic lines for a surface $z = z(x, y)$, substitute $f = \sqrt{1 + y'^2 + z'^2}$ into Euler's equation with $y(x_1) = y_1$ and $y(x_2) = y_2$ as initial data.

The problem of finding minimal and maximal distances between any two points in any space $g_{uv}$, is solved by the same method employed above. Let a path through $g_{uv}$ be a function of a dummy variable $t$, so that the path components are defined by $x^i(t)$. Because the metric is a function of the coordinates $x^i$, as usual, the distance between any two points $x^i(t_1)$ and $x^i(t_2)$ is:

$$s = \int_{t_1}^{t_2} \sqrt{g_{uv} \, (dx^u / dt)(dx^v / dt)} \, dt$$

12.9

Now, we wish to find the path $x^j$ that minimizes the distance between the two points. Assume that $x^u$ minimizes the distance. Any other nearby path can be written as:

$$\overline{x^u} = x^u + h\delta^u$$

$$\overline{x^v} = x^v + h\delta^v \tag{12.10}$$

The $s$ value for any of these paths, of course, is larger than that of $x^u$. The equation in (12.10) was written twice to account for each index. The term $\delta^i$ is not the Kronecker delta because it has only one index symbol; this choice is in keeping with the previous example. The length of the new path $\overline{x^v}$ between the same two points is:

$$s(h) = \int_{t_1}^{t_2} \sqrt{g_{uv}\left(d\overline{x^u}/dt\right)\left(d\overline{x^v}/dt\right)}\,dt$$

As before, $\delta^v(t_1) = \delta^v(t_2) = 0$ so that $\overline{x^v}$ and $x^v$ both intersect the points $x^i(t_2)$ and $x^i(t_1)$. Differentiation with respect to $h$ gives:

$$\frac{ds}{dh} = \int_{t_1}^{t_2} \frac{\partial}{\partial h}\left(g_{uv}\frac{d\overline{x^u}}{dt}\frac{d\overline{x^v}}{dt}\right)^{1/2} dt$$

$$= \int_{t_1}^{t_2} \frac{1}{2}\left(g_{uv}\frac{d\overline{x^u}}{dt}\frac{d\overline{x^v}}{dt}\right)^{-1/2}\left[\frac{d\overline{x^u}}{dt}\frac{d\overline{x^v}}{dt}\frac{\partial g_{uv}}{\partial h} + g_{uv}\frac{\partial}{\partial h}\left(\frac{d\overline{x^u}}{dt}\frac{d\overline{x^v}}{dt}\right)\right]dt$$

Now substitute $\partial g_{uv}/\partial h = g_{uv,k}\,\partial x^k/\partial h$ into the equation above and substitute the time derivatives of the new path $\overline{x^v}$, given in (12.11), into the above equation:

$$\frac{d\overline{x^u}}{dt} = \frac{dx^u}{dt} + h\frac{d\delta^u}{dt}$$

$$\frac{d\overline{x^v}}{dt} = \frac{dx^v}{dt} + h\frac{d\delta^v}{dt} \tag{12.11}$$

Subsituting $Q = (1/2)\left(g_{uv}\left(d\overline{x^u}/dt\right)\left(d\overline{x^v}/dt\right)\right)^{-1/2}$ and $(\partial/\partial h)\left(d\overline{x^u}/dt\right) = d\delta^u/dt$ into the equation, we are left with:

$$\frac{ds}{dh} = \int_{t_1}^{t_2} Q \left[ \frac{d\overline{x}^u}{dt} \frac{d\overline{x}^v}{dt} \frac{\partial x^k}{\partial h} g_{uv,k} + g_{uv} \left( \frac{d\overline{x}^u}{dt} \frac{d\delta^v}{dt} + \frac{d\overline{x}^v}{dt} \frac{d\delta^u}{dt} \right) \right] dt$$

12.12

It is easy to calculate the partial derivatives of the new path, $\partial x^k / \partial h = \delta^k$. Substituting this into (12.12) and splitting the integral leaves us with (12.13):

$$\frac{ds}{dh} = \int_{t_1}^{t_2} Q \delta^k g_{uv,k} \frac{d\overline{x}^u}{dt} \frac{d\overline{x}^v}{dt} dt + \int_{t_1}^{t_2} Q g_{uv} \left( \frac{d\overline{x}^u}{dt} \frac{d\delta^v}{dt} + \frac{d\overline{x}^v}{dt} \frac{d\delta^u}{dt} \right) dt$$

12.13

The two terms in the rightmost integral are of the same form. Integration by parts on one of them means that each term in the second integral results in a term like this:

$$\int_{t_1}^{t_2} Q g_{uv} \frac{d\overline{x}^u}{dt} \frac{d\delta^v}{dt} dt = Q g_{uv} \frac{d\overline{x}^u}{dt} \delta^v \Big|_{t_1}^{t_2} - \int_{t_1}^{t_2} \delta^v \frac{d}{dt} \left( Q g_{uv} \frac{d\overline{x}^u}{dt} \right) dt$$

Because $\delta^v(t_1) = \delta^v(t_2) = 0$, the two terms $Q g_{uv} d\overline{x}^u / dt \, \delta^v \Big|_{t_1}^{t_2}$ are both zero. These modifications change (12.13) to:

$$\frac{ds}{dh} = \int_{t_1}^{t_2} \left[ Q \delta^k g_{uv,k} \frac{d\overline{x}^u}{dt} \frac{d\overline{x}^v}{dt} - \delta^v \frac{d}{dt} \left( Q g_{uv} \frac{d\overline{x}^u}{dt} \right) - \delta^u \frac{d}{dt} \left( Q g_{uv} \frac{d\overline{x}^v}{dt} \right) \right] dt$$

The dummy indices being summed on can be anything. Therefore, to organize this equation the index symbols on all $\delta$ terms can be converted to $\delta^k$. If we change the latter two terms, the sum on the index $v$ and $u$ becomes $k$. Letting $h = 0$ so that $s'(0) = 0$ makes all $\overline{x}^u$ become $x^u$:

$$s'(0) = 0 = \int_{t_1}^{t_2} \delta^k \left[ Q g_{uv,k} \frac{dx^u}{dt} \frac{dx^v}{dt} - \frac{d}{dt} \left( Q g_{uk} \frac{dx^u}{dt} \right) - \frac{d}{dt} \left( Q g_{kv} \frac{dx^v}{dt} \right) \right] dt$$

12.14

Because the $\delta^k(x^1, x^2, x^3, x^4)$ are generally non-zero and the total integral must be zero, the parenthesized term in the integrand must also be zero. It is desirable to replace the dummy variable $t$ by the total distance $s$, as defined in the original equation of $s$ in (12.9). $Q$ was defined so that:

$$Q = (1/2)(dt/ds)$$

In the integral of (12.14), substitute this expression for $Q$, and substitute $dt = ds(dt/ds)$ for the differential $dt$. The result is the integral without the dummy variable, and (12.14) becomes:

$$s'(0) = 0 = \int_{t_1}^{t_2} \delta^k \left[ \frac{1}{2} g_{uv,k} \frac{dx^u}{ds} \frac{dx^v}{ds} - \frac{d}{ds}\left( \frac{1}{2} g_{uk} \frac{dx^u}{ds} \right) - \frac{d}{ds}\left( \frac{1}{2} g_{kv} \frac{dx^v}{ds} \right) \right] ds$$

12.15

By the chain rule, $dg_{ij}/ds = (\partial g_{ij}/\partial x^r)(dx^r/ds) = g_{ij,r}(dx^r/ds)$ because the metric is being expressed as a function of the coordinates and the coordinates as a function of $s$: $g_{ij}(x^r(s))$. The integrand of (12.15) must be zero. After differentiation by $s$, it is given by:

$$0 = \frac{1}{2} g_{uv,k} \frac{dx^u}{ds} \frac{dx^v}{ds} - \frac{1}{2} g_{uk,v} \frac{dx^v}{ds} \frac{dx^u}{ds} - \frac{1}{2} g_{kv,u} \frac{dx^u}{ds} \frac{dx^v}{ds} - g_{uk} \frac{d^2x^u}{ds^2}$$

12.16

These equations solve for the extremal, $x^i(s)$, as a function of length $s$. Of course, the equations could have been kept in terms of the dummy variable $t$, but in relativity it is useful to write them as functions of $s$ instead. With a little algebraic manipulation, equation (12.16) becomes:

$$\frac{d^2x^\sigma}{ds^2} + \frac{1}{2} g^{k\sigma} (g_{uk,v} + g_{vk,u} - g_{uv,k}) \frac{dx^u}{ds} \frac{dx^v}{ds} = 0$$

Finally, the *Christoffel symbols of the first kind* are defined as:

$$[uv,k] = \frac{1}{2}(g_{uk,v} + g_{vk,u} - g_{uv,k})$$

12.17

The *Christoffel symbols of the second kind* are:

$$\left\{ {}^{\sigma}_{uv} \right\} = g^{k\sigma}[uv,k]$$

12.18

These Christoffel symbols are not tensors, and it will become clear later how they transform between coordinate systems. But with them the differential equations for extremals become:

$$\frac{d^2 x^\sigma}{ds^2} + \left\{ {}^{\sigma}_{uv} \right\} \frac{dx^u}{ds} \frac{dx^v}{ds} = 0$$

12.19

These differential equations are not part of the field equations of general relativity, but are simply those used to find geodesics for any given space $g_{ik}$. In general relativity, only some spaces satisfy field equations, which generate various metrics as solutions. Then the Christoffel symbols can be generated and the geodesic equations set up and solved, yielding geodesic paths through space-time. As will be seen later, objects in "free fall" in gravitational fields travel on paths described by equation (12.19) above.

## Exercises

1. In spaces with constant metric components, show that the shortest distance between two points is a straight line.

2. In Euclidean three-space, show that the tensor $C_{ij} = A_i B_j$, operating on an arbitrary vector field $v$, $C_{ij} v^j = A_i B_j v^j$ denoted by $\overline{a} \otimes \overline{b}[\overline{v}]$, is given by $a(\overline{b} \bullet \overline{v})$.

3. Prove that two coordinate transformations, from $A$ to $B$ to $C$, are equivalent to one coordinate transformation from $A$ to $C$ for a vector field. Let $A$ denote the unprimed coordinate system, $B$ the primed system, and $C$ the double primed system.

4. Simplify the following expressions:

$$A^{ij}_{\ kl} B^m_{\ nop} g^{n\alpha} g^{k\beta} g_{i\gamma} g_{m\delta}$$

$$A_i^{\ l} g^{iu} \delta_l^{\ v} - B_{nk} g^{nm} g^{vk} \delta_m^{\ u}$$

$$2 F_m^{\ v} g^{um} - F^u_{\ i} g^{kv} \delta_k^i$$

5. Evaluate the Euler equation $\left[ \partial f / \partial x_i - d/dt \left( \partial f / \partial x_i' \right) \right] = 0$ when $f$ is the difference between kinetic energy and potential energy of an object with mass $m$:
$f(x_i, x_i') = (1/2) m x_i'^2 - V$ .

6.  Find the $y(x)$ that minimizes the integral $\int_0^x y'^2 (1-x^2)dx$ and satisfies $y(2)=1$, $y(3)=2$.

7.  For any two initial conditions $y_1 = y(x_1)$ and $y_2 = y(x_2)$, show that the minimum volume bounded by revolutions of the curve $y(x)$ about the $x$-axis is given by $y(x)=0$.

8.  Derive (12.19) from (12.9).

# CHAPTER 13

# *Overview of Tensor Calculus*

THIS CHAPTER WILL ADDRESS COVARIANT differentiation and affine and metrical manifolds. Covariant differentiation is a way of obtaining new tensors from the differentiation of other tensors. The derivative of a scalar field $\partial h / \partial x^{\alpha} = v_{\alpha}$ always gives a vector field. A scalar is a tensor of rank zero, and a vector is a tensor of rank one. However, the partial derivative of a vector field is not always a second-order tensor field. Consider partial differentiation of the vector field below with respect to the *m*th coordinate variable:

$$v'_k = \frac{\partial x^l}{\partial x'^k} v_l$$

$$\frac{\partial v'_k}{\partial x'^m} = \frac{\partial}{\partial x'^m} \left( \frac{\partial x^l}{\partial x'^k} v_l \right) = \frac{\partial^2 x^l}{\partial x'^m \partial x'^k} v_l + \frac{\partial x^l}{\partial x'^k} \frac{\partial v_l}{\partial x'^m}$$

$$v'_{k,m} = \frac{\partial x^l}{\partial x'^k} \frac{\partial x^n}{\partial x'^m} v_{l,n} + \frac{\partial^2 x^l}{\partial x'^m \partial x'^k} v_l$$

13.1

The $v_{l,n}$ do not transform as second-order tensors would. They would do so only if the mixed partial term in the last equation of (13.1) could somehow be zero. Thus the partial differentiation of tensors must be supplemented in order to guarantee the production of new tensors.

Consider two curvilinear coordinate systems, primed and unprimed. In the unprimed coordinate system a vector field $v_l$ has the same constant vector everywhere:

$$v_l = \text{constant}_l$$

Suppose this unprimed coordinate system to be Euclidean four-space in which each location $(x^1, x^2, x^3, x^4)$ has the same constant vector:

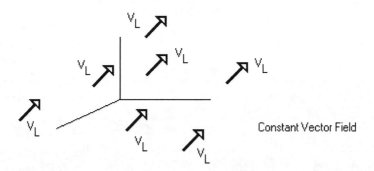

Constant Vector Field

Because the vector field $v_l$ is constant, these components do not change as functions of the coordinates, and their partial derivatives are zero:

$$\frac{\partial v_l}{\partial x^n} = v_{l,n} = 0$$

One might expect the derivative of a vector field to be a second-order tensor field. Any reasonable definition of a new kind of derivative, for vector fields, should yield the second order zero tensor for constant vector fields. A second-order tensor transforms as follows:

$$B'_{ij} = B_{uv} \frac{\partial x^u}{\partial x'^i} \frac{\partial x^v}{\partial x'^j}$$

If the components of $B$ were all zero in one coordinate system, they would have to be zero in every other coordinate system. However if in equation (13.1) the $v_{l,n}$ are zero, then because of the $v_l \, \partial^2 x^l / \partial x'^m \partial x'^k$ term $v'_{k,m}$ will not be zero generally. If this term is subtracted from both sides of the last equation of (13.1) and the $v_l$ are expressed in terms of their primed counterpart, then the last equation of (13.1) becomes:

$$v'_{k,m} - \frac{\partial^2 x^l}{\partial x'^m \partial x'^k} \frac{\partial x'^\sigma}{\partial x^l} v'_\sigma = \frac{\partial x^l}{\partial x'^k} \frac{\partial x^n}{\partial x'^m} v_{l,n}$$

13.2

Note that the right side of this equation transforms as a second-order tensor. If all $v_{l,n}$ vanish, then the left side must also vanish. It is reasonable to define a type of differentiation by meeting the general form of the left-hand side. That is, a type of differentiation which embodies the special case where the derivative of a constant vector field is zero, for all tensor components at all locations, and therefore is zero in all other coordinate systems. However this type of differentiation needs to hold for general vector fields, not simply the case of a constant vector field. To hold generally, the *covariant derivative* of a first-order tensor field must transform as a second-order tensor. Define:

$$\Gamma'^\sigma_{mk} = \frac{\partial^2 x^l}{\partial x'^m \partial x'^k} \frac{\partial x'^\sigma}{\partial x^l}$$

13.3

The covariant derivative of the $k$th component of the vector field $v$, with respect to the $m$th coordinate, is:

$$v_{k;m} = v_{k,m} - \Gamma^\sigma_{mk} v_\sigma$$

13.4

Here the covariant derivative is not necessarily expressed in the primed or unprimed coordinate system specified in (13.1) through (13.3), but in an arbitrary system.

Although equation (13.3) is defined here in such a way that it is symmetric ( $\Gamma^\sigma_{mk} = \Gamma^\sigma_{km}$ ), it does not have to be so, as will be explained later. To ensure that the covariant derivative of a vector field transforms as a second-order tensor in the most general case, it is required that:

$$v'_{k;m} = v_{\alpha;\beta} \frac{\partial x^\alpha}{\partial x'^k} \frac{\partial x^\beta}{\partial x'^m}$$

This can be used as a condition to see how the $\Gamma^\sigma_{km}$ transform:

$$(v'_{k,m} - v'_\sigma \Gamma'^\sigma_{mk}) = (v_{\alpha,\beta} - v_\gamma \Gamma^\gamma_{\alpha\beta}) \frac{\partial x^\alpha}{\partial x'^k} \frac{\partial x^\beta}{\partial x'^m}$$

13.5

To calculate how the $\Gamma^\sigma_{mk}$, must transform, multiply out the right side of this equation and then substitute these terms into the left side:

$$v'_{k,m} = \frac{\partial x^\alpha}{\partial x'^k} \frac{\partial x^\beta}{\partial x'^m} v_{\alpha,\beta} + \frac{\partial^2 x^\gamma}{\partial x'^m \partial x'^k} v_\gamma$$

$$v'_\sigma = v_\gamma \frac{\partial x^\gamma}{\partial x'^\sigma}$$

After rearranging, we get the equation:

$$v_\gamma \left[ \frac{\partial x^\gamma}{\partial x'^\sigma} \Gamma'^\sigma_{mk} \right] = v_\gamma \left[ \frac{\partial^2 x^\gamma}{\partial x'^m \partial x'^k} + \Gamma^\gamma_{\alpha\beta} \frac{\partial x^\alpha}{\partial x'^k} \frac{\partial x^\beta}{\partial x'^m} \right]$$

Dropping $v_\gamma$ from both sides and multiplying through by $\partial x''^i / \partial x^\gamma$ gives:

$$\Gamma'^i_{km} = \Gamma^\gamma_{\alpha\beta} \frac{\partial x^\alpha}{\partial x'^k} \frac{\partial x^\beta}{\partial x'^m} \frac{\partial x'^i}{\partial x^\gamma} + \frac{\partial^2 x^\gamma}{\partial x'^m \partial x'^k} \frac{\partial x'^i}{\partial x^\gamma}$$

13.6

This is how the $\Gamma^a_{bc}$ transform between coordinate systems. The $\Gamma$'s need not be limited to the definition in (13.3) nor to the symmetry implied there. Any quantity $\Gamma^a_{bc}$ that transforms according to (13.6) is called an *affine connection*. Even if an affine connection vanishes in one coordinate system, it does not necessarily do so in another. For a constant vector field, the covariant derivative is zero for all components. In this case, partial derivatives of vector fields in another coordinate system are given by:

$$v_{k,m} = \Gamma^{\sigma}_{mk} v_{\sigma}$$

13.7

The affine connection must transform as defined in (13.6) in order to maintain the tensor character of the covariant derivative. For the special case of (13.3), we assumed that the transformation took place between two curvilinear coordinate systems, each with a metric, and that the unprimed coordinate system was Euclidean four-space. An affine connection without a metric is mathematically possible, but not in relativity theory.

Now let us look more closely at possible types of geometry. All of the calculations above have assumed that a metric and a symmetric affine connection suffice to describe the spaces being considered. While this is enough for general relativity, it is useful to consider broader types of geometry. In differential geometry there is a very general type of "space" called a *differentiable manifold*, which can be thought of as a set of points, each possessing its own coordinates $(x_1,...,x_n)$. Examples are the surface of a sphere, a Klein bottle, or a torus. In a sufficiently small region of the manifold, all points have a one-to-one correspondence with points in an open set of $\mathbb{R}^n$. When an affine connection is defined on a differentiable manifold, affine curvature, affine geodesics, and affine parallel transportation of vectors are all possible. (These will be reviewed and explained in greater detail later.) For angles and distances to be defined, a metric must also be defined on the manifold. If a differentiable manifold has a metric—and therefore an affine connection—defined on it, then it is called a *Riemannian manifold*.

As with vector fields, we must consider the covariant derivative of a second-order tensor field. Consider a second-order tensor field whose values are the same set of constants at each coordinate location in the space. The covariant derivative should be a third-order tensor whose components are all zero. As before, in all other coordinate systems the covariant derivative should also be zero. If the components of a second-order tensor field are all constant, $T_{ab}$, then partial differentiation with respect to any coordinate will be zero: $U_{abc} = T_{ab,c} = 0$. Again, we must evaluate this tensor in another coordinate system, by taking the partial derivative, $\partial/\partial x'^k$, of $T'_{ij} = T_{ab} (\partial x^a/\partial x'^i)(\partial x^b/\partial x'^j)$:

$$\frac{\partial}{\partial x'^k} T'_{ij} = \frac{\partial}{\partial x'^k}\left( T_{ab}\, \frac{\partial x^a}{\partial x'^i}\, \frac{\partial x^b}{\partial x'^j} \right)$$

Using the product rule on these components and expressing the $T_{ab}$, on the right side in terms of $T'_{uv}$, the result is:

$$T'_{ij,k} = T_{ab,c}\, \frac{\partial x^a}{\partial x'^i}\, \frac{\partial x^b}{\partial x'^j}\, \frac{\partial x^c}{\partial x'^k} + T'_{lj}\, \frac{\partial x'^l}{\partial x^a}\, \frac{\partial^2 x^a}{\partial x'^k \partial x'^i} + T'_{im}\, \frac{\partial x'^m}{\partial x^b}\, \frac{\partial^2 x^b}{\partial x'^k \partial x'^j}$$

13.8

The rightmost two monomial terms can be expressed in terms of the affine connection, (13.3), and this can be generalized for any affine connection. Subtracting the rightmost terms from both sides of (13.8) gives us:

$$T'_{ij,k} - T'_{lj}\Gamma'^l_{ki} - T'_{im}\Gamma'^m_{kj} = T_{ab,c}\, \frac{\partial x^a}{\partial x'^i}\, \frac{\partial x^b}{\partial x'^j}\, \frac{\partial x^c}{\partial x'^k}$$

13.9

Once again, if the $T_{ab;c}$ all vanish, then the left side of this equation also vanishes. The right side of 13.9 transforms as a third order tensor would. Therefore, the covariant derivative of a second-order tensor is defined as:

$$T_{ij;k} = T_{ij,k} - T_{lj}\Gamma^l_{ki} - T_{im}\Gamma^m_{kj}$$

13.10

And, if we construct the transformation below, it is easy to show that the affine connections transform by the same law as found in (13.6):

$$T'_{ij;k} = T_{ab;c}\, \frac{\partial x^a}{\partial x'^i}\, \frac{\partial x^b}{\partial x'^j}\, \frac{\partial x^c}{\partial x'^k}$$

The covariant derivative of a second-rank tensor is similar to that of a vector: the first term is a partial derivative, and subsequent terms consist of a copy of the original object multiplied by an affine connection. These terms are subtracted from the partial derivative, with one subtraction for each index in the tensor. This is true in general and can be proven by repeating this analysis for tensors of arbitrary ranks.

So far, we have found covariant derivatives for the covariant components of vectors and tensors. For the covariant derivatives of contravariant components, consider a contravariant vector field $v^l$ with all components constant so that $v^l{}_{,n}$ is zero. Contravariant vector fields transform as follows:

$$v'^k = \frac{\partial x'^k}{\partial x^l} v^l$$

Taking the partial derivative of both sides with respect to a primed coordinate variable $\partial/\partial x'^m$ gives:

$$\frac{\partial v'^k}{\partial x'^m} = \frac{\partial x^n}{\partial x'^m} \frac{\partial}{\partial x^n} \left( \frac{\partial x'^k}{\partial x^l} v^l \right)$$

Expanding out and substituting $v^l = v'' \, \partial x^l / \partial x''$ , results in:

$$v'^k{}_{,m} = \frac{\partial x^n}{\partial x'^m} \frac{\partial x'^k}{\partial x^l} v^l{}_{,n} + v'' \frac{\partial x^l}{\partial x''} \frac{\partial^2 x'^k}{\partial x'^m \partial x^l}$$

$\qquad$ 13.11

Because the right-most term of the right side must be subtracted, to get the form of the covariant derivative, we should express that term as an affine connection in accordance with (13.3). Take the partial derivative $\partial/\partial x'^m$ of the equation below:

$$\delta_t^k = \frac{\partial x'^k}{\partial x''} = \frac{\partial x'^k}{\partial x^l} \frac{\partial x^l}{\partial x''}$$

Because $(\partial/\partial x'^m) \delta_t^k = 0$ , after the differentiation, subtract one of the remaining terms from both sides of the resulting equation:

$$\frac{\partial x^l}{\partial x''} \frac{\partial^2 x'^k}{\partial x'^m \partial x^l} = -\frac{\partial x'^k}{\partial x^l} \frac{\partial^2 x^l}{\partial x'^m \partial x''}$$

After substituting this into (13.11), equation (13.11) becomes:

$$v'^k{}_{,m} = \frac{\partial x^n}{\partial x'^m} \frac{\partial x'^k}{\partial x^l} v^l{}_{,n} - v'' \frac{\partial x'^k}{\partial x^l} \frac{\partial^2 x^l}{\partial x'^m \partial x''}$$

The right-most term is the affine connection given in (13.3). Adding that monomial to both sides gives the following result:

$$v'^k_{,m} + v'^t\Gamma'^k_{mt} = \frac{\partial x^n}{\partial x'^m}\frac{\partial x'^k}{\partial x^l}v^l_{,n}$$

13.12

If the $v^l$ are the components of a contravariant vector field and we assume that all values are constant everywhere in the unprimed coordinate system, then $v^l_{,n} = 0$ always. And, as usual, we assume the right side to be equal to zero.

The left side of equation (13.12), then, represents the covariant derivative of a contravariant vector field. The covariant derivative of a contravariant vector field $v^k$ with respect to the $m$th coordinate is:

$$v^k_{;m} = v^k_{,m} + v^\sigma\Gamma^k_{m\sigma}$$

13.13

Employing a similar analysis for the covariant derivative of a contravariant second-order tensor, we get:

$$T^{ij}_{;k} = T^{ij}_{,k} + \Gamma^i_{kl}T^{lj} + \Gamma^j_{km}T^{im}$$

13.14

For tensors of higher rank a similar law holds. Take the partial derivative of the tensor and add a copy of the affine connection "multiplied" by the tensor for each index of the tensor.

So far, we have considered tensors that are expressed in totally covariant or totally contravariant form. The covariant differentiation law for mixed tensors can be found by the same procedures. As before, assume that the tensor field $T^u_v$ consists of constants for all components. Because they are the same everywhere in space, $T^u_{v,w} = 0$. A tensor field with constant values everywhere should be differentiated to the third-order zero tensor, and zero in all other coordinate systems. A second-order mixed tensor transforms as follows:

$$T'^i_j = \frac{\partial x'^i}{\partial x^u}\frac{\partial x^v}{\partial x'^j}T^u_v$$

Partial differentiation of both sides by $\partial/\partial x'^k$ and substitution of $T^u_v = T'^a_b\left(\partial x^u/\partial x'^a\right)\left(\partial x'^b/\partial x^v\right)$ gives us:

$$T''_{j,k} = \frac{\partial x^w}{\partial x'^k} \frac{\partial x'^i}{\partial x^u} \frac{\partial x^v}{\partial x'^j} T^u_{v,w} + T'^a_j \frac{\partial x^u}{\partial x'^a} \frac{\partial^2 x'^i}{\partial x'^k \partial x^u} + T''^i_b \frac{\partial x'^b}{\partial x^v} \frac{\partial^2 x^v}{\partial x'^k \partial x'^j}$$

13.15

The right-most term of the right side is the affine connection $\Gamma'^b_{kj}$. While the partials of the middle term on the right side is not an affine connection, it can be transformed to one, as before, by the following equation:

$$\frac{\partial x^u}{\partial x'^a} \frac{\partial^2 x'^i}{\partial x'^k \partial x^u} = -\frac{\partial x'^i}{\partial x^u} \frac{\partial^2 x^u}{\partial x'^k \partial x'^a} = -\Gamma'^i_{ka}$$

Substituting these and then moving these two terms to the other side leaves the following equation:

$$T''^i_{j,k} + T'^a_j \Gamma'^i_{ka} - T''^i_b \Gamma'^b_{kj} = \frac{\partial x^w}{\partial x'^k} \frac{\partial x'^i}{\partial x^u} \frac{\partial x^v}{\partial x'^j} T^u_{v,w}$$

13.16

As before, if the $T^u_{v,w}$ are all zero so that the right side of (13.16) is the third-order zero tensor, the left side must be zero as well. This suggests that the covariant derivative of $T^i_j$ is:

$$T^i_{j;k} = T^i_{j,k} + T^a_j \Gamma^i_{ka} - T^i_b \Gamma^b_{kj}$$

13.17

We can see a general trend. The terms of the covariant derivative of a tensor obey the following laws: for each contravariant index, the covariant derivative includes a positive term in the form of the tensor "multiplied" by the affine connection. And for each covariant index, the covariant derivative includes a negative term in the form of the tensor "multiplied" by the affine connection. Remember that affine connections are not necessarily restricted to (13.3), but can be anything that satisfies its transformation law.

There are other ways, as well, to arrive at covariant differentiation. One is to make the coordinate values functions of a dummy variable $s$, and to write the tensors generally as the tensor product of the tensor components multiplied by all its basis vectors. Then, differentiate the result with respect to the dummy variable. Consider a vector field:

$$\bar{v} = v^r \bar{g}_r$$

Differentiate this vector field with respect to $s$:

$$\frac{d\bar{v}}{ds} = v^r_{,\alpha} \frac{dx^\alpha}{ds} \bar{g}_r + v^r \left(\bar{g}_r\right)_{,\alpha} \frac{dx^\alpha}{ds}$$

The $\left(\bar{g}_r\right)_{,\alpha}$ term is evaluated by taking the partial derivative $\partial/\partial x^\alpha$ of $\bar{i}_l \, \partial x^l_* / \partial x^{r}{}^{;\alpha}$ and then substituting $\bar{i}_l = \bar{g}_k \, \partial x^k / \partial x^l_*$ to get:

$$\left(\bar{g}_r\right)_{,\alpha} = \bar{g}_k \frac{\partial x^k}{\partial x^l_*} \frac{\partial^2 x^l_*}{\partial x^\alpha \partial x^r}$$

Substituting this, $d\bar{v}/ds$ becomes:

$$\frac{d\bar{v}}{ds} = v^r_{,\alpha} \frac{dx^\alpha}{ds} \bar{g}_r + v^t \frac{\partial x^r}{\partial x^l_*} \frac{\partial^2 x^l_*}{\partial x^\alpha \partial x^t} \frac{dx^\alpha}{ds} \bar{g}_r = \left(v^r_{,\alpha} + v^t \Gamma^r_{\alpha t}\right) \frac{dx^\alpha}{ds} \bar{g}_r$$

13.18

As an exercise, the reader may show that all sides of this equation are tensors and that the parenthesized term is a tensor embodying the derivative of a vector field. As in ordinary calculus, the product rule applies to the covariant derivative of two multiplied tensors. An example is given below for vectors (that is, tensors of rank one), but this holds true generally. The reader is encouraged to check this if it is unfamiliar. Let $T_{ij} = A_i B_j$, where $A_i$ and $B_j$ are covariant components of two vector fields. We know that:

$$T_{ij;k} = T_{ij,k} - T_{lj}\Gamma^l_{ki} - T_{im}\Gamma^m_{kj}$$

Substituting $T_{ij} = A_i B_j$ into the equation and simplifying, we get:

$$\left(A_i B_j\right)_{;k} = \left(A_i B_j\right)_{,k} - A_l B_j \Gamma^l_{ki} - A_i B_m \Gamma^m_{kj}$$

$$\left(A_i B_j\right)_{;k} = \left(A_{i,k} - A_l \Gamma^l_{ki}\right) B_j + \left(B_{j,k} - B_m \Gamma^m_{kj}\right) A_i$$

$$\left(A_i B_j\right)_{;k} = A_{i;k} B_j + B_{j;k} A_i$$

This proves that the product rule holds.

## Contravariant Differentiation

For manifolds with both an affine connection and a metric, contravariant differentiation results from finding covariant differentiation and then raising the indices with the metric. For example:

$$A^{\alpha\beta;\gamma} = A^{\alpha\beta}_{\;;\theta} g^{\theta\gamma}$$

13.19

For the covariant case:

$$A_{uv}^{\;;w} = A_{uv;y} g^{yw}$$

13.20

Other properties of covariant differentiation also match those of ordinary calculus. For example, covariant and contravariant differentiation is homogeneous. If $\alpha$ and $\beta$ are constants, and $\boldsymbol{A}$ and $\boldsymbol{B}$ are two second-order tensors, then the following is true:

$$(\alpha A^{pq} + \beta B^{pq})_{;r} = \alpha A^{pq}_{\;;r} + \beta B^{pq}_{\;;r}$$

13.21

An analagous law holds for contravariant differentiation, tensors of mixed rank, and higher order tensors. The covariant derivative of a scalar function is simply the partial derivative:

$$\psi_{;b} = \psi_{,b}$$

13.22

To see why, recall that $\psi_{,b}$ provides the components of a gradient and that the gradient of a scalar field is a vector field. Further, the scalar quantity $A^i B_i = \psi$ is defined where $A^i$ and $B_i$ are vector fields, and the sum must be a scalar. Take the covariant derivative of both sides of this and apply the product rule, which proves that $\psi_{;k} = \psi_{,k}$:

$$\psi_{;k} = \left(A^i B_i\right)_{;k}$$

$$= B_i A^i_{\;;k} + B_{i;k} A^i$$

$$= A^i_{\;,k} B_i + A^i \Gamma^i_{kl} B_i + B_{i,k} A^i - B_l \Gamma^l_{ik} A^i$$

$$= A^i_{\;,k} B_i + A^i B_{i,k}$$

$$= \left(A^i B_i\right)_{,k}$$

$$= \psi_{,k}$$

Multiple covariant derivatives are denoted by one semi-colon, as follows:

$$M_{ijk;l;m;n} = M_{ijk;lmn} \qquad\qquad 13.23$$

## *Exercises*

1. Calculate how the Christoffel symbols of the first kind transform between two coordinate systems.

2. By the methods employed in this chapter, show that the definition of the covariant derivative given in (13.14) holds true.

3. Calculate the components of the gradient of the scalar function
$$\varphi(x_*^1, x_*^2, x_*^3) = \sqrt{\left(x_*^1\right)^2 + \left(x_*^2\right)^2}\ \text{ in Cartesian and cylindrical coordinates.}$$
Cylindrical coordinates are related to Cartesian coordinates by the following:

$$x_*^1 = x^1 \cos x^2$$

$$x_*^2 = x^1 \sin x^2$$

$$x_*^3 = x^3$$

4. Show that for a constant vector field in Euclidean space, the changes in a covariant vector field in any other curvilinear coordinate system are given by $\delta v_k = \Gamma^\sigma_{mk} v_\sigma \delta x^m$ , and changes in a contravariant vector field are given by $\delta v^k = -v^\sigma \Gamma^k_{m\sigma} \delta x^m$ . The $\delta x$'s are changes in the coordinates.

5. What is the expression for $P_{ijk;l}$?

6. Consider the partial derivatives of two scalar fields, $\alpha_{,k}$ and $\beta_{,l}$. Is their tensor product another tensor? If so, why? If not, why not?

7. Show that the Christoffel symbols of the second kind transform according to (13.6).

8. Prove the equation $v_{a,m} g^{an} - v^n_{,m} = v^\alpha \Gamma^n_{m\alpha} + g^{kn} v_\sigma \Gamma^\sigma_{mk}$ .

# CHAPTER 14

# *The Symmetric Affine Connection for Spaces with a Metric*

THE AFFINE CONNECTION determines the nature of the covariant or contravariant derivative. Recall that the affine connection was generalized from equation (13.3) to cover any object that transformed according to (13.6). Both a symmetric affine connection and a metric were assumed to exist, and the metric was used to raise and lower indices on tensors. The affine connection was given by:

$$\Gamma^k_{ij} = \frac{\partial^2 x^\alpha_*}{\partial x^i \partial x^j} \frac{\partial x^k}{\partial x^\alpha_*}$$

14.1

This equation makes clear that spaces with a metric, as we have been studying them, imply a symmetric affine connection: symmetry in the $i$ and $j$ indices. In this case the affine connection should be a function of the metric, which will be shown later in this chapter. It can be found in a number of ways, three of which are considered here:

(1) The metric can raise and lower indices on tensors.

(2) If any vector is "parallel"-displaced, its value should not depend on its covariant or contravariant representation.

(3) The lengths of parallel-displaced vectors should not change after parallel displacement.

Now, what is parallel displacement? In a vector field, vectors at different locations will transform between coordinate systems differently from each other because the partials $\partial x_*^l / \partial x'^k$ are also a function of the position of a given vector. To parallel displace a vector, let the vector be evaluated at a point, then let the same vector be evaluated at point nearby the first. The vector components will differ by an amount equal to the equations in (14.2) multiplied times $\Delta x^\sigma$:

$$v^b_{,\sigma} = -\Gamma^b_{\sigma m} v^m$$

$$v_{a,\sigma} = \Gamma^m_{a\sigma} v_m$$

14.2

For these equations the vector field must be constant everywhere in Euclidean space. Because every vector is an identical copy of every other, including those nearby, if a vector is moved to a location nearby it is still the same vector. This means that in the Euclidean coordinate system $v^*_{m,n} = 0$, and all the components of the covariant derivative of the vector field are equal to zero in Euclidean space. Therefore, in any other coordinate system the covariant derivative of the vector field must also be zero. The equations in (14.2) derive from the definitions of the contravariant and covariant derivatives set to zero. In any coordinate system, the partial derivatives of the vector field must be given by (14.2). We see that covariant differentiation is intimately related to the notion of parallel displacement. Generally speaking, parallel displacement of a vector is simply its removal to a location nearby, leaving its direction and length unchanged. In Euclidean four-space parallel displacement does not alter the values of vector components, but in another coordinate system it will. For the following three cases, consider Euclidean space in a Cartesian coordinate system and the other curvilinear coordinates as any general transformation:

## *Case 1*

Because a metric can raise and lower indices, it can change a tensor's covariant index to its corresponding contravariant index. Take the covariant derivative of:

$$v_i = g_{ij} v^j$$

We get:

$$v_{i;k} = \left(g_{ij} v^j\right)_{,k} = g_{ij;k} v^j + v^j_{;k} g_{ij} \tag{14.3}$$

Because $v^j_{;k}$ is a second-order tensor itself, the metric must raise and lower its indices:

$$v_{i;k} = v^j_{;k} g_{ij} \tag{14.4}$$

Comparing (14.3) with (14.4) makes it clear that, because the $v^j$ are arbitrary, these two equations are compatible only if $g_{ij;k} = 0$.

## *Case 2*

The parallel displacement of a vector should not depend on its contravariant or covariant representations. Take the partial derivative $\partial / \partial x^\sigma$ of both sides of:

$$v_a = g_{ab} v^b$$

We get:

$$v_{a,\sigma} = g_{ab,\sigma} v^b + v^b_{,\sigma} g_{ab} \tag{14.5}$$

Substitute the equations of (14.2) into (14.5):

$$\Gamma^m_{a\sigma} v_m = g_{ab,\sigma} v^b - g_{ab} \Gamma^b_{\sigma m} v^m$$

Moving all terms to the right side and standardize all summed indices to the same symbol, the result is:

$$0 = g_{ab,\sigma}v^b - g_{at}\Gamma^t_{\sigma b}v^b - g_{bm}\Gamma^m_{a\sigma}v^b$$

$$0 = v^b\left(g_{ab,\sigma} - g_{at}\Gamma^t_{\sigma b} - g_{bm}\Gamma^m_{a\sigma}\right)$$

$$0 = v^b g_{ab;\sigma}$$

Again, because $v^b$ is an arbitrary vector field, this equation is satisfied only if the covariant derivative of the metric tensor is the third-order zero tensor $g_{ab;\sigma} = 0$. In conclusion, the parallel displacement of a vector is independent of its representation in contravariant or covariant forms if the covariant derivative of the metric is zero. If this process is applied to tensors of higher rank, for example $A^{ijk}g_{kl} = A^{ij}_{\ \ l}$, we also get the constraint $g_{ab;c} = 0$.

## Case 3

The length of a vector should remain the same after parallel displacement to a location nearby. Consider the parallel displacement of a vector $\bar{v}$ over time, along the curve $x^i(t)$. Both its length and the square of its length must remain constant. If we let $S$ be the length of the vector, the derivative of $S$ with respect to time must be zero:

$$S^2 = g_{ik}v^iv^k$$

$$0 = \frac{d}{dt}(S^2) = \frac{\partial g_{ik}}{\partial x^m}\frac{dx^m}{dt}v^iv^k + g_{ik}\frac{d}{dt}(v^iv^k)$$

$$0 = \frac{\partial g_{ik}}{\partial x^m}\frac{dx^m}{dt}v^iv^k + g_{ik}v^i\frac{\partial v^k}{\partial x^m}\frac{dx^m}{dt} + g_{ik}v^k\frac{\partial v^i}{\partial x^m}\frac{dx^m}{dt}$$

Now $dx^m/dt$, which are non-zero, can be factored out. The remaining term must be zero:

$$0 = g_{ik,m}v^iv^k + g_{ik}v^iv^k_{,m} + g_{ik}v^kv^i_{,m} \qquad \text{14.6}$$

Substituting $v^k_{,m} = -\Gamma^k_{ms}v^s$ and $v^i_{,m} = -\Gamma^i_{ms}v^s$ into this equation alters it to:

$$0 = g_{ik,m}v^iv^k - g_{ik}v^iv^s\Gamma^k_{ms} - g_{ik}v^kv^s\Gamma^i_{ms}$$

In each monomial, the indices summed on can be changed to the same summation index and the product of the vector fields can be factored out:

$$0 = v^i v^k \left( g_{ik,m} - g_{is} \Gamma^s_{mk} - g_{sk} \Gamma^s_{mi} \right)$$

Because the $v^i v^k$ are generally non-zero, the parenthesized expression must be zero. This happens to be the covariant derivative of the metric tensor:

$$0 = g_{ik,m} - g_{is} \Gamma^s_{mk} - g_{sk} \Gamma^s_{mi}$$

$$0 = g_{ik;m}$$

In conclusion, the covariant derivative of the metric tensor is required to be zero so that parallel displacement of vectors preserves their lengths.

## Metrical Spaces with a Symmetric Connection

The three requirements considered above for a metrical manifold are:

(1) The metric must always raise and lower indices of tensors.

(2) The parallel displacement of a vector is independent of its contravariant or covariant representation.

(3) Vector lengths are preserved upon parallel displacement.

These requirements hinge on one condition:

$$g_{ij;k} = 0$$

14.7

The covariant derivative of the metric tensor must be the third-order zero tensor. This holds true in any curved space or coordinate system. Equation (14.1) implies that the affine connection is symmetric: $\Gamma^k_{ij} = \Gamma^k_{ji}$. Thus the symmetric affine connection for a metrical space must itself be a function of the metric. In equation (14.7) there are forty equations in forty unknowns, assuming a four-dimensional continuum. The components of the affine connection are uniquely determined by:

$$g_{ij,k} - \Gamma^l_{ik} g_{lj} - \Gamma^l_{jk} g_{il} = 0$$

14.8

To solve for the affine components, consider each index $(i, j, k)$ as representing some fixed value, and cycle through the indices to find two more equations:

$$g_{ki,j} - \Gamma^l_{kj} g_{li} - \Gamma^l_{ij} g_{kl} = 0$$

$$g_{jk,i} - \Gamma^l_{ji} g_{lk} - \Gamma^l_{ki} g_{jl} = 0 \qquad \text{14.9}$$

If we add these together, and subtract (14.8), we get:

$$2\Gamma^l_{ji} g_{lk} = g_{ki,j} + g_{jk,i} - g_{ij,k}$$

Dividing both sides of this equation by two and multiplying by $g^{km}$ we get:

$$\Gamma^m_{ji} = \frac{1}{2} g^{km} (g_{ki,j} + g_{jk,i} - g_{ij,k}) \qquad \text{14.10}$$

The right side of this equation consists of the Christoffel symbols of the second kind. Therefore the symmetric affine connection for a metrical manifold is just the Christoffel symbols of the second kind:

$$\Gamma^m_{ji} = \{^m_{ji}\} \qquad \text{14.11}$$

Throughout the rest of this book the affine connection $\Gamma$ will be taken to mean the Christoffel symbols of the second kind. They transform as an affine connection by construction.

## Exercises

1.   Given that $g_{ab;c} = 0$ is true, prove that $g^{kp}_{;n} = 0$ is true.

2.   Why does $g_{ij;k} = 0$ guarantee that $\{^p_{qr}\}$ transform like an affine connection?

3.   Show that partial derivatives of basis vectors are given by the equation $g_{p,q} = \Gamma^r_{pq} g_r$ in any coordinate system.

4.   Define a curvilinear coordinate system by the transformation from Euclidean space, in Euclidean coordinates $x^i_*$, to another coordinate system given by

$x^1 = x_*^1$, $x^2 = \text{Arcsin}(x_*^2)$, $x^3 = \text{Arccos}(x_*^3)$. Let the vector field $\bar{u}$ be defined by $u_1 = 2x^1, u_2 = 3x^2, u_3 = 4x^3$. Find the covariant derivatives $u_{j;k}$.

5. Simplify the following expressions:

$$(3\delta_p^u g^{ps} \overline{g_s} \bullet \overline{g_w}\delta_v^w - 2g^{us}\overline{g_r} \bullet \overline{g_v}\delta_s^r)_{;k}$$

$$(5g^{mx} H^{\sigma}{}_m \overline{g^i}\delta_x^j - 4g^{jm}H^{\sigma}{}_m \overline{g^i})_{;j} \bullet \overline{g^l} g_{k\sigma}\delta_l^k + (\overline{g^n} g_{n\sigma})_{;j} \bullet \overline{g^i} H_{ac} g^{a\sigma} g^{bj}\delta_b^c$$

6. Show that for any curvilinear coordinate system $\{{}^{\,k}_{i\,j}\}$ reduces to equation (14.1) in Euclidean space.

7. If $\Gamma^i_{k\,m} - \Gamma^i_{m\,k}$ is a tensor, prove it. If it is not a tensor, explain why not.

8. Prove the equation $g^{ab}\overline{g_{b;c}} = \overline{g^a_{;c}}$ .

# CHAPTER 15

# *Special Relativity in Generalized Notation*

AN EVENT IN SPACE-TIME can be written as a space-time vector in four coordinates $(x, y, z, ct) = (x^1, x^2, x^3, x^4)$. (Although events appear here in contravariant components, they could just as easily have been written in covariant form.) The metric can be used to lower the indices to the covariant form of the vector. The four-velocity, four-acceleration, four-momentum, and four-force are defined, in order, as:

$$u^k = \frac{dx^k}{d\tau}$$

$$a^k = \frac{du^k}{d\tau}$$

$$p^k = m\frac{dx^k}{d\tau}$$

$$f^k = \frac{dp^k}{d\tau}$$

15.1

Here $m$ is the rest mass of the given object and $c^2 d\tau^2$ equals $g_{ab}dx^a dx^b$, where the metric components are all zero, with the exception of $g^{ii} = -1$ and $g^{44} = +1$. Thus the line element for special relativity is:

$$ds^2 = (dx^4)^2 - (dx^3)^2 - (dx^2)^2 - (dx^1)^2$$

15.2

This is called the *Minkowski line element* and the associated metric the *Minkowski metric*. When integrated, the line element gives lengths of world lines. For a world-line describing an object moving at a speed $v$ in an inertial frame, the line element above simplifies, with the substitution of $s = c\tau$, to:

$$d\tau = \sqrt{1 - \frac{v^2}{c^2}}\,dt$$

Multiplying both sides of this equation by the speed of light gives:

$$cd\tau = \sqrt{1 - \frac{v^2}{c^2}}\,dx^4$$

Or:

$$\gamma = \frac{dx^4}{cd\tau}$$

15.3

### Special Relativity Expressed in Terms of Four-Vectors

With the definitions in (15.1), the equations of special relativity are expressed in "space-time" terms. For a particle with four-momentum $p^k$, the angular momentum tensor is given by:

$$l^{jk} = x^j p^k - x^k p^j$$

Relativistic electrodynamics can also be expressed in terms of four-vectors or "space-time" terms. The electromagnetic field strengths can be put in terms of the electromagnetic field tensor:

$$F_{pq} = A_{p;q} - A_{q;p} = A_{p,q} - A_{q,p}$$

15.4

Here $A$ is the electromagnetic vector potential. The symmetry of the affine connection is necessary because the Christoffel symbols of the second kind are symmetric in their lower indices:

$$\Gamma^a_{\ bc} = \{^a_{bc}\} = \{^a_{cb}\} = \Gamma^a_{\ cb}$$

This fact allows covariant derivatives to become partial derivatives in the equations of electromagnetism. This, together with the skew symmetry of $F_{pq}$, (that is, $F_{pq} = -F_{qp}$), allows us to write:

$$F_{pq;r} + F_{qr;p} + F_{rp;q} = F_{pq,r} + F_{qr,p} + F_{rp,q} = 0$$

15.5

These equations correspond to Faraday's law and Gauss's law for the magnetic field, which the reader should check. Ampère's law and Gauss's law for the electric field can be found by (15.6):

$$F^{st} = F_{pq} g^{ps} g^{tq}$$

$$F^{st}_{\ ;t} = \mu_0 j^s$$

15.6

Here $(j^1, j^2, j^3, \rho c = j^4)$ are the current densities and $\mu_o = 1/\varepsilon_o c^2$. Next, consider Ampère's law and Gauss's law in terms of four-current and the electromagnetic vector potentials. To find the covariant components of the four-current density $j_i$ as a function of the potentials $A^k$, substitute (15.4) into the first equation of (15.6) and take the covariant derivative with respect to $x^t$:

$$F^{st}_{\ ;t} = A^s_{\ ;qt} g^{qt} - A^t_{\ ;pt} g^{ps}$$

Multiplying this equation by $g_{sm}$ gives the answer:

$$\mu_0 j_m = F_m^{\ t}_{\ ;t} = A_{m;qt} g^{qt} - A^t_{\ ;mt}$$

Other aspects of special relativity can also be put into tensor formalism. For example, the Lorentz transformations can be written as:

$$x'_a = L^b{}_a x_b$$

And the conservation of electric charge can be written as:

$$j^a{}_{;a} = 0$$

Analogous equations can be written for four-momentum, charge and current density, relativistic force, electromagnetic vector potentials, and so on. The four-force exerted by an electromagnetic field on a charged particle $q$, traveling with four-velocity $u^b$, is:

$$f_a = q u^b F_{ab} \qquad \text{15.7}$$

Straightforward substitution will easily verify this.

### The Energy-Momentum Tensor

It is easy to compute the components of the four-velocity vector. If the three-velocity is written as the vector $(w^1, w^2, w^3, c)$, the four-velocity is $u^i = \gamma w^i$:

$$u^1 = \frac{w^1}{\sqrt{1 - \left\lVert \vec{w} \right\rVert^2 / c^2}} \quad u^2 = \frac{w^2}{\sqrt{1 - \left\lVert \vec{w} \right\rVert^2 / c^2}}$$

$$u^3 = \frac{w^3}{\sqrt{1 - \left\lVert \vec{w} \right\rVert^2 / c^2}} \quad u^4 = \frac{c}{\sqrt{1 - \left\lVert \vec{w} \right\rVert^2 / c^2}}$$

$$\text{15.8}$$

Because the vector $\vec{w}$ is the three-velocity, it does not include the fourth component, $c$. The four-momentum is $p^i = mu^i$ and an object's three-velocity is related to its four-velocity by the following equation:

$$w^i = \frac{c d\tau}{dx^4} u^i$$

$$\text{15.9}$$

A continuity equation for the conservation of mass-energy and momentum can also be constructed:

$$div\left[\frac{m\bar{w}}{\sqrt{1-\|\bar{w}\|^2/c^2}}\right] = -\frac{\partial}{\partial t}\left[\frac{m}{\sqrt{1-\|\bar{w}\|^2/c^2}}\right] = -\frac{\partial}{\partial x^4}\left[\frac{mc}{\sqrt{1-\|\bar{w}\|^2/c^2}}\right]$$

Here $m\gamma$ is the total mass-energy. The above equation can be re-written in terms of four-velocity as:

$$(mu^i)_{,i} = 0$$

15.10

It can also be written for three-velocity as:

$$(m\gamma w^i)_{,i} = 0$$

15.11

Although we might be tempted to consider energy density and momentum density as components of a four-vector, we would be wrong. Four-momentum density transforms as a vector according to the equation $A'^i = A^m (\partial x'^i/\partial x^m)$. If densities of energy and momentum transformed in this way, then mass density in the rest frame of $m$ would be related to another Lorentz frame according to the equation $\rho' = \gamma\rho$. But remember length contraction and the fact that mass increases by a factor of $\gamma$ and volume decreases by another factor of $\gamma$. Therefore, mass density transforms as $\rho' = \gamma^2\rho$. Because both $u^i$ and $\rho$ are transformed between inertial frames, this implies that $\rho$ is one component of a second-rank tensor which must transform as follows:

$$T'^{kl} = T^{st}\frac{\partial x'^k}{\partial x^s}\frac{\partial x'^l}{\partial x^t}$$

This second-rank tensor does contain terms that transform with factors of $\gamma^2$ because, in the partial derivatives between two Lorentz transformations, the term $\partial x'^k/\partial x^s$ appears twice. To get an idea of what the components of $T$ represent, consider the simplest case, where the 4-4 component of $T$ represents the density of matter—perhaps a field of dust or a fluid—in a given inertial frame. In the rest frame of the fluid or dust, the term $T^{44} = \rho$ is non-zero and represents the "rest density" of the fluid. All other terms are zero. In the rest frame of the fluid:

$$T^{st} = \begin{bmatrix} 0 & 0 & 0 & 0 \\ 0 & 0 & 0 & 0 \\ 0 & 0 & 0 & 0 \\ 0 & 0 & 0 & T^{44} \end{bmatrix} = \begin{bmatrix} 0 & 0 & 0 & 0 \\ 0 & 0 & 0 & 0 \\ 0 & 0 & 0 & 0 \\ 0 & 0 & 0 & \rho \end{bmatrix}$$

For another inertial frame, we can calculate the components of $T'$ by remembering that the partials in the transformations of $T$ are between Lorentz inertial frames, thus corresponding to Lorentz transformations. If $s = 4$ and $k = 1$, we can use the equation $x'^1 = \gamma(x^1 - vt)$ to get $\partial x'^1 / \partial t = -v\gamma$. When this is carried out for all terms, the $T'^{kl}$ is:

$$T'^{kl} = \begin{bmatrix} v^2\gamma^2 T^{44} & 0 & 0 & -v\gamma^2 T^{44} \\ 0 & 0 & 0 & 0 \\ 0 & 0 & 0 & 0 \\ -v\gamma^2 T^{44} & 0 & 0 & \gamma^2 T^{44} \end{bmatrix}$$

It is clear that $T'^{11} = v^2\gamma^2 T^{44}$, $T'^{14} = T'^{41} = -v\gamma^2 T^{44}$ and $T'^{44} = \gamma^2 T^{44}$. Therefore, $T'^{44} = \rho'$, which concurs with the equation $\rho' = \gamma^2\rho$. We see that momentum density is embodied in the $T'^{41}$. Visualize a cube of fluid with rest density $\rho$ in one inertial frame. In another inertial frame, the cube of fluid travels at a constant arbitrary three-velocity $\overline{w}$. Its density will increase in accordance with the equation $T'^{44} = \gamma^2 T^{44}$ because its mass and volume will increase and decrease, respectively, by a factor of $\gamma$. Further, its density is moving with a speed $w$. Therefore $\rho w \gamma^2$ corresponds to momentum density. The 4-4 component of $T$ is also the energy density because energy and matter are interconvertible. The 4-4 component of $T$ is an energy density and can be written in terms of four-velocity, with the help of (15.3), and rest density $\rho$:

$$T^{44} = \rho c^2 \gamma^2 = \rho \frac{dx^4}{d\tau} \frac{dx^4}{d\tau} = \rho u^4 u^4$$

Because mass increases and volume decreases inversely by the same factor, the momentum densities in each spatial direction are given by $\rho w^j \gamma^2$, with

$j = 1, 2$, or 3. The three-velocity and four-velocity are related by the equation $w^j = u^j(cd\tau/dx^4)$. Multiplying momentum density by the speed of light puts all these terms into the same units, thus allowing the calculation of the $T^{j4}$:

$$T^{j4} = \rho c w^j \gamma^2 = \rho c^2 \frac{d\tau}{dx^4} u^j \frac{dx^4}{cd\tau} \frac{dx^4}{cd\tau} = \rho u^j \frac{dx^4}{d\tau} = \rho u^j u^4$$

This equation allows $j$ to have the values 1, 2, or 3, and the case where $j=4$ was covered previously. Thus the total energy momentum tensor can be generalized as follows:

$$T^{mn} = \rho \frac{dx^m}{d\tau} \frac{dx^n}{d\tau} = \rho u^m u^n$$

15.12

Some components of this tensor correspond to stresses in materials and fluids where the indices take on the values 1, 2, or 3, or the flux of momentum in one direction toward another. The energy momentum tensor $T^{ik} = T^{ki}$ must always be symmetric because the movement of mass-energy from one location to another is embodied in momentum flux, and momentum is conserved. Some further properties follow. For example, let us calculate $T^{mn}u_n$ and interpret the results. From equation (15.12):

$$T^{mn}u_n = \rho u^m u^n u_n$$

All we must do is to find $u^n u_n$. From the definition of four-velocity:

$$u^n u_n = \frac{dx^n}{d\tau} \frac{dx_n}{d\tau}$$

This equation has the coordinate differentials in both covariant and contravariant form. To evaluate $dx^n dx_n$, use the line element:

$$ds^2 = c^2 d\tau^2 = g_{mn} dx^m dx^n = dx_n dx^n$$

Here the metric lowers the index on the differential. Divide both sides of this equation by $d\tau^2$ to get:

$$c^2 = \frac{dx_n}{d\tau}\frac{dx^n}{d\tau}$$

This reduces the problem to:

$$T^{mn}u_n = \rho c^2 u^m$$

We can go a step further to calculate $T^{mn}u_m u_n$. This requires application of the same reasoning to the remaining equation:

$$T^{mn}u_m u_n = \rho c^2 u^m u_m = \rho c^4$$

Thus the inner tensor product of the energy-momentum tensor and the tensor $u_m u_n$ is proportional to the rest density of the fluid. The equation $T^{mn}u_n$ represents the four-momentum per unit volume, with $\Delta B$ a small volume element:

$$T^{mn}u_n = \rho c^2 u^m = \rho c^2 \frac{dx^m}{d\tau} = \frac{mc^2}{\Delta B}\frac{dx^m}{d\tau} = \frac{c^2 p^m}{\Delta B} \qquad 15.13$$

### The Conservation Law for Mass-Energy

To express the conservation of mass-energy and momentum in terms of the energy momentum tensor, consider a fluid or dust whose energy momentum tensor is $T^{ij}$. The mass energy density $T^{44}$ and the momentum density $T^{j4}$, for $j = 1, 2,$ or $3$, should obey a continuity equation, with $\rho_L$ representing the density in a given inertial frame:

$$(\rho w^i \gamma^2)_{,i} = (\rho_L w^i)_{,i} = 0 \qquad 15.14$$

This should correspond to the following equation, where the index $j$ sums from one to three:

$$T^{14}_{,1} + T^{24}_{,2} + T^{34}_{,3} = T^{j4}_{,j} = -T^{44}_{,4}$$

This is merely " $div(T^{j4}) = -(\partial/\partial t)T^{44}$ ". And this equation does correspond to (15.10), which can easily be shown by expressing the energy-momentum tensor in terms of three-velocity:

$$T^{ij} = \rho u^i u^j = \rho \gamma w^i \gamma w^j = \rho \gamma^2 w^i w^j = \rho_L w^i w^j$$

Taking the partial derivative, and summing with respect to the $j$th coordinate, gives:

$$T^{ij}{}_{,j} = w^i \frac{\partial(\rho_L w^j)}{\partial x^j} + \rho_L w^j \frac{\partial w^i}{\partial x^j}$$

For $i = 4$, the last term of this equation is zero, and the first term is zero, for any $i$, because it is the continuity equation (15.14). For $i = 1, 2,$ or $3$, the last term corresponds to a net four-force density. Assuming that there are no internal stresses, the net four-force density must be zero because of Newton's third law. To illustrate, the latter term can be written as a function of three-acceleration:

$$\rho_L w^j \frac{\partial w^i}{\partial x^j} = \rho_L \frac{dx^j}{dt} \frac{\partial w^i}{\partial x^j} = \rho_L \frac{dw^i}{dt} = \widetilde{f^i} = 0$$

If no net external force acts on the region, then Newton's third law requires that the sum of the stresses be zero. The conservation of energy and momentum is embodied in the equation:

$$T^{ij}{}_{,j} = 0$$

15.15

This equation will hold true in Euclidean space. For energy-momentum conservation to hold true in a general coordinate system, equation (15.15) must be generalized from partial to covariant differentiation:

$$T^{ij}{}_{;j} = 0$$

15.16

This conservation law must hold true in a closed system.

Now consider an open system, where momentum and energy flow across a boundary. In an inertial frame, consider a constant differential volume element $\Delta B$ where the energy and momentum of $\Delta B$ can be given by this equation:

$$T^{ij}\Delta B = \rho\Delta Bu^i u^j = mu^i u^j$$

Taking the $j$th partial derivatives and summing on the index $j$ gives:

$$T^{ij}{}_{,j}\Delta B = u^i \frac{\partial(mu^j)}{\partial x^j} + mu^j \frac{\partial u^i}{\partial x^j} = m\frac{dx^j}{d\tau}\frac{\partial u^i}{\partial x^j} = m\frac{du^i}{d\tau} = f^i$$

The first term is zero because of the continuity equation (15.10), and the second term corresponds to a four-force. Dividing both sides by the constant volume element $\Delta B$ and letting the vector $\widetilde{f^i}$ represent a four-force density gives us:

$$T^{ij}{}_{,j} = \widetilde{f^i}$$

Thus in Euclidean space the sum of the partial derivatives of the energy-momentum tensor is equal to the net four-force density. As before, to go from a Cartesian coordinate system to another curvilinear coordinate system, this partial derivative must become the covariant derivative. For the most general case, a net external four-force density acting on matter is given by:

$$T^{ab}{}_{;b} = \widetilde{f^a}$$

15.17

When there is no net external or internal force, $\widetilde{f^a} = 0$. For equation (15.17) to be true in every coordinate system, the contracted third-order tensor $T^{ab}{}_{;b}$ must transform as a vector. The covariant derivative of the energy-momentum tensor must itself be a third order tensor, and transform as follows:

$$T'^{ab}{}_{;c} = T^{pq}{}_{;r} \frac{\partial x'^a}{\partial x^p} \frac{\partial x'^b}{\partial x^q} \frac{\partial x^r}{\partial x'^c}$$

Summing on the indices $c$ equal $b$, we get:

$$T'^{ab}_{\;;b} = T^{pq}_{\;;r} \frac{\partial x'^a}{\partial x^p} \frac{\partial x'^b}{\partial x^q} \frac{\partial x^r}{\partial x'^b} = T^{pq}_{\;;r} \frac{\partial x'^a}{\partial x^p} \delta^r_q$$

$$T'^{ab}_{\;;b} = T^{pr}_{\;;r} \frac{\partial x'^a}{\partial x^p}$$

$$\widetilde{f}'^a = \widetilde{f}^p \frac{\partial x'^a}{\partial x^p}$$

Thus the four-force density transforms as a vector, and if it is zero in one coordinate system, it is zero in an all others. For that reason equation (15.16) embodies the conservation of mass-energy and momentum in the most general sense.

The energy-momentum tensor for an ideal frictionless fluid, with the pressure of the fluid $p$ and the rest density of the fluid $\rho$, is:

$$T^{jk} = \left( \rho + \frac{p}{c^2} \right) u^j u^k - \frac{p}{c^2} g^{jk}$$

15.18

In this equation, each four-velocity is divided by the speed of light so that the units work out correctly.

### The Electromagnetic Energy-Momentum Tensor

The electromagnetic field can store and release energy. We have seen that the power density was given by $\overline{j} \bullet \overline{E}$. Letting $\rho_c$ represent charge density, this can be generalized to:

$$j^\sigma F^u_{\;\sigma} = T^{uv}_{\;;v} = \widetilde{f}^u = \rho_c w^b F^u_{\;b}$$

15.19

This equation makes sense because $T^{44}_{\;;4}$ is part of the power density given in (15.19), and $F^u_{\;\sigma}$ are the electric and magnetic field strengths, $\boldsymbol{E}$ and $\boldsymbol{B}$. The constant $\mu_o$ equals $1/\varepsilon_o c^2$. Ampère's law and Gauss's law are embodied in the equation:

$$\mu_0 j^\sigma = F^{\sigma v}_{\;;v}$$

Substituting this expression into (15.19) gives:

$$T^{uv}_{\;\;;v} = \frac{1}{\mu_0} F^{u}_{\;\sigma} F^{\sigma v}_{\;\;;v}$$

15.20

    This formula shows the relationship between the energy-momentum tensor for the electromagnetic field and the electromagnetic field tensor. To find the energy-momentum tensor in terms of the electromagnetic field tensor with no derivatives, the equation must be manipulated to eliminate the covariant derivative. (Maxwell's equations are traditionally studied in flat space where covariant differentiation and partial differentiation are interchangeable.) All the following calculations will use covariant differentiation, covering partial differentiation trivially. The solution is:

$$T^{uv} = \frac{1}{\mu_0} \left( -F^{u}_{\;\sigma} F^{v\sigma} + \frac{1}{4} g^{uv} F^{\sigma\rho} F_{\sigma\rho} \right)$$

15.21

To prove this, take the covariant derivative of both sides with respect to $x^v$, and change indices on the right-most term:

$$\mu_0 T^{uv}_{\;\;;v} = (F^{u}_{\;\sigma} F^{\sigma v})_{;v} + \frac{1}{4} g^{u\rho} (F^{\sigma v} F_{\sigma v})_{;\rho}$$

15.22

Here the minus sign vanishes because of the skew symmetry of the electromagnetic field tensor ( $F^{\sigma v} = -F^{v\sigma}$ ). The right-most term on the right side can be multiplied out:

$$(F^{\sigma v} F_{\sigma v})_{;\rho} = F^{\sigma v}_{\;\;;\rho} F_{\sigma v} + F^{\sigma v} F_{\sigma v;\rho}$$

Now:

$$F^{\sigma v}_{\;\;;\rho} F_{\sigma v} = g^{s\sigma} g^{tv} F_{st;\rho} F^{mn} g_{m\sigma} g_{nv} = F_{st;\rho} F^{mn} \delta^{s}_{m} \delta^{t}_{n} = F_{mn;\rho} F^{mn}$$

Changing indices by letting $m = \sigma$ and $n = v$, the monomial sum is identical to the other term so that:

$$(F^{\sigma v} F_{\sigma v})_{;\rho} = 2 F^{\sigma v} F_{\sigma v;\rho}$$

Equation (15.22) then becomes:

$$\mu_0 T^{uv}{}_{;v} = (F^u{}_\sigma F^{\sigma v})_{;v} + \frac{1}{2} g^{u\rho} F^{\sigma v} F_{\sigma v;\rho} \qquad 15.23$$

Faraday's law and Gauss's law for the magnetic field are expressed as:

$$F_{\rho\sigma;v} + F_{\sigma v;\rho} + F_{v\rho;\sigma} = 0$$

Solving for $F_{\sigma v;\rho}$ and substituting it into (15.23) gives us:

$$\mu_0 T^{uv}{}_{;v} = (F^u{}_\sigma F^{\sigma v})_{;v} - \frac{1}{2} F^{\sigma v} g^{u\rho} F_{\rho\sigma;v} - \frac{1}{2} F^{\sigma v} g^{u\rho} F_{v\rho;\sigma} \qquad 15.24$$

Due to the skew symmetry of the electromagnetic field tensor, the middle term on the right side changes to $F^{\sigma v} = -F^{'v\sigma}$ and the right-most term on the right side changes to $F_{v\rho} = -F_{\rho v}$. Using the metric to raise its corresponding index eliminates it from the equations, leaving as a final result:

$$\mu_0 T^{uv}{}_{;v} = (F^u{}_\sigma F^{\sigma v})_{;v} + \frac{1}{2} F^{v\sigma} F^u{}_{\sigma;v} + \frac{1}{2} F^{\sigma v} F^u{}_{v;\sigma} \qquad 15.25$$

Now it is apparent that the right-most two monomial sums are the same, but simply use different indices. We can change indices for the middle monomial on the right side to add those two terms. Substituting $F^{v\sigma} = -F^{\sigma v}$ gives:

$$\mu_0 T^{uv}{}_{;v} = (F^u{}_\sigma F^{\sigma v})_{;v} - F^{\sigma v} F^u{}_{\sigma;v}$$

When we use the product rule to expand the left-most monomial on the right side and simplifying the result, we have:

$$\mu_0 T^{uv}{}_{;v} = F^u{}_\sigma F^{\sigma v}{}_{;v}$$

This equation matches (15.20) and proves that the energy-momentum tensor given in (15.21) for the electromagnetic field energy is correct.

## Exercises

1. Let $T^{uv}$ be the energy-momentum tensor for the electromagnetic field. Prove that $T^{uv}g_{uv}=0$.

2. Calculate the electromagnetic field tensor for a charged particle in motion along the x-axis of an inertial frame.

3. Show that conservation of electric charge is given by $j^a{}_{;a} = 0$.

4. For an ideal frictionless fluid, show that $T^{jk}u_k = u^j\rho$.

5. Show that the covariant derivatives in (15.4) reduce to partial derivatives.

6. Show that the covariant derivatives in (15.5) reduce to partial derivatives.

7. Prove that equation (15.7) reduces to $d(m'\vec{v})/dt = q(\vec{E} + \vec{v} \times \vec{B})$.

8. Show that equation (15.5) corresponds to Faraday's law and Gauss's law for the magnetic field and show that equation (15.6) corresponds to Gauss's law and Ampère's law.

9. Show that the angular momentum tensor is a tensor and is skew symmetric $l^{mn} = -l^{nm}$.

10. From the definitions given in this chapter, calculate the four-force in terms of the space-time position vector.

11. The coordinate location of a particle in an inertial frame is given below as a function of its proper time. The term $\tau_o$ is a constant. Suppose that at $t = 0$, $\tau = 0$. Calculate the four-momentum, four-force, four-velocity, time coordinate as a function of proper time and $x(t)$:

$$x(\tau) = \frac{2}{3}c\tau_0\left(\frac{\tau}{\tau_0}\right)^{3/2}, \quad y(\tau) = z(\tau) = 0$$

# PART 5

## *Gravity*

# CHAPTER 16

## *The Foundations of General Relativity*

SCIENCE, IT HAS BEEN SAID, began with Galileo's rolling objects down inclined planes. This was the first mathematical examination of falling objects in the gravitational field to be based on experiment. Galileo found that, assuming the same initial conditions and neglecting air resistance, the motion of all objects in the gravitational field is the same, regardless of mass. In particular, if two objects of different mass are dropped from the same height, they will fall to the ground in the same amount of time. Neglecting air resistance, the equation of motion for an object freely falling near the surface of the earth is given by the following equation, whose solutions are parabolas:

$$\left( \frac{d^2x}{dt^2}, \frac{d^2y}{dt^2}, \frac{d^2z}{dt^2} \right) = \left( 0, 0, -9.82 \frac{m}{\sec^2} \right)$$

16.1

Johannes Kepler found three laws of planetary motion and Isaac Newton unified these with Galileo's equations into one description of gravitational motion. Newton also discovered that masses exert gravitational forces on one another. Newton's universal theory of gravitation calculates the force between two masses, $M$ and $m_*$, given by the equation:

$$F = -\frac{GMm_*}{r^2}$$

16.2

Here $G$ is the gravitational constant and $r$ is the spatial separation between the two centers of mass for $M$ and $m_*$. In Newtonian gravity, the gravitational field can store potential energy, and the gravitational potential is the gravitational potential energy of the mass $m_*$ divided by its mass $m_*$. For a spherically symmetric object of mass $M$, the gravitational potential is:

$$\phi = \frac{GM}{r}$$

16.3

At any point in this gravity field, the gravitational acceleration can be calculated by taking the gradient of the potential:

$$\bar{g} = -grad\phi = -\frac{GM}{r^3}\bar{r}$$

In this equation, $\bar{r} = (x, y, z)$ is the position vector. The force on a second mass, $m_*$, is $\bar{F} = m_* \bar{g}$, the vector form of equation (16.2). At any radius $r$ from the center of a spherically symmetric object of mass $M$, the gravitational acceleration, multiplied over the surface area, is a constant:

$$(g) \cdot (4\pi r^2) = \left(-\frac{GM}{r^2}\right) \cdot (4\pi r^2) = -4\pi GM$$

This implies that the surface integral of $\bar{g}$ over a general surface enclosing $M$ should be the constant $-4\pi GM$, similar to Gauss's law:

$$\iint_{\partial V}\left[\bar{g} \bullet \bar{n}\right] dS = -4\pi GM$$

When we rewrite the left side of this equation, use the divergence theorem, and write $M$ as the integral of mass density over the volume region $V$, this equation becomes:

$$\iiint\limits_{V} div\,(\overline{g}\,)dV = -4\pi G \iiint\limits_{V} \rho\,dV$$

In differential form it is:

$$div\,(\overline{g}\,)= -4\pi G\rho$$

From vector calculus, the divergence of a gradient equals the Laplacian. For that reason, substituting the gradient of the gravitational potential for **g** into the equation above gives:

$$lap(\phi) = 4\pi G\rho$$

16.4

This equation relates mass density to the gravitational potential at any point in space for static Newtonian gravity fields. In special relativity electromagnetic impulses cannot propagate faster than the speed of light, and objects with mass cannot be accelerated to speeds at or beyond the speed of light. The reason is that any object going faster than light could send impulses backward in time, possibly enabling genuine contradictions.

Newton's theory of universal gravitation allows for *instantaneous* propagation of impulses. Note that in equation (16.2) when one mass changes its position, its force on another mass at any distance *r* changes instantly as well. This means that Newtonian gravitation and special relativity are incompatible. Another disagreement between Newtonian gravity and relativity has to do with simultaneity. Because special relativity shows that simultaneity is relative, if the simultaneous influences in Newtonian gravity existed in one inertial frame, they would not exist simultaneously in another inertial frame. Clearly Newton's theory of gravity is not compatible with special relativity.

Although special relativity shows that uniform motion is relative, Einstein thought that accelerated motion might still be absolute. One could distinguish between inertial and non-inertial frames by forces in the non-inertial frames. An astronaut accelerating in a rocket will feel pushed back in his or her seat by the acceleration, and relative to the astronaut, the "inertial frame" left behind accelerates in the opposite direction. But observers in that inertial frame feel no forces of acceleration at all. An observer stuck to the interior surface of a large rotating cylinder in space feels a centrifugal force. Relative to the observer, the rest of the universe rotates in the opposite direction but without feeling any centrifugal force. Apparently inertial forces allow one to distinguish accelerated motion in an absolute way. Einstein faced two questions: (1) Is accelerated motion relative, as uniform motion is, and if so how? (2) What theory of gravity would prohibit faster than light impulses? Einstein was delighted to discover that these two problems had the same solutions: the *principle of equivalence* and the *principle of general relativity*.

Einstein discovered the principle of equivalence by imagining a rocket's acceleration in the vacuum of outer space, far from the gravitational fields of stars or planets. Astronauts inside the accelerating rocket are pushed toward its back wall. To an observer floating in space outside, astronauts inside the rocket are thrust toward its rear by inertial effects. As Einstein realized, if accelerated motion is relative, then the coordinate system of the rocket and its astronauts is a rest frame from which the rest of the universe accelerates backwards. If so, the rocket's coordinate system is as valid as any other. But how, then, can accelerated motion be relative? Einstein's solution was simple: relative to astronauts in the rocket, there exists a gravitational field whose force pulls them toward the back wall and keeps them there. Relative to the rocket, in other words, the rocket is at rest in a gravitational field and fires its engines to keep from falling in that gravity field. The rest of the universe is falling in this gravitational field.

Similarly, someone inside an elevator in free fall in the earth's gravitational field is not affected by gravity inside the elevator because, relative to the elevator, there is no gravitational field. According to the *principle of equivalence*, gravitational fields are accelerated, or non-inertial, frames of reference. This principle explains Galileo's discovery that objects of different masses fall toward the ground in exactly the same way. Two different masses, floating far from the earth and at rest relative to each other, will accelerate in exactly the same way according to a rocket accelerating nearby. Thus Einstein found that accelerated motion is relative. Astronauts in an accelerated frame of reference accelerate relative to an inertial frame. Relative to astronauts, they are at rest in a gravitational field and the rest of the universe accelerates in the opposite direction because a gravitational field pulls it in that direction. Is the astronaut really accelerating, or really at rest while the universe accelerates because it is caught in one gigantic gravitational field? As with special relativity, neither is actually correct, because accelerated motion is not absolute. The rocket accelerates only relative to inertial frames. A huge gravitational field accelerates the entire universe, but only relative to an astronaut in the rocket. This principle holds for all other types of accelerated motion, including accelerations due to rotations. An observer stationed on the interior of a rotating cylinder makes measurements of a gravitational field and also measures the entire universe rotating around the stationary cylinder. An observer outside the cylinder measures no gravitational field and no rotating universe, but measures the cylinder's rotation. Because accelerated motion is relative, measurements in both frames of reference are equally right and accurate. The relativity of accelerated motion is embodied in the idea that the accuracy of a measuring device is independent of the frame of reference in which it is stationed. Also, the laws of physics have to be the same for the observer rotating within the cylinder as well as for the outside observer. If the laws of physics were different for one of them then accelerated motion would be deducible from the laws of physics and therefore absolute.

Now, a measuring device may function differently in a strong gravitational field. For instance, the friction between moving parts of a mechanical clock may be greater than usual under very high gravity. Assuming the gravitational pull on the components of a measuring device does not interfere with its normal operation, the *principle of general relativity* can be stated this way: the accuracy of any measuring device is independent of the frame of reference it is stationed in and, in every frame of reference, all physical laws are the same. This extends the special theory of relativity so that accelerated motion is relative and the laws of physics are the same in any frame of reference, not just inertial frames. The principle of equivalence and the principle of general relativity can be stated simply:

## *The Law of Equivalence*

A frame of reference consisting of changing special relativistic inertial frames is a stationary frame of reference in a local gravitational field.

### *The Law of General Relativity*

In every frame of reference, all physical laws are the same.

Applying the principle of general relativity to the principle of equivalence, it follows that no experiment can decide between an accelerated coordinate system and a gravitational coordinate system. This is because there is no difference between them: *gravity* and *inertia* are simply two different words for the same thing. Because the laws of physics have to be the same in gravity fields as in accelerated frames of reference, it is necessary that space-time is curved.

### *Curved Space-Time*

A consequence of the principle of equivalence is that a description of a gravitational field can be uncovered simply by studying acceleration in special relativity. Thus it is useful to examine some properties of a non-inertial frame of reference: a coordinate system composed of changing special relativistic inertial frames. Consider an inertial frame with two stationary points, *A* and *B*, and a stream of photons sent continuously from *A* to *B* in a straight line. Imagine that this takes place far from the gravitational influence of any mass such as the earth.

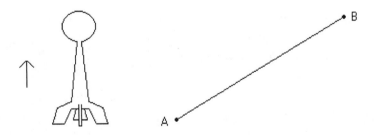

Rocket With Constant Upward Acceleration

Suppose that a rocket moves past these two points in constant acceleration. From special relativity, we know that a photon of light sent from *A* directly to

*B* will arrive in the shortest time possible because light moves at the fastest speed possible. How does an observer on the accelerating rocket observe this situation? Relative to the rocket's frame of reference, the photon stream travels on a curved path:

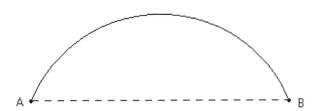

According to the principle of equivalence, the rocket is at rest in a gravitational field that pulls everything, including the universe, downward. From the rocket's perspective the gravity field bends the ray of light. The principle of equivalence predicts that gravitational fields bend light rays: that gravity simply pulls light rays down. From the point of view of the rocket, the light ray is not traversing the shortest possible spatial distance between points *A* and *B*. Relative to the accelerating rocket, the shortest possible distance is given by the dashed line in the diagram above. Would a photon of light traversing the dashed line get from *A* to *B* more quickly than, or in the same amount of time as, along the curved path? Although gravity tends to pull photons down, suppose that a photon of light were somehow forced to traverse the dashed line, perhaps with mirrors. Would it arrive at *B* faster than along the curved path?

Imagine how the dashed line would look in the original inertial frame. Consider a photon that traverses the dashed path in an attempt to go from *A* to *B* in the same amount of time as along the curved path:

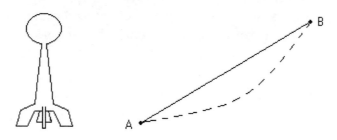

In the original inertial frame the path of the dashed line is a spatially greater distance than the original path. A photon forced along the dashed path would thus reach *B* after a photon sent along the original straight-line path, assuming that both photons left point *A* at the same time. Because special relativity is true in this inertial frame, there is no way a photon traveling the dashed path could get to *B* in the same time, or less, than one traveling on the straight line path. To do so would mean photons traveling on the dashed path would have to move faster than the speed of light and this is ruled out. Therefore, in the rocket's frame of reference, light traversing the dashed path must take more time than light traversing the curved path. But how can this be? For the rocket, the dashed line is spatially shorter and the speed of light along it is constant. Einstein solved this apparent contradiction in the rocket's frame of reference by realizing that, relative to the rocket, time runs more slowly along the dashed path than it runs at higher altitudes where the curved path resides, and this difference more than compensates for the extra spatial distance. In fact, in the rocket's frame of reference, photons traveling along the curved path get from *A* to *B* as quickly as possible. No other route can be faster in any frame of reference.

Several important discoveries follow from this. First, space-time is curved relative to an observer in an accelerating rocket, because changing special relativistic inertial frames is curved space-time. (By the principle of equivalence, changing special relativistic inertial frames are gravitational fields and so gravitational fields must be curved space-time.) Second, time itself slows down in a gravitational field, relative to locations of higher altitude in that gravitational field. Third, photons in "free fall" in a gravitational field travel on geodesics of the curved space-time, which means that they move from one location to another in the shortest time possible. Light travels along the shortest distances through space-time. By similar reasoning, objects "free falling" in gravity fields travel on straight-line courses through space-time. The space-time itself is curved which is why objects freely traveling through gravity fields move along "curved" paths. In this sense gravity is not a force. The earth, for example, travels on a straight line through space-time, but that space-time is curved around the sun.

The fact that gravity is a curvature of space-time can be made clearer in other situations. Consider a disk that rotates at a constant angular speed in an inertial frame. To the inertial frame, each small segment of distance along the perimeter contracts in the direction of its motion because of the length contraction of special relativity. To an observer riding along the perimeter of the rotating disk, the ratio of the disk's circumference to its radius is not $2\pi$ but:

$$\frac{Circumference}{Radius} = \frac{2\pi}{\sqrt{1 - v^2/c^2}}$$

16.5

An observer in the inertial frame would say that this is due to special relativistic length contraction. But relative to an observer stuck to the perimeter of the rotating disk, a gravitational field curves space-time in such a way that there is a greater spatial distance around the circumference. The space is not Euclidean.

The principle of equivalence also predicts changes in photon frequencies in gravity fields. Consider a photon of frequency $f$, emitted at point $A$ and received at point $B$, and a large box with height equal to the distance between $A$ and $B$. At the moment the photon leaves $A$, the box, stationed between $A$ and $B$, begins accelerating upward with constant acceleration.

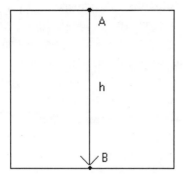

The box reaches speed $v = at$, where $t$ is the time the photon takes to reach $B$. The time interval $t$ is so brief that the box moves upward comparatively little and $t$ is very nearly equal to the height of the box divided by the speed of light:

$$t = \frac{h}{c}$$

The speed of the box after time $t$ is:

$$v = \frac{ah}{c}$$

Because $v \ll c$, the photon's frequency will make a Doppler shift by the classical amount relative to the moving box:

$$f' = f\left(1 + \frac{v}{c}\right)$$

Or:

$$f' = f\left(1 + \frac{ah}{c^2}\right) = f\left(1 + \frac{\phi}{c^2}\right)$$

16.6

By the principle of equivalence, because the box's acceleration is constant, it is stationary in a gravitational field. This means that gravity fields can blue-shift photons moving down a gravitational potential. If the photon moves from $B$ to $A$ it red-shifts by the following amount:

$$f' = f\left(1 - \frac{\phi}{c^2}\right)$$

16.7

For weak potentials $|\phi| << c^2$, calculation of the change in frequency of a photon in a gravitational field implies that time should run faster at the top of the potential, $\phi = ah$ (of height $h$), by a factor of $(1 + \phi/c^2)$. A way to calculate the effect of gravity on time for a weak potential $\phi = ah$ confirms this intuition. At the perimeter of a rotating cylinder, the tangential speed is $v = kr$, where $k$ is a constant. The acceleration at that radial distance is given by the equation: $v^2/r = k^2r^2/r = k^2r = a$. Consider a cylinder of radius $r_2 = r_1 + h$ where $h << r_1$ so that $r_2 \approx r_1$, and imagine a box of height $h$ resting at the perimeter of the rotating cylinder, at $r_2$:

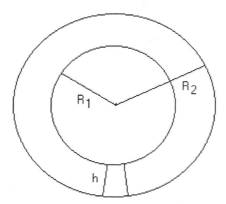

From special relativity, the rate at which time runs at $r_1$, relative to the inertial frame of the rotating disk, is:

$$t_1' = t\sqrt{1 - (kr_1)^2/c^2}$$

And the rate at which time runs at $r_2$, relative to the same inertial frame, is:

$$t_2' = t\sqrt{1 - (kr_2)^2/c^2}$$

Relative to $r_2$, time at $r_1$ runs at a rate given by the ratio of these:

$$\frac{t_1'}{t_2'} = 1 + \frac{k^2}{2c^2}(r_2 - r_1)(r_2 + r_1)$$

This equation is calculated by dividing Taylor approximations of the primed quantities and factoring. Substituting $h$ for $r_2 - r_1$ and substituting $2r_2$ for $r_2 + r_1$ (because they are very nearly equal) leaves:

$$\frac{t_1'}{t_2'} = 1 + \frac{k^2 r_2}{c^2} h$$

16.8

Because the acceleration at $r_2$ is $a = k^2 r_2$ and the potential there is $\phi = ah$, the relation between $t_1'$ and $t_2'$ is:

$$t_1'/t_2' = 1 + \phi/c^2$$

16.9

This holds true only for very weak gravity fields, $|\phi| << c^2$, and was calculated from the principle of equivalence alone.

Gravitational fields can have many different shapes. In weak uniform gravity fields we can easily calculate how much a ray of light drops. It is known that a ray of light will travel in a straight line in flat space-time. A rocket accelerating through space perpendicular to the light ray will move by a distance of $\frac{1}{2} at^2$ for $v << c$. This distance measures the drop of the light ray in a gravitational field. A light ray will traverse a closed room on the surface of the earth in time $x/c$, where $x$ is the width of the room. Substituting this time interval into $\frac{1}{2} at^2$ gives the distance light drops:

$$\Delta z = \frac{ax^2}{2c^2}$$

16.10

Here $a$ is the acceleration of gravity on the surface of the earth. On the surface of the earth, the distance the light ray drops is very small.

The principles of equivalence and of general relativity predict many features of gravitational fields, borne out by experiments:

(1) That gravity is a curvature of space-time.

(2) That light travels on geodesic paths in that curved space-time

(3) That light is red-shifted and blue-shifted by gravity depending on whether it climbs up a gravitational potential or falls through a gravitational potential.

(4) That time at the base of a gravitational potential runs more slowly than at higher altitudes in the potential.

(5) Starlight passing close to the sun, should be deflected slightly in the direction of the sun.

As stated previously, the two principles also show that accelerated motion is relative, not absolute, thus paving the way for a relativistic theory of gravity. The above examples show that the principle of equivalence and the principle of general relativity predict many qualitative and quantitative features of the gravitational field. All of these predictions have tested true experimentally. Gravity is the curvature of space-time and that curvature is a function of the distribution of mass-energy. But if space-time is curved, how can we calculate its shape $g_{uv}$? All curved and flat spaces with a metric are described by a metric tensor. Some subset of all possible shapes will characterize the gravitational field. The field-equations of general relativity allow one to calculate how space-time is shaped for a given distribution of mass-energy $T_{uv}$; that is the field equations are differential equations of the metric tensor. Relativity theory shows that there is no natural intrinsic or preferred coordinate system. This means that all laws of nature are coordinate-independent and embodied by tensors. This very modest requirement is called the *principle of general covariance*.

## *Exercises*

1. Imagine a uniform gravitational field with a constant acceleration of 300 m/sec$^2$ at all altitudes. Relative to zero altitude, how fast is time running at an altitude of $3.00 \times 10^{20}$ meters?

2. Suppose a light ray travels horizontally across a stadium 170 meters in length on earth. How far down is the light ray pulled by gravity during its journey across the stadium?

3. To an observer on the interior of a rotating disk, with a radius of 1000 Km and perimeter speed 99.2 percent of the speed of light, what is the circumference of the disk?

4. A photon of frequency 7.61 megahertz is emitted at the top of a 100-meter building and travels toward the ground. Assuming that this takes place at the surface of the earth, what is the change in frequency of the photon when it hits the ground?

5. Using the same methods employed in this chapter, show that a weak uniform gravity field red shifts light by the equation (16.7).

6. Imagine a disk that starts with no rotation. Supposing that a disk could withstand arbitrarily high centripetal forces, would it remain intact as it rotated faster and faster at the perimeter? What would happen to the disk?

7. Imagine a large rod stretched from the sun to Barnard's star, with a set of thrusters at each mile to accelerate the rod to any speed less than light. In the Sol-Barnard inertial frame, if all thrusters fired simultaneously, what would happen to the rod? Would it accelerate to a given speed?

8. In Newtonian gravity, suppose that a stationary cloud of matter is distributed through space so that the gravitational potential at any point is given by $\phi = \alpha e^{-\beta xyz}$, where $\alpha$ and $\beta$ are constants. What is the density of the cloud at each point in space?

# CHAPTER 17

# The Field Equations of General Relativity

A CURVILINEAR COORDINATE TRANSFORMATION can represent two different things: for one, a simple change of coordinates, as in the Cartesian plane, where rectangular Cartesian coordinates can be changed to polar coordinates. Or it can represent a mapping from one space to another, as in the mapping of a flat circular area to the points on a hemisphere. Applied to any space, transformations of the former type will leave the intrinsic curvature and other properties of that space unaltered, but transformations of the latter type will alter them. Transforming three-dimensional Euclidean space from Cartesian coordinates to cylindrical co-ordinates leaves the nature of that space unchanged. All mathematical properties of a given space are independent of the coordinate system imposed on it. To understand the field equations of general relativity, then, it is useful to understand transformations between coordinate systems on a given space, which leave the space's mathematical properties unaltered. Euclidean spaces, and flat spaces generally, have two properties: (1) the *equality of mixed partials*, and (2) the fact that parallel displacements of vectors along arbitrary curves leave their orientations and magnitudes unchanged. When coordinates are changed in a flat space, these two properties are retained. Consider any vector field $v$ in Euclidean space. From vector calculus the equality of mixed partials holds true:

$$\frac{\partial^2 v_i}{\partial x \partial y} - \frac{\partial^2 v_i}{\partial y \partial x} = 0$$

Or:

$$B_{ijk} = \frac{\partial^2 v_i}{\partial x^j \partial x^k} - \frac{\partial^2 v_i}{\partial x^k \partial x^j} = 0$$

17.1

When changing to a new coordinate system, covariant differentiation replaces partial differentiation. For example, if the vector field above (in Euclidean space) is expressed in cylindrical coordinates, then covariant differentiation replaces partial differentiation. Therefore the equality of mixed partials implies that the difference between the order of covariant differentiation should be zero when any flat-space vector field is expressed in an arbitrary coordinate system. A different way of saying this is as follows: for any given vector field, if the difference of the order of two covariant derivatives is zero, then the vector field resides in a flat space. In that case there must be a coordinate transformation to that flat space such that the metric tensor has constant values. In fact, the initial coordinate system described a flat space to begin with, but may have been unrecognizable because of the coordinate system chosen. If equation (17.1) is thought of as a third-order tensor whose values are all zero, they must be zero in any other coordinate system by the transformation properties of tensors. Therefore (17.1) is generalized to:

$$B_{pqr} = v_{p;qr} - v_{p;rq} = 0$$

17.2

If this equation holds true for an arbitrary vector field, then the metric describes a flat space. The principle of equivalence shows that a local region of curved space-time devoid of matter can be transformed into a flat Minkowski space-time by going to a state of "free fall" in that region. This implies that the curved space-time is really flat space-time, but in a different coordinate system. Therefore, to describe a gravitational field, all we must do is to transform a flat space to a curved space by means of a different set of coordinates. Likewise, any localized curved space-time region devoid of matter should be transformable to a flat space-time by a coordinate transformation.

Let us examine coordinate transformations that transform a "curved" metric $g'_{\alpha\beta}$ to a flat metric $g_{\alpha\beta}$. It is not always easy to determine the kind of space a metric describes because the coordinate system in which it is expressed may be convoluted. But we know that if equation (17.2) holds true, a coordinate transformation from the "curved" metric to a flat metric exists. This is the mathematical embodiment of the principle of equivalence. The field equations of general relativity should thus be expressed somehow in terms of a curvature tensor. The field equations must also satisfy some other conditions, such as the conservation of mass-energy and momentum and approximate Newtonian gravitation in the weak-field case. Because general relativity takes place in a space with a symmetric affine connection and a metric, the affine connections are the Christoffel symbols of the second kind:

$$\Gamma^l_{ij} = \{^{\,l}_{ij}\} = g^{lk}[ij,k]$$

Here the Christoffel symbols of the first kind are given by:

$$[ij,k] = \frac{1}{2}\left(\frac{\partial g_{jk}}{\partial x^i} + \frac{\partial g_{ik}}{\partial x^j} - \frac{\partial g_{ij}}{\partial x^k}\right)$$

To calculate $v_{p;qr} - v_{p;rq}$, note that the first covariant derivatives are:

$$B_{pq} = v_{p;q} = v_{p,q} - v_\sigma \Gamma^\sigma_{pq}$$

$$B_{pr} = v_{p;r} = v_{p,r} - v_\sigma \Gamma^\sigma_{pr}$$

And to find the second covariant derivative, substitute these second-order tensors into:

$$v_{p;qr} = B_{pq;r} = B_{pq,r} - B_{lq}\Gamma^l_{pr} - B_{pl}\Gamma^l_{rq}$$

$$v_{p;rq} = B_{pr;q} = B_{pr,q} - B_{lr}\Gamma^l_{pq} - B_{pl}\Gamma^l_{rq}$$

This yields:

$$v_{p;qr} = v_{p,qr} - v_{\sigma,r}\Gamma^{\sigma}_{pq} - v_{\sigma}\Gamma^{\sigma}_{pq,r} - \Gamma^{l}_{pr}(v_{l,q} - v_{\sigma}\Gamma^{\sigma}_{lq}) - \Gamma^{l}_{rq}(v_{p,l} - v_{\sigma}\Gamma^{\sigma}_{pl})$$

$$v_{p;rq} = v_{p,rq} - v_{\sigma,q}\Gamma^{\sigma}_{pr} - v_{\sigma}\Gamma^{\sigma}_{pr,q} - \Gamma^{l}_{pq}(v_{l,r} - v_{\sigma}\Gamma^{\sigma}_{lr}) - \Gamma^{l}_{rq}(v_{p,l} - v_{\sigma}\Gamma^{\sigma}_{pl})$$

Forming the differences between these two, canceling common terms, and factoring, we get:

$$v_{p;qr} - v_{p;rq} = v_{\sigma}R^{\sigma}_{pqr} \qquad\qquad 17.3$$

With:

$$R^{\sigma}_{pqr} = \Gamma^{\sigma}_{pr,q} - \Gamma^{\sigma}_{pq,r} + \Gamma^{\sigma}_{lq}\Gamma^{l}_{pr} - \Gamma^{\sigma}_{lr}\Gamma^{l}_{pq} \qquad\qquad 17.4$$

Here $R^{\sigma}_{pqr}$ is the *Riemann-Christoffel curvature tensor*. Equation (17.4) describes a fourth-order tensor because the left side of (17.3) is a tensor, as is the vector field *v*. Because the quotient theorem proves that the inner and outer product of one tensor with another results in another tensor, this result makes sense.

## *Parallel Displacement of a Vector*

Imagine a Euclidean, or flat space, with a vector at any point. Move this vector along any curve to a point nearby, and move an identical copy of the vector from the same starting point along a different path to the same destination.

Parallel Displacement in a Flat Space.

Same Flat Space in Curvilinear Coordinate System.

The difference between these two vectors is the zero vector. In any coordinate transformation of this flat space to another coordinate system, the vector differences must remain zero. Suppose that the paths on which the vectors are parallel displaced are in the direction of the coordinate variables. That is, the first path parallel displaces the vector along the $x^q$ coordinate curve, then along the $x^r$ curve. The second path parallel displaces the other vector along the $x^r$ coordinate curve and then along the $x^q$ curve. Total changes in both vectors should be exactly equal, so that their differences are zero. Changes in a vector's coordinates will be given by multiplying both sides of the below equation by $\delta x^q$ and summing over the index $q$:

$$v_{p,q} = \Gamma^{\sigma}_{pq} v_{\sigma}$$

This formula is simply the definition of the covariant derivative set to zero.

Because, in flat space, the changes in the vector are zero, the covariant derivative must be zero in flat space and in all other coordinate systems. Multiplying the equation by the change in the $x^q$ coordinate variable $\delta x^q$ gives the change in the vector in another coordinate system. Take the partial derivative of this with respect to the $x^r$ coordinate and, after substituting a copy of $v_{p,q}$ for $v_{\sigma,r}$ and changing dummy variables, we get:

$$v_{p,qr} = \Gamma^{\sigma}_{pq,r} v_{\sigma} + \Gamma^{\sigma}_{pq} v_{\sigma,r} = v_{\sigma} \left( \Gamma^{\sigma}_{pq,r} + \Gamma^{l}_{pq} \Gamma^{\sigma}_{lr} \right)$$

Multiplying this equation by the product of the changes in the $x^q$ and $x^r$ coordinate variables $\delta x^q \delta x^r$ gives the total change in the vector along the $q$-$r$ route. Doing the same things along the $r$-$q$ route gives an equation identical to this one except with $q$ and $r$ interchanged. Because these must be equal, the difference $v_{p,qr} - v_{p,rq}$ is equal to the vector multiplied by the curvature tensor, as before.

If all components of the curvature tensor are zero then the following will be true:

(1) The order of covariant differentiation does not matter.

(2) Parallel displaced vectors change by the same amount, regardless of the paths they take between two locations.

(3) There exists a coordinate transformation from a "curved" metric to a flat metric.

All metric tensors with constant components are flat spaces, and all the components of the curvature tensor equal zero. Thus flat space can be defined as any space where all the components of the curvature tensor are zero:

$$R^{\sigma}_{pqr} = 0$$

The curvature tensor can be used to test the metric of a space to see if it is flat. For example, if a sheet of paper is crumpled up, its new shape can be described by a metric of complicated equations if expressed in three-space. A two-dimensional creature living on that surface would see its space as flat and would have no idea that the space was "crumpled up" in three dimensions. From this crumpled up sheet of paper, no matter how complicated its metric tensor is, its corresponding curvature tensor will vanish. Since all components of that tensor are zero, the space is really flat, and there is a coordinate transformation that maps it to a metric with constant components which does not change any properties of that space. In general, when the curvature tensor is zero there always exists coordinate transformations which changes the components of the metric tensor to constant values and alters no properties of the space. If one or more of the components of the curvature tensor is non-zero, then it measures the curvature of the space.

The metric tensor for space-time given by special relativity is:

$$g_{uv} = \begin{bmatrix} 1 & 0 & 0 & 0 \\ 0 & -1 & 0 & 0 \\ 0 & 0 & -1 & 0 \\ 0 & 0 & 0 & -1 \end{bmatrix}$$

17.5

This is certainly a flat space. Now, the principle of equivalence says that when special relativistic inertial frames are changing, as in the coordinate system of an accelerating rocket, there exists a gravitational field *i.e.* a curved space-time. For the rocket, the metric components $g_{uv}$ are not constants but functions of the rockets' coordinates. However, the curvature tensor should still be zero because when all its components are zero in one coordinate system (the starting inertial frame of the rocket), they must be zero in all others (for example the rockets'). For gravitational fields in empty space, the metric tensors are functions of the coordinates but their corresponding curvature tensors are zero. Because the curvature tensor is geometrically sophisticated enough to distinguish all flat spaces from all curved spaces, Einstein's idea was to coax it into generating curved spaces consistent with the principle of equivalence. By reversing the role of the curvature tensor, so to speak, it can be transformed from a curvature test on a metric to differential equations that generate metric spaces consistent with the principle of equivalence.

In order to exploit the curvature tensor in this fashion, we should understand some of its geometric properties.

## Properties of the Riemann Christoffel Curvature Tensor

The *Ricci tensor* is defined as a contraction of the curvature tensor:

$$R_{pq} = R^{\sigma}_{pq\sigma}$$
$$R_{pq} = \Gamma^{\sigma}_{p\sigma,q} - \Gamma^{\sigma}_{pq,\sigma} + \Gamma^{\sigma}_{lq}\Gamma^{l}_{p\sigma} - \Gamma^{\sigma}_{l\sigma}\Gamma^{l}_{pq} \qquad 17.6$$

Direct substitution shows us that the curvature tensor is skew-symmetric in the indices $q$ and $r$:

$$R^{\sigma}_{pqr} = -R^{\sigma}_{prq} \qquad 17.7$$

Likewise, it is easy to show that:

$$R^{\sigma}_{pqr} + R^{\sigma}_{qrp} + R^{\sigma}_{rpq} = 0 \qquad 17.8$$

The *Ricci scalar*, $R$, is defined by:

$$R = g^{pq}R_{pq} \qquad 17.9$$

The curvature tensor is also found through covariant differentiation of higher rank tensors. We can take the covariant derivative of a second-rank tensor twice and subtract a copy of it with the order of the covariant derivatives changed. Although we can do this with any second-rank tensor, the example below demonstrates the special case where the second-rank tensor equals the tensor product of two vector fields. For the second-rank tensor $B_{sp} = u_s v_p$, take the covariant derivative twice:

$$(u_s v_p)_{;qr} = (u_{s;q} v_p + u_s v_{p;q})_{;r} = u_{s;qr} v_p + u_{s;q} v_{p;r} + u_{s;r} v_{p;q} + u_s v_{p;qr}$$

Creating an identical copy of this equation, but with the indices $q$ and $r$ interchanged, and subtracting it from the original leaves:

$$(u_s v_p)_{;qr} - (u_s v_p)_{;rq} = v_p(u_{s;qr} - u_{s;rq}) + u_s(v_{p;qr} - v_{p;rq})$$

Because the parenthesized expressions on the right side can be expressed as functions of the curvature tensor, the right side becomes:

$$v_p u_\sigma R^\sigma_{sqr} + v_\sigma u_s R^\sigma_{pqr}$$

Letting $B_{\sigma p} = u_\sigma v_p$ and $B_{s\sigma} = u_s v_\sigma$ gives:

$$B_{sp;qr} - B_{sp;rq} = B_{\sigma p} R^\sigma_{sqr} + B_{s\sigma} R^\sigma_{pqr} \qquad 17.10$$

As in the case of vector fields, the order of covariant differentiation is unimportant if all components of the curvature tensor are zero.

### The Bianchi Identities and the Einstein Tensor

The curvature tensor satisfies important differential identities known as the *Bianchi identities*. To find these, take the covariant derivative of the equation (17.3) with respect to $x^t$:

$$v_{p;qrt} - v_{p;rqt} = v_{\sigma;t} R^\sigma_{pqr} + v_\sigma R^\sigma_{pqr;t} \qquad 17.11$$

Making two more copies of this equation and cyclically rotating the indices $q$, $r$, and $t$ gives:

$$v_{p;rtq} - v_{p;trq} = v_{\sigma;q} R^\sigma_{prt} + v_\sigma R^\sigma_{prt;q}$$

$$v_{p;tqr} - v_{p;qtr} = v_{\sigma;r} R^\sigma_{ptq} + v_\sigma R^\sigma_{ptq;r} \qquad 17.12$$

For the three equations in (17.11) and (17.12), the left-most term of the left side can be expressed by treating $v_{p;q}$ as the second-order tensor $B_{pq}$ from equation (17.10). When we do so, the left-most term of the left sides of these equations becomes the left-most term of the left side of the following equation:

$$v_{p;qrt} - v_{p;qtr} = v_{\sigma;q}R^{\sigma}_{prt} + v_{p;\sigma}R^{\sigma}_{qrt}$$

$$v_{p;rtq} - v_{p;rqt} = v_{\sigma;r}R^{\sigma}_{ptq} + v_{p;\sigma}R^{\sigma}_{rtq}$$

$$v_{p;tqr} - v_{p;trq} = v_{\sigma;t}R^{\sigma}_{pqr} + v_{p;\sigma}R^{\sigma}_{tqr}$$

17.13

Solving these three equations for the left-most term of the left side, and then substituting them into the previous set of equations in (17.12) and (17.11) yields three more equations which, after we add together and cancel redundant terms, we have:

$$v_{p;\sigma}(R^{\sigma}_{qrt} + R^{\sigma}_{rtq} + R^{\sigma}_{tqr}) = v_{\sigma}(R^{\sigma}_{pqr;t} + R^{\sigma}_{prt;q} + R^{\sigma}_{ptq;r})$$

The parenthesized expression on the left side is zero by equation (17.8), the entire left side of this equation is zero. And because the vector field $v_{\sigma}$ is arbitrary, the parenthesized expression on the right side is zero.

$$R^{\sigma}_{pqr;t} + R^{\sigma}_{prt;q} + R^{\sigma}_{ptq;r} = 0$$

17.14

These Bianchi identities are satisfied for the curvature tensor. Other properties of the curvature tensor can best be seen when it is expressed completely in covariant form. Lowering the contravariant index on the curvature tensor gives:

$$R_{spqr} = g_{\sigma s}R^{\sigma}_{pqr}$$

$$R_{spqr} = g_{\sigma s}\Gamma^{\sigma}_{pr,q} - g_{\sigma s}\Gamma^{\sigma}_{pq,r} + [l\,q,s]\Gamma^{l}_{pr} - [l\,r,s]\Gamma^{l}_{pq}$$

17.15

To evaluate the first two monomial sums on the right side, use the relationship between the Christoffel symbols of the first and second kind:

$$g_{\sigma s}\Gamma^{\sigma}_{pr} = [pr,s]$$

$$g_{\sigma s}\Gamma^{\sigma}_{pq} = [pq,s]$$

Taking partial derivatives with respect to the coordinate variable $x^q$ for the first equation, and the partial derivative of the coordinate variable $x^r$ for the second equation, and rearranging leaves:

$$g_{\sigma s}\Gamma^{\sigma}_{pr,q} = [pr,s]_{,q} - g_{\sigma s,q}\Gamma^{\sigma}_{pr}$$

$$g_{\sigma s}\Gamma^{\sigma}_{pq,r} = [pq,s]_{,r} - g_{\sigma s,r}\Gamma^{\sigma}_{pq}$$

17.16

The right-most monomial sums on the right side contain partial derivatives of the metric. These can be substituted with:

$$g_{\sigma s,r} = [\sigma r,s] + [sr,\sigma]$$

$$g_{\sigma s,q} = [\sigma q,s] + [sq,\sigma]$$

17.17

We can easily verify these expressions by substituting the definition of the Christoffel symbols of the first kind. Finally, substitute the results from (17.16) and (17.17) into equation (17.15) and simplify:

$$R_{spqr} = [pr,s]_{,q} - [pq,s]_{,r} - [sq,\sigma]\Gamma^{\sigma}_{pr} + [sr,\sigma]\Gamma^{\sigma}_{pq}$$

From the definition of Christoffel symbols of the second kind, this equation can be rewritten entirely in terms of the Christoffel symbols of the first kind:

$$R_{spqr} = [pr,s]_{,q} - [pq,s]_{,r} - g^{\sigma l}\left([sq,\sigma][pr,l] - [sr,\sigma][pq,l]\right)$$

17.18

It is easy to see that:

$$R_{spqr} = -R_{psqr}$$

Consider the equation:

$$R_{spqr} = R_{qrsp}$$

We can prove that this is true by making an identical copy of this equation, but with the indices swapped, and then verifying the equation below. Substitute the definitions of the Christoffel symbols and simplify to show this.

$$[pr,s]_{,q} - [pq,s]_{,r} = [r\,p,q]_{,s} - [r\,s,q]_{,p}$$

The following summarizes the symmetries of the curvature tensor as calculated so far:

$$R_{spqr} = -R_{sprq} \quad or \quad R^{\sigma}_{pqr} = -R^{\sigma}_{prq}$$
$$R_{spqr} = -R_{psqr}$$
$$R_{spqr} = R_{qrsp}$$

17.19

When we apply the first and second equations of (17.19) to the third equation of (17.19), we have:

$$R_{spqr} = R_{rqps}$$

17.20

Multiplying (17.20) by $g^{rs}$ gives the equation:

$$R_{pq} = R_{qp}$$

17.21

This demonstrates that the Ricci tensor is symmetric.

### Contracting the Bianchi Identities

When we set the index $r$ equal to the index $\sigma$, and sum over those indices, the Bianchi identities in (17.14) can be contracted:

$$R^{\sigma}_{pq\sigma;t} + R^{\sigma}_{p\sigma t;q} + R^{\sigma}_{ptq;\sigma} = 0$$

Applying the first equation of (17.19) to two of the terms and expressing one term in its completely covariant form changes the contracted Bianchi identities to:

$$R^{\sigma}_{pq\sigma;t} - R^{\sigma}_{pt\sigma;q} - g^{s\sigma} R_{spqt;\sigma} = 0$$

The first two monomial sums are Ricci tensors $R_{pq;t}$ and $R_{pt;q}$. Substitute them into the equation above and multiply the tensor product $g^{pq}g^{tu}$ by the result. Next, the third equation of (17.19) is applied to the right-most monomial sum, and the equations become:

$$(R_{pq;t} - R_{pt;q} - g^{s\sigma} R_{qtsp;\sigma})g^{pq}g^{tu} = 0$$

This simplifies to:

$$(Rg^{tu})_{;t} - R^{qu}_{;q} - g^{s\sigma}g^{tu}R^{p}_{tsp;\sigma} = 0$$

The right-most curvature term is $R_{ts;\sigma}$. Substituting this and using the metric to raise the remaining indices leaves:

$$(Rg^{tu})_{;t} - R^{qu}_{;q} - R^{u\sigma}_{;\sigma} = 0$$

The dummy indices $t$, $q$, and $\sigma$ can all be expressed as $t$. Using the symmetry of the Ricci tensor gives:

$$(Rg^{tu})_{;t} - 2R^{tu}_{;t} = 0$$

Multiplying both sides by negative one-half and factoring, this expression becomes:

$$\left( R^{tu} - \frac{1}{2}g^{tu} R \right)_{;t} = 0$$

17.22

The *Einstein tensor*, $G^{uv}$, is defined as:

$$G^{uv} = R^{uv} - \frac{1}{2}g^{uv} R$$

17.23

Thus the Einstein tensor is symmetric and its divergence vanishes:

$$G^{uv}_{;v} = 0$$

## *The Field Equations of General Relativity*

The principles of equivalence and of general relativity require that space-time be curved. This curvature is gravity. We must now find the equations needed to calculate how that curvature is generated by mass-energy, which is expressed in terms of the energy-momentum tensor. As previously mentioned, while the curvature tensor embodies the principle of equivalence, it does not by itself relate the distribution of mass-energy to curvature. We can find a relationship between the metric tensor and the energy-momentum tensor via some modified version of the curvature tensor. Such a relationship can be found by recognizing certain properties that the concepts of general relativity impose on its equations. Our knowledge of general relativity and Newtonian gravity suggests that the equations of general relativity should obey the following constraints:

(1) The gravitational field equations should satisfy the conservation of mass-energy, momentum, and angular momentum.

(2) The tensor describing the curvature of space-time should be built from the curvature tensor to embody the principle of equivalence and nothing else.

(3) For weak static gravity fields, the theory should very nearly approximate Newtonian gravity. For example the gravitational potential $\phi$ should be proportional to $g_{44}$ and satisfy $lap(\phi)=4\pi G\rho$.

(4) Because of (3) above, the tensor describing the curvature of space-time should be a function of second-order differential equations of the metric.

(5) The tensor describing the curvature of space-time should be proportional to the energy-momentum tensor. Hence, it must be a symmetric second-order tensor. Thus greater energy density gives greater curvature, just as greater mass yields greater gravity in Newton's universal theory of gravitation.

(6) The gravitational field equations should reduce to the flat space of special relativity when all the components of the energy momentum tensor are zero.

Only the Einstein tensor meets all of these requirements. The full field equations of general relativity are:

$$kT^{uv} = R^{uv} - \frac{1}{2}g^{uv}R$$

17.24

The constant $k$ is a constant of proportionality. The conservation of energy and momentum, for example, is automatically satisfied because of (17.22). From mathematical considerations, the covariant derivative of the metric tensor is zero for spaces with a symmetric affine connection. Since $g^{uv}_{\ ;v} = 0$ holds true always, the covariant derivative of $\Lambda g^{uv}$ is always zero. This suggests that the field equations can be increased in complexity and still satisfy $T^{uv}_{\ ;v} = 0$ by adding the "cosmological term" $\Lambda g^{uv}$:

$$kT^{uv} = R^{uv} - \frac{1}{2}g^{uv}R + \Lambda g^{uv}$$

17.25

These are the complete field equations of general relativity with a cosmological term. What is left is to calculate the so far undetermined constants $k$ and $\Lambda$. The *cosmological constant*, $\Lambda$, gives space-time a curvature with no ordinary matter present. This constant corresponds to a vacuum energy and its value need not be zero. (The possibility of a non-zero vacuum energy term, or even a time-varying vacuum energy term, will be explored later.) We can determine the value of $k$ by approximating Newtonian gravitation. Multiply the field equations (17.25) by the covariant metric tensor $g_{uv}$ and let $T=T^{uv}g_{uv}$:

$$R - 2R + 4\Lambda = kT$$

Solving for the Ricci scalar $R$ gives:

$$R = -kT + 4\Lambda$$

Substituting this value for the Ricci scalar back into the original field equations and then solving for the Ricci tensor gives:

$$R^{ij} = k\left(T^{ij} - \frac{1}{2}g^{ij}T\right) + \Lambda g^{ij}$$

17.26

To help find $k$, consider the $R_{44}$ component alone:

$$R^{44} = k\left(T^{44} - \frac{1}{2}g^{44}T\right) + \Lambda g^{44}$$

17.27

The field equations must reduce to Newtonian gravity for weak-static fields. In the previous chapter we found that in such fields, time at the higher point $h$ in a gravitational potential $\phi = ah$ runs faster relative to the base of $h$ by the approximate amount:

$$dt' = \left(1 + \frac{\phi}{c^2}\right)dt$$

Multiply both sides of this equation by the speed of light and then square both sides, noting that $w$ is the coordinate time:

$$ds^2 = \left(1 + \frac{2\phi}{c^2} + \varepsilon\right)dw^2$$

Here $(1 + \phi/c^2)^2$ is approximately $(1 + 2\phi/c^2)$, and $\varepsilon$ represents a function whose values return small numbers ($\varepsilon << \phi/c^2$) which can be neglected for purposes of approximation. Thus, for a weak-static gravity field, the line element is given by:

$$ds^2 = \left(1 + \frac{2\phi}{c^2}\right)dw^2 - dx^2 - dy^2 - dz^2$$

17.28

This line element must approximate Newtonian gravitation. For this case $g_{44} \doteq 1 + 2\phi/c^2$, $g_{33} = g_{22} = g_{11} = -1$ is found by reading off the metric terms, $ds^2 = g_{uv}dx^u dx^v$, from the line element (17.28). All other components of the metric are zero. Using these values of the metric, $R_{44}$ is calculated. Hence $R^{44}$ is also calculated and $T^{44}$ and $T$ can be evaluated by using the formula $T^{44} = \rho c^2$:

$$T^{44} = \rho c^2$$
$$T = T^{ij}g_{ij} = T^{44}g_{44} \approx \rho c^2$$
$$g_{44} \approx 1,\ g^{44} \approx 1$$

This gives the right side of (17.27). To find $R^{44}$, note that $R^{44} = R_{ab}g^{a4}g^{b4} = R_{44}g^{44}g^{44} \cong R_{44}$:

$$R_{44} = \Gamma^{\sigma}_{4\sigma,4} - \Gamma^{\sigma}_{44,\sigma} + \Gamma^{\sigma}_{l4}\Gamma^{l}_{4\sigma} - \Gamma^{\sigma}_{l\sigma}\Gamma^{l}_{44}$$

The product terms $\Gamma\Gamma$ will all be of the order $\left(\partial\phi/\partial x^{i}\right)^{2} \cdot \left(1/c^{4}\right)$ and are so small that they can be neglected. And the sum $\Gamma^{\sigma}_{4\sigma,4}$ will be zero because we assume a static gravitational field and the potential $\phi(x, y, z)$ is not a function of time. Thus $g_{44}$ is not a function of time, and the only substantial term left is $\Gamma^{\sigma}_{44,\sigma}$. Therefore $R^{44}$ is:

$$R_{44} \approx -\Gamma^{\sigma}_{44,\sigma} = -\Gamma^{1}_{44,1} - \Gamma^{2}_{44,2} - \Gamma^{3}_{44,3}$$

$$= -\frac{1}{2}g_{44,11} - \frac{1}{2}g_{44,22} - \frac{1}{2}g_{44,33}$$

$$= -\frac{1}{2}lap(g_{44})$$

$$= -\frac{1}{2}lap(1 + 2\phi/c^{2})$$

$$= -\frac{1}{c^{2}}lap(\phi)$$

This gives the left side of (17.27). Substituting all of these results into (17.27), we find:

$$R^{44} = k\left(T^{44} - \frac{1}{2}g^{44}T\right) + \Lambda g^{44}$$

$$-\frac{1}{c^{2}}lap(\phi) = k\left(\rho c^{2} - \frac{1}{2}\rho c^{2}\right) + \Lambda = \left(\frac{k\rho c^{2}}{2} + \Lambda\right)$$

$$lap(\phi) = \left(-\frac{k\rho c^{4}}{2} - \Lambda c^{2}\right) = 4\pi G\rho$$

Solving for $k$ gives:

$$k = -\frac{8\pi G}{c^4} - \frac{2\Lambda}{\rho c^2}$$

Because $k$ must be a constant, and the density $\rho$ is a variable function, this implies that $\Lambda = 0$. The constant $k$ then equals $-8\pi G/c^4$, assuming that all components of the energy momentum tensor was expressed in terms of energy. That tensor could equally well be written in terms of mass, in which case all its components would need the extra factor of the square of the speed of light. In that case $k$ equals $-8\pi G/c^2$. The full field equations of general relativity are then:

$$-\frac{8\pi G}{c^4} T^{pq} = R^{pq} - \frac{1}{2} g^{pq} R$$

17.29

But for cosmology it is useful to consider the possibility of a cosmological term:

$$-\frac{8\pi G}{c^4} T^{pq} = R^{pq} - \frac{1}{2} g^{pq} R + \Lambda g^{pq}$$

In this case, the constant $k$ is determined solely as in (17.29) and $\Lambda$ is treated simply as another constant to be determined. A property of these field equations is that influences do not propagate at speeds faster than light. Since these field equations have gravitational influences travel out in waves at the speed of light, general relativity also predicts the existence of gravitational waves.

The field equations can also be derived by means of other methods. Using the calculus of variations, the right side of (17.25) can be derived from the lagrangian $(R + 2\Lambda)\sqrt{-g}$, where $R$ is the Ricci scalar, $g = \det g_{ij}$, and $\Lambda$ is a cosmological constant.

## Exercises

1.  Prove equation (17.10) for any second-rank tensor.

2. Consider the surface of a canister. For this two-space, calculate the curvature tensor, the Ricci tensor, the Ricci scalar, and the Einstein tensor.

3. Using the equations of this chapter, find an approximate form for the line element of a very weak, spherically symmetric, gravity field.

4. Prove the equations in (17.17).

5. Given that $R = g^{mn}R_{mn}$, show that the Ricci scalar $R$ equals $R^\sigma_\sigma$.

6. Would the equations of (17.19) and (17.20) hold true if $\Gamma \neq \{\ \}$? Why or why not?

7. Why are the requirements (1) through (6) for the field equations not satisfied with a cosmological term? Explain why the field equations can have a vacuum term $\Lambda$.

8. Write the field equations of general relativity in "mixed" components $T^p_{\ \sigma}$ .

9. Find the appropriate constant to express the cosmological term in terms of an energy density.

10. Re-derive the Riemann Christoffel curvature tensor using a contravariant vector field instead of the covariant field assumed in this chapter.

11. What is the curvature of a wrinkled sheet of paper?

12. Show that this equation is true: $[pr,s]_{,q} - [pq,s]_{,r} = [r\,p,q]_{,s} - [r\,s,q]_{,p}$

13. Express all equations in (17.19) in completely contravariant form.

14. Calculate the gravitational red shift on light for any weak, *i.e* approximately Newtonian, gravity field.

15. Does equation (17.14) hold for any Riemannian space? If so, why? If not, why not?

# CHAPTER 18

## *Solving the Field Equations*

.

THE FULL FIELD EQUATIONS of general relativity are:

$$-\frac{8\pi G}{c^4}T_{pq} = R_{pq} - \frac{1}{2}g_{pq}R$$

18.1

And the curvature tensors are given in terms of Christoffel symbols of the second kind:

$$\Gamma^{\sigma}_{ij} = \frac{1}{2}g^{\sigma k}(g_{ik,j} + g_{jk,i} - g_{ij,k})$$

$$R_{pq} = \Gamma^{\sigma}_{p\sigma,q} - \Gamma^{\sigma}_{pq,\sigma} + \Gamma^{\sigma}_{lq}\Gamma^{l}_{p\sigma} - \Gamma^{\sigma}_{l\sigma}\Gamma^{l}_{pq}$$

$$R = R_{pq}g^{pq}$$

The energy-momentum tensor $T_{pq}$ gives the distribution of mass-energy, momentum, and stresses. Although in (18.1) the field equations have been written in covariant form, they can be put into contravariant form if we multiply them by the tensor product $g^{pm}g^{qn}$ to raise the indices. The equations of general relativity are differential equations relating the distribution of mass-energy, $T_{pq}$, to the shape of space-time $g_{pq}$. The energy momentum tensor can be expressed in terms of energy (Joules) or mass (kilograms) because special relativity requires that matter and energy are interchangeable. In previous chapters, the energy-momentum tensor was expressed in Joules. But it could just as easily have been expressed in kilograms, in which case $k$ would have been $-8\pi G/c^2$. The constant of proportionality between energy density and curvature is:

$$k = -\frac{8\pi G}{c^4} = -2.07612 \times 10^{-43} \; Sec^2 / kg \; m$$

When the energy-momentum tensor is expressed in terms of mass density, the constant is:

$$k = -\frac{8\pi G}{c^2} = -1.86592 \times 10^{-26} \; m / kg$$

Because this constant is small, to curve space-time substantially requires a great deal of matter. However, moderate amounts of matter occupying *small* regions of space will also create large curvatures.

Solving the equations will generally be very difficult, for four major reasons. First, most ordinary differential equations cannot be solved analytically and require the techniques of numerical analysis. Second, the field equations of general relativity are a nonlinear system of partial differential equations of the second order in the ten unknowns, $g_{pq}$. Third, because initial-value and boundary value data are given in space-time, they are difficult to visualize. Fourth, the equations sometimes yield bogus or non-physical solutions. What makes the nonlinear character of the equations so difficult is the self-influencing dynamic aspect of space-time: the curvature of space and the distribution of energy are constantly influencing each other. But the problem is not intractable, and for some cases of high symmetry it is possible to obtain exact solutions. Other cases can be solved by approximations or, with the help of digital supercomputers, by the use of numerical methods. Such difficulties have existed throughout the history of physics. In classical physics, for example, the three-body problem must be analyzed by means of numerical computations on computers. The influences of three-gravitational bodies upon each other cannot be solved in an analytical way.

We might think that the metric of any curved space-time would have a corresponding distribution of energy-momentum throughout space-time—an associated energy-momentum tensor—or that any distribution of mass-energy and momentum would have a corresponding metric. If this were true, however, matter could behave in an arbitrary fashion. Particles, for instance, could have negative inertia. But neither experiments in subatomic accelerators nor studies of cosmic rays have ever found particles with negative mass.

This is one example of constraints on the energy momentum tensor. Further constraints come from other well-known properties of matter: the behavior of electrically charged matter is constrained by Maxwell's laws and that of fluids by equations governing fluid dynamics. In general, the laws of physics must limit the properties of any energy-momentum tensor. Because the energy-momentum tensor acts as a source to the curvature terms, it limits the metric tensors coming out of the field equations. Therefore, neither the energy-momentum tensor nor the metric tensor can be arbitrary. Mathematically speaking, for any coordinate system, if the energy-momentum tensor is known, there are ten unknown quantities in the metric. Or, if the metric is known, the energy-momentum tensor can be calculated. Because the coordinate system is arbitrary, we are free to specify the form of some components of both the metric and energy-momentum tensors, as we can with regular differential equations. (For example, a differential equation in Cartesian coordinates can be transformed to polar coordinates, yielding a modified equation embodying the same geometrical situation.) This degree of freedom is necessary because the standard tensor transformation laws can be used to transform both tensors to new coordinate systems.

In many cases, although the metric and energy-momentum tensors are not precisely known, their broad outline can be found from other considerations. For example, the properties of a fluid can be specified in $T_{pq}$ and geometric symmetry assumed in the form $g_{pq}$. In these cases the field equations act like a bread pan. When a blob of dough is put into the pan, the pan makes the dough assume the shape of the pan exactly. But if the dough's shape is not in the approximate shape of the pan, it will not go into the pan. If the broad form of a metric and/or the energy momentum tensor is known, it can be put into the field equations, which prune the broad forms to specific solutions satisfying general relativity. However, this type of approach will only work if the broad form of the metric tensor or energy-momentum tensor is guessed correctly.

This approach can best be illustrated with the following example. The principle of equivalence shows that a rocket undergoing constant uniform acceleration is in the same situation as a rocket at rest in a uniform gravitational field. From the rocket's perspective, space-time has a curved shape. What is the character of this gravitational field?

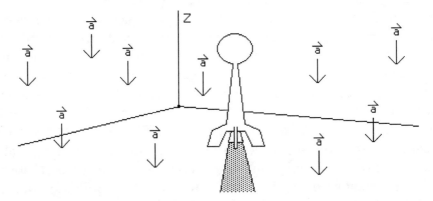

The spatial coordinates should be Euclidean. However, as we have noted, time will run faster at higher altitudes relative to lower altitudes. Therefore the line element must have this broad form:

$$ds^2 = g_{\lambda\gamma}dx^\lambda dx^\gamma$$
$$= g_{44}dw^2 + g_{11}dx^2 + g_{22}dy^2 + g_{33}dz^2$$
$$= g_{44}(z)dw^2 - dx^2 - dy^2 - dz^2 \qquad \text{18.2}$$

Because the rate at which time runs is altitude relative, $g_{44}$ should be a function of $z$ alone. Thus the metric components can be read off from the line element.

$$g_{44} = g_{44}(z)$$
$$g_{11} = -1$$
$$g_{22} = -1$$
$$g_{33} = -1$$

All other components of the metric tensor are zero. This is the broad outline of the shape of the four-space for this case. The coordinates are given by:

$$x^4 = w$$
$$x^1 = x$$
$$x^2 = y$$
$$x^3 = z$$

The $g_{44}$ term is some function of $z$, but so far it is an entirely unknown function. An object that is stationary in this gravitational field makes no spatial contributions to its world line. In this case the proper distance of the world line is:

$$ds^2 = g_{44}dw^2$$
$$d\tau = \sqrt{g_{44}}\,dt$$

Because in this space there is no matter (if we neglect the mass of the rocket), $T_{pq} = 0$ for all components. From the contracted version of the field equations $(8\pi G/c^4)T = R$, and because $T_{pq} = 0$, $T = 0$. Thus $R = 0$, and the field equations reduce to:

$$R_{pq} = 0$$

18.3

With the metric in (18.2), the first step is to form the Christoffel symbols of the first kind. When all indices are different, $[i\,j,k]$ will be zero because those components of the metric will be zero. Only those of the form $g_{ii}$ will be non-zero. This means that Christoffel symbols of the form $[i\,k,i]$ and $[i\,i,k]$ are the only non-zero Christoffel symbols of the first kind. Because these symbols are partial derivatives in the coordinates, any partial derivative of the $g_{11} = g_{22} = $

$g_{33} = -1$ will be zero. And because $g_{44}$ is a function of $z$ only, the only non-zero Christoffel symbols of the first kind are:

$$[4\ 3,4] = \frac{1}{2} g_{44,3}$$

$$[4\ 4,3] = -\frac{1}{2} g_{44,3}$$

Only the diagonal components of the metric are non-zero, so it follows from the equation $g_{ij} g^{jk} = \delta_i^k$ that the contravariant components are the reciprocals of the covariant components:

$$g^{44} = 1/g_{44}$$

$$g^{33} = 1/g_{33} = -1$$

$$g^{22} = 1/g_{22} = -1$$

$$g^{11} = 1/g_{11} = -1$$

The only non-zero Christoffel symbols of the second kind are those that relate to the Christoffel symbols of the first kind:

$$\Gamma_{44}^3 = g^{33}[4\ 4,3] = \frac{1}{2} g_{44,3}$$

$$\Gamma_{43}^4 = g^{44}[4\ 3,4] = \frac{1}{2g_{44}} g_{44,3}$$

18.4

All components of the Ricci tensor are zero except $R_{44}$ and $R_{33}$, and $R_{33} = -R_{44}/g_{44}$ (see the exercises at the end of this chapter). Here $R_{44}$ is given by:

$$R_{44} = \Gamma_{4\sigma,4}^\sigma - \Gamma_{44,\sigma}^\sigma + \Gamma_{l4}^\sigma \Gamma_{4\sigma}^l - \Gamma_{l\sigma}^\sigma \Gamma_{44}^l = 0$$

After substituting in the non-zero affine components of (18.4), we have:

$$R_{44} = -\Gamma_{44,3}^3 + \Gamma_{43}^4 \Gamma_{44}^3 = 0$$

Or, expressed in terms of metric components:

$$-g_{44,33} + \frac{1}{2g_{44}}\left(g_{44,3}\right)^2 = 0$$

18.5

Because $g_{44}$ is a function of $z$ only, the partial derivatives become ordinary derivatives. Let $Q = g_{44}$ and multiply the equation (18.5) by $-2Q$:

$$2Q\frac{d^2Q}{dz^2} - \left(\frac{dQ}{dz}\right)^2 = 0$$

The solution to this differential equation is computed to be:

$$Q = D(A + Bz)^2$$

Here $A$, $B$ and $D$ are constants. This means that the line element in (18.2) is of the form $ds^2 = D(A + Bz)^2 dw^2 - dx^2 - dy^2 - dz^2$. Now this line element must approximate the Newtonian case when the potential obeys $|\phi| << c^2$ or $D\left(A^2 + 2ABz + B^2z^2\right) \approx \left(1 + 2az/c^2\right)$, which means that $A = D = 1$ and $B = a/c^2$. Thus, the final line element is:

$$ds^2 = \left(1 + \frac{az}{c^2}\right)^2 dw^2 - dx^2 - dy^2 - dz^2$$

18.6

This solution holds generally, not just for cases where $az << c^2$. We are done! This procedure is a common way of solving the field equations. First, guess the form of the line element by guessing the form of the metric, then form the Christoffel symbols of the first kind, then the second kind (the affine connection). Next, form the Ricci tensor, the Ricci scalar, and finally the Einstein and energy-momentum tensors. This produces a system of partial differential equations that can sometimes be solved analytically. After finding analytical solutions, determine the values of any constants. The final line element, or simply the metric, is the solution describing the curved space-time under investigation. This procedure usually works for cases of very high symmetry for example stationary and rotating objects of spherical symmetry. It also gives solutions for expanding and contracting universes and for cases of cylindrically symmetrical geometry, such as cosmic strings or rotating cylinders. The solution can be used to calculate other information, such as the rate at which time runs at a location, relative to other locations, or the paths of light rays and other objects traveling freely in this metric. To illustrate this, both of these are done for the line element found in (18.6). Consider a world line $x^i(s)$ through space-time along the time dimension alone so that there are no spatial contributions. The spatial differentials are zero, $dx = dy = dz = 0$, and $dw$ is non-zero. Thus, (18.6) becomes:

$$ds^2 = \left(1 + \frac{az}{c^2}\right)^2 dw^2$$

After taking square roots and integrating, we have:

$$\tau = \left(1 + \frac{az}{c^2}\right) t$$

18.7

This equation gives the now familiar relation between the rate at which time runs at height $z$ relative to height zero. Objects in free fall in this gravitational field will travel on geodesics:

$$\frac{d^2 x^\sigma}{ds^2} + \Gamma^\sigma_{uv} \frac{dx^u}{ds} \frac{dx^v}{ds} = 0$$

18.8

We must solve these equations in the case where the space-time is described as in (18.6). Because the only non-zero components of the affine connection are given in (18.4), the geodesic equations in (18.8) for this case are:

$$0 = \frac{d^2x^4}{ds^2} + 2\Gamma^4_{43} \frac{dx^4}{ds} \frac{dx^3}{ds}$$

$$0 = \frac{d^2x^3}{ds^2} + \Gamma^3_{44} \left( \frac{dx^4}{ds} \right)^2$$

$$0 = \frac{d^2x^2}{ds^2}$$

$$0 = \frac{d^2x^1}{ds^2}$$

18.9

Computing the non-zero affine terms gives:

$$\Gamma^3_{44} = \frac{1}{2} g_{44,3} = \frac{1}{2} \frac{\partial}{\partial z} \left( 1 + \frac{az}{c^2} \right)^2 = \frac{a}{c^2} \left( 1 + \frac{az}{c^2} \right)$$

$$\Gamma^4_{43} = \frac{1}{2 g_{44}} g_{44,3} = \frac{a}{c^2} \frac{(1 + az/c^2)}{(1 + az/c^2)^2} = \frac{a/c^2}{(1 + az/c^2)}$$

Substituting these non-zero affine terms, and changing notation to $x^4 = w, x^3 = z, x^2 = y, x^1 = x$, the equations for the path (18.9) become:

$$0 = \frac{d^2w}{ds^2} + \left( \frac{2a/c^2}{1 + az/c^2} \right) \frac{dw}{ds} \frac{dz}{ds}$$

$$0 = \frac{d^2z}{ds^2} + \frac{a}{c^2} \left( 1 + \frac{az}{c^2} \right) \left( \frac{dw}{ds} \right)^2$$

$$0 = \frac{d^2y}{ds^2}$$

$$0 = \frac{d^2x}{ds^2}$$

18.10

These are the equations of motion for objects in free fall in this case. In the weak field limit $s \approx ct = w$ and $az << c^2$ the equations (18.10) are very nearly approximated by:

$$\frac{d^2z}{dt^2} = -a \qquad \frac{d^2y}{dt^2} = 0 \qquad \frac{d^2x}{dt^2} = 0$$

The solutions to these equations are parabolas, according both with Galileo's finding that the acceleration of objects is independent of their mass and with the principle of equivalence, which shows that objects freely falling in a weak uniform gravity field traverse parabolas. This simple example has illustrated a popular technique for solving problems in general relativity.

## Exercises

1. Show, for the uniform gravitational field considered in this chapter, that $R_{44} = -R_{33}g_{44}$.

2. Suppose a kind of "magic matter" which could have any dynamic properties at all. Given an arbitrary metric, how could we calculate the distribution of this "magic matter" throughout space-time?

3. In a uniform gravitational field of arbitrary extension in space, at what height does time come to a complete stop? Express the answer in terms of coordinate systems given in this chapter.

4. Consider the metric $ds^2 = dw^2 - e^{-\beta(x-w)^2} dx^2 - dy^2 - dz^2$ where $\beta$ is a constant. For this space, find:

   a. The non-zero Christoffel symbols of the first and second kind.

   b. $R_{11}, R_{00}, R_{10}, R$.

   c. The energy momentum tensor.

   d. The Einstein tensor.

   What do the field equations say for this space?

5. Suppose the curvature scalar for a given region of space is $R = 2.50 \times 10^{-26} m^{-2}$. What is the energy-momentum scalar, $T$, for this curvature?

6. An *event horizon* (for the metric in 18.6) is the location at which time comes to a complete halt. In a uniform gravitational field with acceleration of $g = 10 m/sec^2$, how far below the $x$-axis is the event horizon?

7. Show that if the terms $g_{ab,c} g_{de,f}$ are small enough to be ignored, the curvature tensor can be approximated by $R_{spqr} \doteq (1/2)(g_{rs,pq} - g_{pr,sq} + g_{pq,sr} - g_{qs,pr})$.

8. For the metric below, find the Christoffel symbols of the first and second kind, the Ricci and Einstein tensors, and the Ricci scalar. The terms $w_0$ and $x_0$ are both constant.

$$ds^2 = \left( \sin \frac{w}{w_0} \right) dw^2 - \left( \cos \frac{x}{x_0} \right) dx^2 - dy^2 - dz^2$$

# PART 6

## Relativity and the Cosmos

# CHAPTER 19

# *The Schwarzschild Solution and Black Holes*

THE PREVIOUS CHAPTER demonstrated a general procedure for solving the field equations. This procedure allowed calculation for a very common and simple case: a uniform gravitational field, approximated by gravitational fields near the surface of the earth. While the gravity field of the earth is not globally uniform, it generally diminishes with distance from the earth. Many objects in the universe (stars, planets, moons, white dwarfs, brown dwarfs, and so on) are also primarily spherical, with symmetrical mass distributions and slow rotation in comparison to the speed of light. The procedures outlined in the previous chapter can to be applied to these cases by means of the *Schwarzschild solution*, which covers the exterior space-time surrounding a non-rotating spherically symmetric mass. It is named for Karl Schwarzschild, who discovered it shortly after Einstein published the general theory of relativity.

To simplify calculations, it is convenient to write special relativity's line element with the spatial variables in spherical coordinates. Consider the familiar three-dimensional Euclidean space with the following line element:

$$ds^2 = g_{kl}dx^k dx^l = dx^2 + dy^2 + dz^2$$

19.1

The only non-zero metric components are $g_{11} = g_{22} = g_{33} = +1$, and the indices in (19.1) sum only from one to three. Spherical coordinates are related to rectangular coordinates by the following transformation:

$$x = r\cos\varphi\sin\theta$$
$$y = r\sin\varphi\sin\theta$$
$$z = r\cos\theta$$

Because the line element for three-dimensional Euclidean space can be written in spherical coordinates, we can define the following:

$$x^1 = x \qquad x'^1 = r$$
$$x^2 = y \qquad x'^2 = \varphi$$
$$x^3 = z \qquad x'^3 = \theta$$

To put the metric tensor into spherical coordinates, let the summation over the two indices range from one to three rather than the usual one to four, and use the familiar transformation law:

$$g'_{kl} = g_{ts}\frac{\partial x^t}{\partial x'^l}\frac{\partial x^s}{\partial x'^k}$$

After carrying out this calculation, the only non-zero components of $g'_{kl}$ are:

$$g'_{11} = 1$$
$$g'_{22} = r^2\sin^2\theta$$
$$g'_{33} = r^2$$

These metric components provide the line element for three-dimensional Euclidean space expressed in spherical coordinates:

$$ds^2 = g'_{kl}dx'^k dx'^l = dr^2 + r^2 d\theta^2 + r^2\sin^2\theta\, d\varphi^2$$

19.2

The Minkowski line element, with the spatial variables in spherical coordinates, is given by:

$$ds^2 = dw^2 - dr^2 - r^2 d\theta^2 - r^2 \sin^2 \theta d\varphi^2 \qquad 19.3$$

Here, as before, $w = ct$. To determine the modifications that would describe the space surrounding spherically symmetric objects, recall that while time runs more slowly at the base of a gravitational well relative to higher altitudes, the amount should be the same at all distances away from the center of the spherical mass. The mass distribution is assumed to be spherically symmetric. Also, radial distances can be distorted while still retaining spherical symmetry. This means that the $g_{44}$ and $g_{11}$ metric components can be arbitrary functions of the radial variable $r$. Thus the line element in (19.3) can be generalized to this form:

$$ds^2 = e^{2v} dw^2 - e^{2\lambda} dr^2 - r^2 d\theta^2 - r^2 \sin^2 \theta d\varphi^2 \qquad 19.4$$

Here $v$ and $\lambda$ are two arbitrary functions of the radial coordinate. In keeping with convention, the metric terms $g_{44}$ and $g_{11}$ are expressed exponentially as a function of $v$ and $\lambda$. Because these two variables can be viewed as natural logarithms of any arbitrary functions, generality is not lost. To find $v(r)$ and $\lambda(r)$, the same procedure from the previous chapter can be used. The metric terms are:

$$g_{44} = e^{2v}$$
$$g_{11} = -e^{2\lambda}$$
$$g_{22} = -r^2 \sin^2 \theta$$
$$g_{33} = -r^2$$

Here $x^1 = r, x^2 = \varphi, x^3 = \theta, x^4 = w$, and all other components of the metric tensor are zero. All of the energy-momentum tensor's components are zero because the exterior space-time surrounding spherically symmetric masses is assumed to contain no material. The character of that space-time is the only question presently of interest.

For the Schwarzschild solution, the field equations of general relativity reduce to $R_{kl} = 0$ because the energy-momentum tensor is zero. By the equation

$g_{ab}g^{bc} = \delta_a^c$ , the contravariant components of the metric tensor are given by $g^{kl} = 1/g_{kl}$ because only the diagonal elements of the metric are non-zero. The contravariant components of the metric are as follows:

$$g^{44} = e^{-2v}$$
$$g^{11} = -e^{-2\lambda}$$
$$g^{22} = -r^{-2}\sin^{-2}\theta$$
$$g^{33} = -r^{-2}$$

The non-zero Christoffel symbols of the first kind are:

$$[4\ 4,1] = -v'e^{2v}$$
$$[1\ 1,1] = -\lambda'e^{2\lambda}$$
$$[2\ 2,1] = r\sin^2\theta$$
$$[2\ 2,3] = r^2\sin\theta\cos\theta$$
$$[3\ 3,1] = r$$
$$[4\ 1,4] = [1\ 4,4] = v'e^{2v}$$
$$[1\ 2,2] = [2\ 1,2] = -r\sin^2\theta$$
$$[2\ 3,2] = [3\ 2,2] = -r^2\sin\theta\cos\theta$$
$$[1\ 3,3] = [3\ 1,3] = -r$$

Because $v$ and $\lambda$ are functions of $r$ alone, the partial derivatives become ordinary derivatives with respect to $r$, denoted with a prime. And because only the $g^{mm}$ are non-zero, the Christoffel symbols of the first kind are used with the $g^{mm}$ to calculate the non-zero Christoffel symbols of the second kind:

$$\Gamma^1_{44} = v'e^{2v-2\lambda}$$

$$\Gamma^1_{11} = \lambda'$$

$$\Gamma^1_{22} = -re^{-2\lambda}\sin^2\theta$$

$$\Gamma^1_{33} = -re^{-2\lambda}$$

$$\Gamma^3_{22} = -\sin\theta\cos\theta$$

$$\Gamma^2_{23} = \Gamma^2_{32} = \cot\theta$$

$$\Gamma^4_{41} = \Gamma^4_{14} = v'$$

$$\Gamma^2_{12} = \Gamma^2_{21} = \Gamma^3_{13} = \Gamma^3_{31} = \frac{1}{r} \qquad 19.5$$

Here the primes denote differentiation with respect to $r$. It turns out that the only non-zero components of the Ricci tensor are the diagonal components:

$$0 = R_{44} = \left(-v'' + \lambda'v' - (v')^2 - \frac{2v'}{r}\right)e^{2v-2\lambda}$$

$$0 = R_{11} = \left(v'' - \lambda'v' + (v')^2 - \frac{2\lambda'}{r}\right)$$

$$0 = R_{22} = (-1 + e^{-2\lambda}[1 - r\lambda' + rv'])\sin^2\theta$$

$$0 = R_{33} = (-1 + e^{-2\lambda}[1 - r\lambda' + rv']) \qquad 19.6$$

These equations have been set to zero in accordance with the field equations. There is no mass-energy in the empty space surrounding the spherically symmetric mass for this problem. For reasons that will become apparent shortly, the fact that the Ricci scalar is not zero does not alter the situation. The truth of these relations will be seen later on:

$$R_{44} = -R_{11}e^{2v-2\lambda}$$

$$R_{22} = R_{33}\sin^2\theta$$

Thus the Ricci scalar is:

$$R = R_{ik}g^{ik} = R_{44}g^{44} + R_{33}g^{33} + R_{22}g^{22} + R_{11}g^{11} = -\frac{2R_{33}}{r^2} - 2e^{-2\lambda}R_{11}$$

Substituting this expression and the values for the non-zero Ricci tensor components into the field equations allows calculation of the Einstein tensor:

$$0 = -\frac{8\pi G}{c^4}T_{ik} = R_{ik} - \frac{1}{2}g_{ik}R$$

It turns out that each of the four non-zero Einstein tensor components is equal to a function multiplied by one of the $R_{kk}$ components. This is true because the energy momentum tensor has all of its components equal to zero. Thus the Einstein tensor reduces to the Ricci tensor set equal to the second-order zero tensor, and we do not lose generality by solving the equations in (19.6) for $v(r)$ and $\lambda(r)$. Dividing both sides of the first equation of (19.6) by $e^{2v-2\lambda}$ and adding the result to the second equation of (19.6), we get:

$$\lambda' = -v' \qquad\qquad 19.7$$

Integrating both sides with respect to $r$ gives us:

$$\lambda = -v \qquad\qquad 19.8$$

The fourth equation of (19.6) can be expressed totally in terms of $v$ and $v'$ by substituting (19.7) and (19.8) into the fourth equation of (19.6):

$$e^{2v}\left[1 + 2rv'\right] = 1$$

Or:

$$\frac{d}{dr}\left[re^{2v}\right] = 1$$

$$\left[re^{2v}\right] = r - \mathbb{C}_0$$

$$e^{2v} = 1 - \frac{\mathbb{C}_0}{r}$$

Here $\mathbb{C}_0$ is a constant of integration. Thus the other previously undetermined function is $e^{2\lambda} = e^{-2\nu} = 1/(1 - \mathbb{C}_0/r)$. The constant $\mathbb{C}_0$ is equal to $2GM/c^2$, where $M$ is the mass of the spherical object as determined by Kepler's laws for objects moving at large distances from $M$. This choice, as will be clear later, very nearly approximates the Newtonian potential in weak gravity fields $r \gg 2GM/c^2$. The full line element can now be written:

$$ds^2 = \left(1 - \frac{2GM}{c^2r}\right)dw^2 - \frac{1}{\left(1 - \dfrac{2GM}{c^2r}\right)}dr^2 - r^2d\theta^2 - r^2\sin^2\theta\,d\varphi^2$$

19.9

This line element describes the exterior space-time geometry for spherically symmetric, non-rotating, non-charged, objects of mass $M$. This is the Schwarzschild solution, and the line element in (19.9) is the *Schwarzschild line element*. To justify the choice of the constant, $\mathbb{C}_0$, remember again that time runs at different rates in a gravitational field. Relative to the base of a gravitational potential $\phi$, time at the height of the potential is running at a rate $\sim 1 + \phi/c^2$. Relative to the top of that potential, time at the base of the potential is running at $1/(1 + \phi/c^2) \approx (1 - \phi/c^2)$. Substituting the Newtonian potential $\phi = GM/r$ yields:

$$d\tau = \left(1 - \frac{GM}{c^2r}\right)dt$$

For an object resting on the surface of a planet, the radial and angular contributions to its world line are zero. Therefore, the relative rate at which time runs on the surface of a planet, compared to far away from the planet, is given by:

$$d\tau = \sqrt{1 - \frac{\mathbb{C}_0}{r}}\,dt \approx \left(1 - \frac{\mathbb{C}_0}{2r}\right)dt$$

Comparing this with the previous equation gives us:

$$d\tau = \sqrt{1 - \frac{2GM}{c^2r}}\,dt \approx \left(1 - \frac{GM}{c^2r}\right)dt$$

From this, it is clear that $\mathbb{C}_0 = 2GM/c^2$ is the correct choice.

### Red-shifts and Time Dilation in the Schwarzschild Space

It is easy to see how radiation should red-shift and blue-shift in the region of a spherical object. Depending on the direction in which the radiation travels, the red or blue shift is proportional to the relative rates at which time runs. This makes geometric sense because the frequency of oscillation of an object will be reduced in proportion to relative time slowing. Consider a radiation source at a distance $r_b$ from $M$ and a receiver at a distance $r_a > r_b$ from $M$. The wavelength of radiation will be red-shifted by the following equation:

$$\lambda_a = \lambda_b \sqrt{\frac{1 - 2GM/r_a c^2}{1 - 2GM/r_b c^2}}$$

19.10

A similar relation holds for the amount of time elapsed at the two different points:

$$t_a = t_b \sqrt{\frac{1 - 2GM/r_a c^2}{1 - 2GM/r_b c^2}}$$

19.11

For observation points very far away from $M$, this relation is very nearly as follows:

$$t_\infty = \frac{t_b}{\sqrt{1 - \dfrac{2GM}{r_b c^2}}}$$

If we assume that all the mass of $M$ is under $r_b$, when $r_b = 2GM/c^2$, $t_\infty$ becomes infinite for any finite $t_b$. In other words, relative to an observer at a distance greater than $r_b$ from $M$, time has come to a stop at the distance $r_b$. This means that a very heavy star, collapsing on its way to becoming a black hole, collapses more and more slowly as its surface approaches its Schwarzschild radius (defined next) relative to distant observers. (Black holes were originally called "frozen stars" because, their time elapses so slowly relative to the rest of the universe that it has almost halted.)

The *Schwarzschild radius, r,* is defined as:

$$r = \frac{2GM}{c^2}$$

19.12

The escape velocity at the Schwarzschild radius is equal to the speed of light, and radiation emitted here is red-shifted toward infinity. Because nothing can move faster than light, anything at or under the Schwarzschild radius cannot escape. This is a non-rotating, non-charged black hole. The surface, consisting of all points at the Schwarzschild radius, equidistant from the center of $M$, is called the *event horizon*.

## Rotating and Charged Black Holes

Black holes can rotate and, in theory, can have a net electromagnetic charge. The surrounding space-times of rotating black holes are distorted into a kind of twist. This effect, called *frame-dragging*, can be though of as follows: a rotating black hole causes the space-time around it to rotate as well, like the rotation of liquid or air around a vortex. Objects traveling through the gravitational field of a rotating black hole can gain or lose energy from it. Spherically symmetric masses can also be electrically charged, but for these cases the Schwarzschild solution will not describe the surrounding space-time.

An electrically charged non-rotating black hole, with charge $Q$ and mass $M$, is described by the *Reissner-Nordström solution*, which can be found by calculating the energy-momentum tensor for a spherically symmetric charge and equating it with the Einstein tensor for spherically symmetric space. The result of this lengthy but straightforward calculation, where $\mu_o = 4\pi \times 10^{-7}$ $kg$–$m/C^2$, is stated below:

$$ds^2 = \left(1 - \frac{2GM}{rc^2} + \frac{\mu_0 GQ^2}{4\pi c^2 r^2}\right)dw^2 - \frac{dr^2}{\left(1 - \frac{2GM}{rc^2} + \frac{\mu_0 GQ^2}{4\pi c^2 r^2}\right)} - r^2 d\theta^2 - r^2 \sin^2\theta \, d\varphi^2$$

For electrically charged rotating black holes the *Kerr-Newman solution* describes the surrounding space-time. Because the calculations are quite involved, only the Kerr-Newman metric, in what are known as "Boyer-Lindquist coordinates," will be stated here. Let the mass, charge, and angular momentum, as measured by distant observers, be given by $M$, $Q$, and $L$. Let the helper variables be defined as:

$$\Delta = \left( r^2 - \frac{2GM}{c^2}r + \frac{\mu_0 G}{4\pi c^2}Q^2 + \frac{L^2}{M^2 c^2} \right)$$

$$\rho^2 = \left( r^2 + \frac{L^2}{M^2 c^2}\cos^2\theta \right)$$

$$a = \frac{L}{Mc}$$

19.13

The line element, then, is:

$$ds^2 = \left(\frac{\Delta}{\rho^2}\right)\left[ dw - a\sin^2\theta\, d\varphi \right]^2 - \left(\frac{\sin^2\theta}{\rho^2}\right)\left[ (r^2 + a^2)d\varphi - a dw \right]^2$$

$$- \left(\frac{\rho^2}{\Delta}\right)dr^2 - \rho^2 d\theta^2$$

19.14

The geometry of the surrounding space-time is entirely characterized by $M$, $Q$, and $L$, similar to the way subatomic particles are described by their masses, charges, and spins.

In the Kerr-Newman solution, the special case of zero charge is called the *Kerr solution*. It describes rotating black holes that are electrically neutral. The closer to the equatorial regions of the black hole, the faster the frame dragging effect becomes, while at the "poles" there is almost no frame dragging at all. These effects occur with all rotating objects, such as neutron stars. Even the Earth itself drags space-time as it rotates, but the effect is quite small. Other interesting observations also come out of the Kerr-Newman solution. Kerr-Newman space-time has two event horizons, an ergosphere, and a ring singularity (unlike the Schwarzschild solution, which has a singularity at the origin $(w, 0, 0, 0)$). In the Kerr-Newman solution there is a ring singularity in the plane of rotation: the greater the rotation, the greater the radius of the ring. The ergosphere is a region defined by the outer event horizon and the stationary limit (a surface where space-time is rotationally dragged around the rotating black hole at a speed equal to the speed of light). No object at or under the stationary limit can remain at a fixed angular coordinate relative to distant observers. The angular momentum and rotational energy of rotating black holes can, in principle, be extracted, even though no material inside the black hole actually escapes. For further reading about black holes, see the bibliography at the end of this book.

## Exercises

1. For the Schwarzschild solutions, show that $G_{kk} = f_k R_{kk}$ where $f_k$ is a function. These allow the Einstein tensor and the Ricci tensor both to be zero.

2. If the earth were to collapse to a black hole, what would its Schwarzschild radius be?

3. If the sun were to collapse to a black hole, what would its Schwarzschild radius be?

4. Ignoring the sun and the Milky Way galaxy, how much does time slow on the surface of the earth relative to locations very far away?

5. Prove that the escape velocity from the Schwarzschild geometry is $\sqrt{2GM/r}$ .

6. In terms of the radial coordinate, what is the spatial distance between any two points along the same radial line from the center of a spherical, non-rotating, non-charged object?

7. Show that (19.2) comes from (19.1) via the transformations given.

8. Show that the affine connection in (19.5) corresponds to the metric in (19.4). Then derive (19.6) from the result.

9. Calculate $g = \det g_{ij}$ for the space given in (19.9).

# CHAPTER 20

# Further Calculations
# in the Schwarzschild Geometry

IN THE LAST CHAPTER some properties of the Schwarzchild geometry were explored, including the Schwarzschild radius and changes in wavelengths of photons moving in gravity fields. General relativity also predicts that light should bend slightly when passing close to the sun and that Mercury's orbit should shift slightly because of the curvature of space-time. Experimental tests of these are in excellent agreement with general relativity. The sun's gravitational field is approximately described by the Schwarzschild solution, which can be used to calculate the sun's bending of starlight and Mercury's orbital shift, though only for weak gravity fields where $r >> 2GM/c^2$. The metric tensor components are:

$$g_{44} = \left(1 - \frac{2GM}{c^2 r}\right) \qquad g_{11} = -1 \Big/ \left(1 - \frac{2GM}{c^2 r}\right)$$

$$g_{22} = -r^2 \sin^2 \theta \qquad g_{33} = -r^2$$

And the inverse, or contravariant, metric components are:

$$g^{44} = 1 \Big/ \left(1 - \frac{2GM}{c^2 r}\right) \qquad g^{11} = -\left(1 - \frac{2GM}{c^2 r}\right)$$

$$g^{22} = -r^{-2} \sin^{-2}\theta \qquad g^{33} = -r^{-2}$$

From these we can calculate the Christoffel symbols of the second kind. The bending of light around the sun and Mercury's orbit change can be found by restricting the motion to one plane. If we set the angle to $\theta = \pi/2$, then $\Gamma^3_{22} = -\sin\theta\cos\theta = 0$ and $\Gamma^2_{23} = \Gamma^2_{32} = \cot\theta = 0$. The only non-zero Christoffel symbols of the second kind are:

$$\Gamma^1_{22} = \Gamma^1_{33} = -r\left(1 - \frac{2GM}{c^2 r}\right)$$

$$\Gamma^2_{12} = \Gamma^2_{21} = \Gamma^3_{13} = \Gamma^3_{31} = \frac{1}{r}$$

$$\Gamma^4_{14} = \Gamma^4_{41} = (GM/c^2 r^2) \Big/ \left(1 - \frac{2GM}{c^2 r}\right)$$

$$\Gamma^1_{44} = \frac{GM}{c^2 r^2}\left(1 - \frac{2GM}{c^2 r}\right)$$

$$\Gamma^1_{11} = (-GM/c^2 r^2) \Big/ \left(1 - \frac{2GM}{c^2 r}\right)$$

20.1

### The Bending of Light by the Sun

In special relativity, light traveling through the vacuum has proper distance and proper time of zero. This can be verified by substituting the spatial distance traveled, $\Delta x^2 + \Delta y^2 + \Delta z^2$, into the Minkowski metric, which equal $c^2\Delta t^2$, so for any photon traveling in the vacuum $\Delta s^2 = 0$. Any geodesic world line with a proper distance of zero is called a *null geodesic*. Electromagnetic radiation travels through the vacuum on null geodesics, both in curved spaces and in flat space. In any coordinate system, null geodesics are described by equation (20.2), where $s$ is an affine parameter:

$$g_{ik}\frac{dx^i}{ds}\frac{dx^k}{ds}=0$$

20.2

In the case of weak gravitational fields $ds \approx dw$, and for special relativity equation (20.2) is:

$$0=\frac{\Delta w^2}{\Delta s^2}-\frac{\Delta x^2}{\Delta s^2}-\frac{\Delta y^2}{\Delta s^2}-\frac{\Delta z^2}{\Delta s^2}=\left(1-\frac{v^2}{c^2}\right)$$

This is true only when $v = c$. To calculate the paths of light rays, we must solve the geodesic equations:

$$\frac{d^2x^\sigma}{ds^2}+\Gamma^\sigma_{uv}\frac{dx^u}{ds}\frac{dx^v}{ds}=0$$

Substitution of the appropriate Christoffel symbols, (20.1), into the geodesic equations gives (20.3). These equations give the path as a function of an affine parameter $s$ $[x^4(s), x^1(s), x^2(s), x^3(s)] = [w(s), r(s), \varphi(s), 0]$:

$$0=\frac{d^2r}{ds^2}-\frac{GM/c^2r^2}{(1-2GM/c^2r)}\left(\frac{dr}{ds}\right)^2-r\left(1-\frac{2GM}{c^2r}\right)\left(\frac{d\varphi}{ds}\right)^2$$

$$+\frac{GM}{c^2r^2}\left(1-\frac{2GM}{c^2r}\right)\left(\frac{dw}{ds}\right)^2$$

$$0=\frac{d^2\varphi}{ds^2}+\frac{2}{r}\frac{dr}{ds}\frac{d\varphi}{ds}$$

$$0=\frac{d^2w}{ds^2}+\frac{2GM/c^2r^2}{(1-2GM/c^2r)}\frac{dr}{ds}\frac{dw}{ds}$$

20.3

And equation (20.2) is:

$$\left(1-\frac{2GM}{c^2r}\right)\left(\frac{dw}{ds}\right)^2-\frac{1}{(1-2GM/c^2r)}\left(\frac{dr}{ds}\right)^2-r^2\left(\frac{d\varphi}{ds}\right)^2=0$$

20.4

Because the path is restricted to one plane, $\theta(s) = 0$. Multiply the third equation of (20.3) by $(1-2GM/c^2r)$ and the second by $r^2$. Factoring the two equations gives:

$$\frac{d}{ds}\left(r^2\frac{d\varphi}{ds}\right) = 0$$

$$\frac{d}{ds}\left(\left(1-\frac{2GM}{c^2r}\right)\frac{dw}{ds}\right) = 0$$

Both of these equations can be integrated:

$$r^2\frac{d\varphi}{ds} = A_0$$

$$\left(1-\frac{2GM}{c^2r}\right)\frac{dw}{ds} = 1$$

20.5

The first equation's constant of integration must be proportional to the angular momentum of the photon grazing the sun's surface, and must be constant because angular momentum is conserved. The second equation's constant of integration must be the number one because when $M$ is very small, $s = w$. Solving these two equations for $d\varphi/ds$ and $dw/ds$ and substituting them into equation (20.4) gives:

$$0 = \frac{1}{(1-2GM/c^2r)} - \frac{1}{(1-2GM/c^2r)}\left(\frac{dr}{ds}\right)^2 - \frac{A_0^2}{r^2}$$

Substitute $dr/ds = (dr/d\varphi)(d\varphi/ds)$ into this equation, use the first equation in (20.5) again, and multiply the result by $r^2(1-2GM/c^2r)$ to get:

$$0 = r^2 - \frac{A_0^2}{r^2}\left(\frac{dr}{d\varphi}\right)^2 - A_0^2\left(1-\frac{2GM}{c^2r}\right)$$

20.6

Solving for $dr/d\varphi$ and integrating yields an integral that cannot be solved analytically. For weak gravity fields an approximation to this integral can be found by a variety of methods, the simplest of which is that used by Bergmann. Substitute $g = 1/r$ into (20.6) to get:

$$\left(\frac{dg}{d\varphi}\right)^2 = \frac{1}{A_0^2} - g^2 + \frac{2GM}{c^2}g^3$$

20.7

When $M = 0$, equation (20.7) is a straight line. The point of closest approach is $g' = 1/r'$, and is found when $dg/d\varphi = 0$. The point of closest approach by light is found by solving the cubic equation for $g'$:

$$0 = \frac{1}{A_0^2} - g'^2 + \frac{2GM}{c^2}g'^3$$

Subtracting this equation from (20.7) leaves an equation that can be approximated by letting $L = (g'^2 - g^2)$ and $\Delta L = (-2GM/c^2)(g'^3 - g^3)$. The result is:

$$\frac{d\varphi}{dg} = (L + \Delta L)^{-\frac{1}{2}}$$

In the case when $M=0$ and $\Delta L=0$, the above equation is $d\varphi'/dg = L^{-1/2}$. The difference in the angle, from the point of closest approach to infinity, between the straight-line solution and the general solution is defined to be $\Delta\varphi = \varphi - \varphi'$. Hence:

$$\frac{d\varphi}{dg} - \frac{d\varphi'}{dg} = \frac{d}{dg}(\Delta\varphi) = (L + \Delta L)^{-1/2} - L^{-1/2} \doteq \Delta L \frac{d}{dL}(L^{-1/2}) = \frac{-\Delta L}{2L^{3/2}}$$

Integrating this equation gives:

$$\Delta\varphi = \int_{g=1/r'}^{g=1/\infty=0} \left(-\Delta L/2L^{3/2}\right)dg = \frac{GM}{c^2r'}\left[\frac{g^2/g'^2 + g/g' - 2}{\sqrt{1-g^2/g'^2}}\right]_{1/r'}^{1/\infty}$$

Because $\Delta\varphi$ ranges from $r'$ to infinity, it should represent half of the bending angle on a light ray. Substituting $g' = 1/r'$, $g = 1/r$ and $\alpha = |2\Delta\varphi|$, the total angle by which light is bent is given by (20.8):

$$\alpha = \frac{2GM}{c^2 r'} \left[ \frac{r'^2/r^2 + r'/r - 2}{\sqrt{1 - r'^2/r^2}} \right]_{r=r'}^{r=\infty} = \frac{4GM}{c^2 r'}$$

20.8

The angular units are in radians. Assuming that light has mass and is pulled on by gravity as in Newtonian physics, this angle is twice the prediction of Newtonian gravity.

### The Shift in the Perihelion of Mercury

General relativity predicts that the sun's gravitational field is slightly stronger at the point of Mercury's closest approach than it would be in Newtonian gravity. Because of this, Mercury's elliptical orbit will shift a tiny amount on each orbit. This shift can be calculated by making an approximation. At speeds small in comparison to light, Mercury falls freely in the sun's gravitational field. Because its proper distance, therefore, is approximately equal to $ct$, it is very nearly approximated by equation (20.9):

$$g_{ik} \frac{dx^i}{ds} \frac{dx^k}{ds} = 1$$

20.9

The equations in (20.5), used to calculate the deflection of light around the sun, are useful here. We need only change the constant of integration on the first equation, to:

$$r^2 \frac{d\varphi}{ds} = \frac{r_0 v_0}{c}$$

20.10

Here $v_0$ is the speed of the planet Mercury at closest approach $r_0$. From Newtonian gravity we know that elliptical orbits such as Mercury's are described by the equation:

$$u(\varphi) = \frac{1}{r(\varphi)} = \frac{GM}{v_0^2 r_0^2} (1 + e \cos \varphi)$$

Here the eccentricity, $e$, is $\left[v_0^2 r_0/GM\right]-1$. Equation (20.9) can be written out as:

$$\left(1-\frac{2GM}{c^2 r}\right)\left(\frac{dw}{ds}\right)^2 - \frac{1}{(1-2GM/c^2 r)}\left(\frac{dr}{ds}\right)^2 - r^2\left(\frac{d\varphi}{ds}\right)^2 = 1$$

20.11

Substituting the second equation of (20.5) and equation (20.10) into (20.11) gives:

$$\left(\frac{dr}{ds}\right)^2 + \frac{r_0^2 v_0^2}{r^2 c^2}\left(1-\frac{2GM}{c^2 r}\right) = \frac{2GM}{c^2 r}$$

Then, we substitute $dr/ds = (dr/d\varphi)(d\varphi/ds)$ and use the second equation of (20.5) again. After simplifying, we have:

$$\left(\frac{dr}{d\varphi}\right)^2 + r^2\left(1-\frac{2GM}{c^2 r}\right) = \frac{2GM}{v_0^2 r_0^2}r^3$$

This equation can be further changed by letting $r = 1/u$:

$$\left(\frac{du}{d\varphi}\right)^2 + u^2 - \frac{2GM}{c^2}u^3 = \frac{2GM}{v_0^2 r_0^2}u$$

20.12

Differentiating both sides of this equation with respect to the angle $\varphi$ gives:

$$\frac{d^2 u}{d\varphi^2} + u = \frac{GM}{v_0^2 r_0^2}\left(1+\frac{3v_0^2 r_0^2}{c^2}u^2\right)$$

20.13

The corresponding equation in Newtonian gravity is:

$$\frac{d^2 u}{d\varphi^2} + u = \frac{GM}{v_0^2 r_0^2}$$

20.14

Because the term $3v_0^2 r_0^2 u^2/c^2$ is very small, the solution to (20.13) should be very nearly an ellipse. The solution to (20.14) is of the form $u = A(1 + e\cos\varphi)$, where $e$ is the eccentricity and $A = GM/v_0^2 r_0^2$. Letting $L = 3v_0^2 r_0^2/c^2$, the solution to (20.13) will be periodic. So it is natural to assume the solution to the equation

$$u'' + u = A(1 + Lu^2)$$
20.15

will be of the form:

$$u = A(1 + e\cos(\varphi\psi)) + LB$$
20.16

Here $\psi$ is a constant factor changing the angle slightly, and $B$ is a constant. Substituting (20.16) into the left side of (20.15) gives:

$$u'' + u = A + LB + (1 - \psi^2) \cdot (Ae\cos(\varphi\psi))$$
20.17

And substituting (20.16) into the right side of (20.15) and neglecting second-order terms gives:

$$A(1 + Lu^2) = A + (LA^3 + (LA^3 e^2/2)) + 2eLA^3 \cos(\varphi\psi)$$
$$+ (LA^3 e^2/2)\cos(2\varphi\psi)$$
20.18

If we equate the right-hand terms of (20.17) and (20.18), it is clear that the following equations hold true:

$$LB = L(A^3 + A^3 e^2/2)$$
$$2eLA^3 = Ae(1 - \psi^2)$$

Solving for $\psi^2$ gives $\psi^2 = 1 - 2LA^2$, which can be approximated by:

$$\psi \doteq 1 - LA^2 = 1 - \frac{3G^2 M^2}{v_0^2 r_0^2 c^2}$$

For one orbit, the change in the angle between two successive perihelions is $\Delta\varphi'$:

$$\Delta\varphi' = 2\pi\Delta\psi = 2\pi(1 - \psi) = \frac{6\pi G^2 M^2}{v_0^2 r_0^2 c^2}$$

Solving the equation $e = v_0^2 r_0 / GM - 1$ for $v_0^2 r_0^2$ gives $v_0^2 r_0^2 = GMr_0(1+e)$, and substituting this into the above equation yields the final result:

$$\Delta\varphi' = \frac{6\pi GM}{(1+e)r_0 c^2}$$

20.19

If $M$ = the mass of the sun and $r_0$ = Mercury's closest approach to the sun, then $\Delta\varphi'$ is 43 seconds of arc per century. Because equation (20.19) is only approximate, it is accurate only in weak gravity fields such as the sun's. For strong gravity fields, paths are best found by using numerical techniques on the equations.

## Circular Orbits in the Schwarzschild Space

Circular geodesic paths are possible in the Schwarzschild space. The nature of these paths and their implications for light rays can be found. An object that is much less massive than the black hole it orbits travels at a constant speed $v$ at a constant radial coordinate distance $r$. The speed $v$ is relative to points at the radial distance $r$, but not to distant observers. For them, the coordinate variables are, to a very high degree, their local variables of space and time. Due to gravitational time dilation, relative to distant observers at "infinity," objects in circular orbit travel at slower angular speeds:

$$v\sqrt{1 - \frac{2GM}{c^2 r}} = r\frac{d\varphi}{dt}$$

20.20

Circular orbits can be found by setting $d^2r/ds^2 = 0$ and $dr/ds = 0$ in the first equation of (20.3) and changing the constants of integration in (20.5). The terms $d^2r/ds^2$ and $dr/ds$ are zero because the radial coordinate does not change over time for circular orbits. The equations then become those in (20.21):

$$0 = -r\left(1 - \frac{2GM}{c^2 r}\right)\left(\frac{d\varphi}{ds}\right)^2 + \frac{GM}{r^2 c^2}\left(1 - \frac{2GM}{c^2 r}\right)\left(\frac{dw}{ds}\right)^2$$

$$0 = \frac{d}{ds}\left(r^2 \frac{d\varphi}{ds}\right)$$

$$0 = \frac{d}{ds}\left(\left(1 - \frac{2GM}{c^2 r}\right)\frac{dw}{ds}\right)$$

20.21

Integrating the last two equations of (20.21) gives:

$$r^2 \frac{d\varphi}{ds} = K_1$$

$$\left(1 - \frac{2GM}{c^2 r}\right)\frac{dw}{ds} = K_0$$

20.22

The constant $K_1$ corresponds to the angular momentum of the object in circular orbit around mass $M$. The units for $K_1$ are in terms of distance—meters, for example—and $K_1$ is the angular momentum divided by rest mass and the speed of light:

$$K_1 = \frac{vr/c}{\sqrt{1 - v^2/c^2}}$$

20.23

Because $v$ and $r$ are both constant for circular orbits, $K_1$ is constant. Although equation (20.23) may appear awkward, it can be derived from (20.24). Rewriting the first equation in (20.22) by means of the chain rule will also help justify equation (20.23):

$$r^2 \frac{d\varphi}{dt}\frac{dt}{ds} = r^2 \frac{d\varphi}{dt}\frac{dw}{ds}\frac{1}{c} = K_1$$

Multiplying equation (20.20) by $r$ and substituting it into the equation above gives:

$$\frac{rv}{c}\sqrt{1-\frac{2GM}{c^2r}}\frac{dw}{ds}=\frac{vr/c}{\sqrt{1-v^2/c^2}}$$

Solving for *dw/ds* gives:

$$\frac{dw}{ds}=\frac{1}{\sqrt{1-v^2/c^2}\sqrt{1-2GM/c^2r}}$$

20.24

This equation makes sense because $dt/d\tau = dw/ds$. For distant observers, the proper time for any object circling around mass $M$ will be subject to two time-dilation factors: gravity and orbital speed. Starting with (20.24) it is easy to derive (20.23) hence the justification of (20.23). Substituting (20.24) into the last equation of (20.22) gives $K_0$:

$$K_0=\frac{\sqrt{1-\frac{2GM}{c^2r}}}{\sqrt{1-\frac{v^2}{c^2}}}$$

20.25

Now both constants of integration, $K_0$ and $K_1$ are known. The first equation of (20.21) is:

$$-r\left(\frac{d\varphi}{ds}\right)^2+\frac{GM}{r^2c^2}\left(\frac{dw}{ds}\right)^2=0$$

Substituting (20.24) and $d\varphi/ds = K_1/r^2$ into this equation and simplifying allows for the calculation of local orbital velocity:

$$v=\sqrt{\frac{GM/r}{1-\frac{2GM}{c^2r}}}$$

20.26

An object traveling at speed $v$ orbits $M$ in a circle. However, when $r$ equals the Schwarzschild radius, the orbital speed is infinite. Because nothing can go faster than the speed of light, there must be a minimum radius at which circular orbits are possible. Setting $v = c$ in (20.26) and solving for $r$ gives:

$$r = \frac{3GM}{c^2}$$

20.27

The set of points at this radial coordinate distance is called the *photon sphere*. At this distance, light can orbit circularly around $M$, but this orbit is not stable. Slight deviations will cause photons to spiral toward or away from the black hole. "Free fall" orbits between the photon sphere and the event horizon is not possible. To orbit in this region requires some downward thrust to counterbalance the pull of gravity. The escape velocity in Schwarzschild space is equal to its Newtonian equation and so black holes will accelerate in falling material to speeds ever closer to the speed of light. As falling objects approach the event horizon, their local speed creeps asymptotically closer to the speed of light. Locally, the kinetic energy of these objects increases without limit. But distant observers observe the total energy of the black hole (and any material falling in) as constant. The local increase in energy of falling material is, essentially, an attribute of the coordinate system, and physical quantities are relative to coordinate systems. Because energy and momentum are not absolute in character, the principles of special and general relativity resolve the apparent contradiction between local and distant observers.

In special relativity motion, time, distance, and mass are relative to inertial frames. This is expanded in general relativity, where motion, time, distance, and mass are relative to different locations in gravitational fields. Consider a stationary spherical shell of $n$ asteroids, each of rest mass $m$, surrounding a neutron star at the center of the sphere. The asteroids are very far from the neutron star. The total mass-energy of the asteroids is $nm$ relative to stationary observers distant from the neutron star. Each asteroid falls directly toward the neutron star, all reaching its surface at the same time and with the same kinetic energy. Relative to the surface of the neutron star, the total mass-energy of all the asteroids is $nm'$, where $m' > m$ due to the kinetic energy of each asteroid. But relative to an observation point far from the neutron star, the total mass-energy of all the asteroids is still $nm$. The mass energy of each asteroid is relative and depends upon its location in the gravitational field. An object's mass and energy depends both on its location and speed in a gravity field, and on the location and speed of an observer. That is, mass-energy is relative in general relativity, just as it is in special relativity.

## *Exercises*

1. Calculate the angular deflection of a light ray grazing past the surface of the sun.

2. Show that, for circular orbits, $K_0$ and $K_1$ both satisfy the line element
$$1 = \left(1 - 2GM/c^2 r\right)\left(dw/ds\right)^2 - r^2 \left(d\varphi/ds\right)^2 .$$

3. For an object falling directly toward a non-rotating, non-charged black hole, show that $d^2 r/d\tau^2 = -GM/r^2$ .

4. Calculate the time it takes a photon of light to fall from any distance $r_2$ to the Schwarzschild radius, relative to distant observers. Assume that the photon travels directly toward the center of the black hole.

5. Distant observers, watching an object in a circular orbit in Schwarzschild space, see slowed orbital speed due to gravitational time dilation. Taking this effect into account, what measurement of orbital speed would a distant observer make?

6. For an object orbiting circularly in Schwarzschild space, find the relationship between proper time and coordinate time.

7. A Jupiter-mass planet orbits a non-rotating, non-charged black hole of 60.0 solar masses. The eccentricity of the orbit is 0.121 and its closest approach to the black hole is $3.51 \times 10^{10}$ meters (radial coordinate distance). Assuming that no other objects are present, calculate the shift in the perihelion of that planet's orbit for one revolution about the black hole.

8. Calculate the approximate number of revolutions a planet with eccentricity $e$ would need for the shift in the perihelion to take the perihelion back to its approximate starting position. Assume that the point of closest approach is $R_0$ and that the planet and star are the only two bodies in the system.

9. Show that (20.1) is true via calculation on (19.5) for the plane $\theta = \pi/2$.

# CHAPTER 21

# *General Relativity and Cosmology*

GENERAL RELATIVITY DESCRIBES the long-range force of gravity as a curvature of space-time. Electromagnetism, the other long-range force, plays no essential role on the large scale of the universe because the universe is electrically neutral. The strong and weak nuclear forces have no effect on the global properties of the universe because they operate over distances comparable to those of atomic nuclei. It is therefore felt that only the gravitational force—and possibly some type of vacuum force—governs the large-scale dynamics of the universe.

The universe is composed of galaxies grouped together in clusters and super-clusters. Also the universe is expanding, all groups of galaxies are moving away from each other and within their own groups. This strongly supports the *big bang theory:* that in the remote past the material of which the galaxies are made was all together and then expanded outward. Because the purpose of this book is to introduce the theory of relativity, the large and controversial topic of cosmology—a branch of astronomy that studies of the structure and dynamics of the universe as a whole—will not be explored here in detail. This chapter will focus on relativity as it is used in cosmology, primarily in modeling the expansion of the universe.

The expanding universe model, according to which all matter and energy in the universe was once concentrated in a single spot that exploded outward, can be treated in general relativity under the *Robertson-Walker models*. These models assume that the universe is homogeneous and isotropic: that the galaxies are distributed similarly in all directions and distances. This assumption is called the *cosmological principle*. In reality the universe is not perfectly homogenous and isotropic but on the largest scales it is thought to be very nearly so. This means that, at any cosmic time, each region of space-time should be approximately the same as all others. Therefore cosmological models that embody the cosmological principle should be restricted to spaces of constant curvature. Astronomers have found that the farther away a galaxy is from the earth, the faster it is moving away relative to the earth. In fact, as *Hubble's law* states, the relative speed of a galaxy is proportional to its distance from the earth. Because observations have upheld Hubble's law, any accurate model of the universe must be compatible with it. The expansion of the universe results from a giant explosion that occurred about twelve to eighteen billion years ago. Evidence for this is found in the cosmic background radiation that has a present temperature of 2.7 degrees Kelvin. What caused that explosion? The big bang may have been the result of a previous large-scale collapse of the universe but ideas such as these are still speculative. At present there is no scientific answer to this question.

The Robertson-Walker models are consistent with the cosmological principle and with Hubble's law. Ignoring the time dimension for the moment, three-dimensional spaces of constant curvature satisfy the equations:

$$R_{ijkl} = K\left(g_{il}g_{jk} - g_{ik}g_{jl}\right)$$

Assuming that the metric is for a three-dimensional space, we can find the Ricci tensor by summing on the indices from one to three:

$$R_{jk} = g^{il}R_{ijkl} = K\left(3g_{jk} - \delta^l_k g_{jl}\right) = 2Kg_{jk}$$

The curvature scalar $R$ is then:

$$R = g^{jk} R_{jk} = 6K$$

The curvature scalar is the same function at all locations in space: $R(x, y, z) = 6K_0$. For spherical spaces, it is best to use spherical coordinates. In fact, a simple generalization of spherical coordinates can be used for spaces with more than three dimensions. Consider the following space with a constant radius $\hat{S}$:

$$y = \hat{S} \sin \alpha \sin \theta \sin \varphi$$
$$x = \hat{S} \sin \alpha \sin \theta \cos \varphi$$
$$z = \hat{S} \sin \alpha \cos \theta$$
$$w = \hat{S} \cos \alpha$$

This space has the line element:

$$ds^2 = \hat{S}^2 \left[ d\alpha^2 + \sin^2 \alpha \, (d\theta^2 + \sin^2 \theta d\varphi^2) \right]$$

Making the substitution $\hat{r} = \sin \alpha$ and its differential $d\hat{r} = \cos\alpha d\alpha$, we can easily calculate $d\alpha^2$:

$$d\alpha^2 = \frac{d\hat{r}^2}{\cos^2 \alpha} = \frac{d\hat{r}^2}{1 - \sin^2 \alpha} = \frac{d\hat{r}^2}{1 - \hat{r}^2}$$

Expressing the line element as a function of this variable, by substitution, gives the result:

$$ds^2 = \hat{S}^2 \left[ \frac{d\hat{r}^2}{1 - \hat{r}^2} + \hat{r}^2 \, (d\theta^2 + \sin^2 \theta d\varphi^2) \right]$$

Letting $K$ be proportional to the constant curvature scalar for this space, this equation can be generalized to an identical equation except that $1 - K\hat{r}^2$ replaces $1 - \hat{r}^2$. The constant $K$ can be written as $K = k |K|$, where $k$ is +1 or

–1 depending on the sign of the curvature. We can then verify the constant curvature of the resulting space by calculating the curvature tensor directly from the given metric elements. Further, if we make the substitution $\hat{r}$ equals $r/\sqrt{K}$ and $S$ equals $S\sqrt{K}$, with $K = k|K|$ where $k = \pm 1$ depending on positive or negative global curvature, then the line element becomes:

$$ds^2 = S^2 \left[ \frac{dr^2}{1 - kr^2} + r^2 \left( d\theta^2 + \sin^2 \theta \, d\varphi^2 \right) \right]$$

Using this, it is possible to define the Robertson-Walker line element that defines their corresponding cosmological models:

$$ds^2 = c^2 dt^2 - (S(t))^2 \left[ \frac{dr^2}{1 - kr^2} + r^2 \left( d\theta^2 + \sin^2 \theta \, d\varphi^2 \right) \right]$$

21.1

Here $S(t)$ is the scale factor of the universe as a function of time, and $k = -1$, 0, +1 for an open universe, a flat universe, and a closed universe, respectively. For an object co-moving along a chosen coordinate system homogenous to all other such locations in the universe, the variable $t$ is the total amount of proper time since the big bang. If we think of the expanding universe as an expanding balloon painted with dots, each dot on the balloon is "co-moving" with the expansion of the balloon. No dots are moving across the surface of the balloon. Thus all differential volume regions with world lines of the same proper distance from the big bang are identical in curvature and other properties.

Assume that matter in the universe is an electrically neutral dust, or frictionless fluid, with the same density at each "co-moving" point. Let $\{u^i\}$ = (1, 0, 0, 0) be the four-velocity vector of any fluid or dust element. The coordinates for this element are $x^0 = ct$, $x^1 = r$, $x^2 = \theta$, $x^3 = \varphi$. And from the Robertson-Walker line element, the general form of the metric is:

$$g_{00} = 1$$

$$g_{11} = -\frac{S^2(t)}{(1 - kr^2)}$$

$$g_{22} = -r^2 S^2(t)$$

$$g_{33} = -r^2 S^2(t) \sin^2 \theta$$

Because the diagonal elements of the metric are the only non-zero terms, the contravariant form of the metric is made up of the reciprocals of each covariant metric component:

$$g^{00} = 1$$

$$g^{11} = -\left(\frac{1 - kr^2}{S^2(t)}\right)$$

$$g^{22} = -\frac{1}{r^2 S^2(t)}$$

$$g^{33} = -\frac{1}{r^2 S^2(t) \sin^2 \theta}$$

As $S$ is a function of $t$ alone, partial derivatives become ordinary derivatives in calculations of Christoffel symbols. Letting $\dot{S} = \partial S/\partial t = dS/dt$ denote differentiation of $S$ with respect to $t$, a long but direct calculation gives the non-zero Christoffel symbols of the first kind $[i\ j, k] = (1/2)(g_{ik,j} + g_{jk,i} - g_{ij,k})$:

$$[0\,1,1]=[1\,0,1]=\frac{-S\dot{S}}{c\,(1-kr^{2})} \qquad\qquad [0\,2,2]=[2\,0,2]=\frac{-r^{2}S\dot{S}}{c}$$

$$[0\,3,3]=[3\,0,3]=\frac{-r^{2}S\dot{S}\sin^{2}\theta}{c} \qquad [1\,2,2]=[2\,1,2]=-rS^{2}$$

$$[1\,3,3]=[3\,1,3]=-rS^{2}\sin^{2}\theta \qquad [2\,3,3]=[3\,2,3]=-r^{2}S^{2}\sin\theta\cos\theta$$

$$[1\,1,0]=\frac{S\dot{S}}{c\,(1-kr^{2})} \qquad [1\,1,1]=\frac{-krS^{2}}{\left(1-kr^{2}\right)^{2}} \qquad [2\,2,0]=\frac{r^{2}S\dot{S}}{c}$$

$$[2\,2,1]=rS^{2} \qquad [3\,3,0]=\frac{r^{2}S\dot{S}\sin^{2}\theta}{c} \qquad [3\,3,1]=rS^{2}\sin^{2}\theta$$

$$[3\,3,2]=r^{2}S^{2}\sin\theta\cos\theta$$

Non-zero Christoffel symbols of the second kind, $\Gamma^{\sigma}_{i\,j}=g^{\sigma k}[i\,j,k]$, are given in (21.2):

$$\Gamma^{1}_{01}=\Gamma^{1}_{10}=\Gamma^{2}_{02}=\Gamma^{2}_{20}=\Gamma^{3}_{03}=\Gamma^{3}_{30}=\frac{\dot{S}}{cS}$$

$$\Gamma^{2}_{12}=\Gamma^{2}_{21}=\Gamma^{3}_{13}=\Gamma^{3}_{31}=\frac{1}{r} \qquad\qquad \Gamma^{0}_{11}=\frac{S\dot{S}}{c\,(1-kr^{2})}$$

$$\Gamma^{0}_{22}=\frac{r^{2}S\dot{S}}{c} \qquad \Gamma^{0}_{33}=\frac{r^{2}S\dot{S}\sin^{2}\theta}{c} \qquad \Gamma^{1}_{11}=\frac{kr}{(1-kr^{2})}$$

$$\Gamma^{1}_{22}=-r\,(1-kr^{2}) \qquad \Gamma^{1}_{33}=-r\,(1-kr^{2})\sin^{2}\theta$$

$$\Gamma^{2}_{33}=-\sin\theta\cos\theta \qquad \Gamma^{3}_{23}=\Gamma^{3}_{32}=\cot\theta$$

21.2

Next we must compute the field equations $kT_{uv}=R_{uv}-\tfrac{1}{2}g_{uv}R+\Lambda g_{uv}$ for the affine connection above. After we find the curvature side of the field equations, we must equate it with the proper energy-momentum tensor of the universe. The energy-momentum tensor of the universe must be based on considerations of homogeneity and isotropy. All of the components of the Ricci tensor except for the diagonal ones are zero. They are:

$$R_{00} = \frac{3\ddot{S}}{c^2 S}$$

$$R_{11} = -\left[2\dot{S}^2 + S\ddot{S} + 2kc^2\right]\frac{1}{c^2(1-kr^2)}$$

$$R_{22} = -\left[2\dot{S}^2 + S\ddot{S} + 2kc^2\right]\frac{r^2}{c^2}$$

$$R_{33} = -\left[2\dot{S}^2 + S\ddot{S} + 2kc^2\right]\frac{r^2\sin^2\theta}{c^2}$$

The double dot denotes second time derivatives. And the curvature scalar $R$ is $R = R_{pq}g^{pq}$:

$$R = \frac{6}{c^2 S^2}\left[\dot{S}^2 + S\ddot{S} + kc^2\right]$$

The non-zero components of the Einstein tensor, added to any cosmological term $G_{pq} + \Lambda g_{pq}$, calculate to:

$$G_{00} + \Lambda g_{00} = \left[-3\dot{S}^2 - 3kc^2 + \Lambda S^2 c^2\right]\frac{1}{c^2 S^2}$$

$$G_{11} + \Lambda g_{11} = \left[\dot{S}^2 + kc^2 + 2S\ddot{S} - \Lambda S^2 c^2\right]\frac{1}{c^2(1-kr^2)}$$

$$G_{22} + \Lambda g_{22} = \left[\dot{S}^2 + kc^2 + 2S\ddot{S} - \Lambda S^2 c^2\right]\frac{r^2}{c^2}$$

$$G_{33} + \Lambda g_{33} = \left[\dot{S}^2 + kc^2 + 2S\ddot{S} - \Lambda S^2 c^2\right]\frac{r^2\sin^2\theta}{c^2}$$

21.3

These equations give the geometric shape of space-time for spaces obeying the Robertson-Walker geometry. But the distribution of energy and momentum, $T_{uv}$, needs to be that of the aforementioned dust or fluid at rest in volume elements with the same proper distance from the big bang. The four-velocity of that fluid is $u_0 = (d/dx^0)(ct, 0, 0, ,0)=(1, 0, 0, 0)$ and the energy momentum tensor for a perfect fluid or dust field is:

$$T_{ij} = (\rho + p)u_i u_j - pg_{ij}$$

Here $\rho$ is the rest energy density of the fluid/dust and $p$ is the local pressure. Substituting the four-velocity and the metric components from the equation (21.1) into this energy-momentum tensor gives us the energy-momentum tensor for the universe:

$$T_{00} = \rho$$

$$T_{11} = \frac{pS^2}{(1 - kr^2)}$$

$$T_{22} = pS^2 r^2$$

$$T_{33} = pS^2 r^2 \sin^2 \theta$$

21.4

Multiplying these by the constant $-8\pi G/c^4$ and equating them with their counterparts in (21.3) gives the complete field equations for Robertson-Walker cosmological models. In doing this there are three copies of one equation. Eliminating this redundancy leaves two equations:

$$\frac{\dot{S}^2 + kc^2 - \Lambda S^2 c^2/3}{S^2} = \frac{8\pi G}{3c^2}\rho$$

21.5

$$\frac{2S\ddot{S} + \dot{S}^2 + kc^2 - \Lambda S^2 c^2}{S^2} = \frac{-8\pi G}{c^2}p$$

21.6

These equations govern the evolution of any Robertson-Walker universe. To summarize: $S(t)$ shows change in size of the universe over cosmic time $t$; $k = -1, 0, +1$ is an index specifying an open, flat, or closed shape; and $p(t)$ and $\rho(t)$

show variation of total energy density and total pressure over cosmic proper time. The constant $\Lambda$ represents a possible cosmological term.

The remainder of this chapter will study these two equations and the cosmological models they contain. First, some general properties of these equations need to be explored. Differentiating equation (21.5) with respect to time, multiplying equation (21.6) by $-3\dot{S}/S$, and adding the results together yields:

$$\frac{-\dot{S}}{S}\left(3\dot{S}^2 + 3kc^2 - \Lambda S^2 c^2\right) = \frac{8\pi G}{c^2}\left(\dot{\rho}S^2 + 2\rho S\dot{S} + 3pS\dot{S}\right)$$

The parenthesized expression on the left is $(8\pi G/c^2)\rho S^2$ by equation (21.5). After substituting it into this equation, we obtain:

$$-\rho S\dot{S} = \dot{\rho}S^2 + 2\rho S\dot{S} + 3pS\dot{S}$$

Simplifying this equation and multiplying both sides of the result by $S$ yields an equation that can be factored to:

$$0 = \frac{d}{dt}(\rho S^3) + p\frac{d}{dt}(S^3)$$

21.7

Equation (21.7) is just the conservation of energy: $\rho S^3$ can be thought of as energy and $S^3$ as volume. The rate of loss of energy equals the negative of pressure multiplied by change in volume. Therefore, with a non-zero pressure the universe must do work to increase its expansion rate. Because general relativity was derived to satisfy the conservation laws of energy, momentum, and angular momentum, this is no surprise. This equation could be derived directly from $T^{uv}_{;v} = 0$. It can also be written as:

$$0 = \dot{\rho} + 3\frac{\dot{S}}{S}(\rho + p)$$

The conservation of energy is not the only global property of Robertson-Walker models. They can also be examined in terms of global cosmic expansion speed and deceleration. Multiply equation (21.5) by three, multiply (21.6) by (–1), and add the two together to get:

$$\frac{\dot{S}^2 + kc^2 - S\ddot{S}}{S^2} = \frac{4\pi G}{c^2}(\rho + p)$$

From (21.5) we see that $(\dot{S}^2 + kc^2)/S^2 = (8\pi G/3c^2)\rho + \Lambda c^2/3$. Substituting this into the equation above gives:

$$-\frac{\ddot{S}}{S} = \frac{4\pi G}{3c^2}(\rho + 3p) - \Lambda c^2/3$$

21.8

Two important quantities in cosmology are the Hubble constant and the deceleration parameter, which are not truly constant but vary with cosmic proper time. At any cosmic time their values are defined as:

$$H = \frac{\dot{S}}{S}$$

$$q = \frac{-S\ddot{S}}{\dot{S}^2}$$

21.9

These quantities can be expressed in terms of cosmic energy density $\rho$, curvature $k$, "radius or scale factor" $S$, and any cosmological term $\Lambda$. First, substitute the definition of $H$ into (21.5) and the definition of $q$ into (21.8). The results are:

$$H^2 = \frac{8\pi G}{3}\rho_m - \frac{kc^2}{S^2} + \frac{\Lambda c^2}{3}$$

$$q = \frac{(4\pi G/3)(\rho_m + p_m) - \Lambda c^2/3}{(8\pi G/3)\rho_m - kc^2/S^2 + \Lambda c^2/3}$$

Here, both pressure and energy density are expressed in units of mass per unit volume, denoted with a subscript $m$.

## The Cosmological Red Shift

All Robertson-Walker models have in common cosmological red shift for an expanding universe and cosmological blue shift for a contracting universe. With cosmological red shift, electromagnetic waves of wavelength $\lambda_1$ emitted at one location in space-time are stretched to a new wavelength $\lambda_0$ at a different location. A wave of light travels along a geodesic from one location to another in the empty space between the galaxies. Consider a photon of light emitted at one location, traveling along a path $r(t)$, and received at another location. In this case, of the four components $(t, r, \theta, \varphi)$, the path through space-time is fixed in the two angular co-ordinates and variable in $t$ and $r$. Because light travels on null geodesics, $ds^2 = 0$, and because there are no changes on the two angular coordinates for this null geodesic, the general Robertson-Walker line element along the geodesic reduces to:

$$0 = c^2 dt^2 - \frac{S^2 dr^2}{(1 - kr^2)}$$

Or:

$$\int_{t_1}^{t_0} (c/S)dt = \int_{r_1}^{r_0} d/\sqrt{1 - kr^2}\, dr$$

21.10

The light wave is emitted at $(t_1, r_1, \theta_0, \varphi_0)$ and received at $(t_0, r_0, \theta_0, \varphi_0)$. For the calculations that follow, assume that the wavelength of light at emission is small in comparison to the spatial distance it travels. The first wave crest is emitted at time $t_1$ and received at time $t_0$. The second crest is emitted at time $t_1 + \Delta t_1$ and received at time $t_0 + \Delta t_0$. Over these small times, $\Delta t_1$ and $\Delta t_0$, the source and receiver of the wave travel the same radial distance $r_1$ to $r_0$. This means that the right-hand side of equation (21.10) will not change:

$$\int_{t_1 + \Delta t_1}^{t_0 + \Delta t_0} (c/S)dt = \int_{r_1}^{r_0} d/\sqrt{1 - kr^2}\, dr$$

Equating this equation with (21.10) makes it clear that the following equality holds:

$$\int_{t_1+\Delta t_1}^{t_0+\Delta t_0} (c/S(t))dt = \int_{t_1}^{t_0} (c/S(t))dt$$

By using the integration law $\int_a^b f + \int_b^c f = \int_a^c f$, each side can be written as:

$$\int_{t_1+\Delta t_1}^{t_1} (c/S)dt + \int_{t_1}^{t_0+\Delta t_0} (c/S)dt = \int_{t_1}^{t_0+\Delta t_0} (c/S)dt + \int_{t_0+\Delta t_0}^{t_0} (c/S)dt$$

After simplification, this becomes:

$$\int_{t_1}^{t_1+\Delta t_1} (c/S)dt = \int_{t_0}^{t_0+\Delta t_0} (c/S)dt$$

Now over the comparably small time intervals, $\Delta t_1$ and $\Delta t_0$, $S$ does not change substantially so this equation becomes:

$$\frac{c\Delta t_1}{S(t_1)} = \frac{c\Delta t_0}{S(t_0)}$$

Further, because the time interval between successive wave crests, $\Delta t_1$ and $\Delta t_0$, is small in comparison to travel time, the wavelength at source and reception are related by the equations $c\Delta t_0 = \lambda_0$ and $c\Delta t_1 = \lambda_1$. By definition, $(\lambda_0 - \lambda_1)/\lambda_1 = \Delta\lambda_1/\lambda_1 = z$. Therefore the ratio of cosmological shift in wavelength is given by:

$$\frac{S(t_0)}{S(t_1)} = \frac{\lambda_0}{\lambda_1} = z+1$$

21.11

This is the cosmological red shift for all Robertson-Walker cosmological models, or, for a contracting universe, a cosmological blue shift. The shift in wavelength results from the expansion or contraction of space. It is not a Doppler shift in the sense that Doppler shifts were explored earlier. All Robertson-Walker models obey Hubble's law when the speed of recession between two galaxies is small in comparison to the speed of light. Let $t_1 = t_0 - \Delta t_0$, and equation (21.11) will be approximated by Taylor's theorem:

$$1 + z \doteq 1 + \frac{\dot{S}(t_0)}{S(t_0)} \Delta t_0$$

21.12

Using equation (21.10) with comparatively small values of $\Delta t_0$ and $r_1$ gives:

$$\frac{c \Delta t_0}{S(t_0)} \approx \int_{t_0 - \Delta t_0}^{t_0} (c/S(t)) dt = \int_0^{r_1} \left( 1 / \sqrt{1 - kr^2} \right) dr \approx r_1$$

When we substitute these approximations into equation (21.12) and solve for $z$, the result is:

$$z \doteq \frac{\dot{S}(t_0) r_1}{c} = \frac{\dot{S}(t_0)}{S(t_0)} \frac{r_1 S(t_0)}{c} = \frac{H_0 x}{c}$$

In this approximation, the distance $x$ between galaxies is very nearly $r_1 S(t_0)$. If we treat $z = v/c$ as if it were a regular Doppler shift for objects traveling slowly in comparison with the speed of light, we find that Hubble's law, $v = H_0 x$, is compatible with any Robertson-Walker model. When astronomers study the red or blue shift of an astronomical object, they look at radiation that is potentially subject to three major kinds of wavelength shift: Doppler shift, gravitational red shift, and cosmological red shift. Cosmological red shifts are assumed to be Robertson-Walker in character. If $\lambda$ is the wavelength of the radiation in the source's rest frame and if the wavelength of the radiation received by astronomers on earth is $\lambda'$, then $z+1$ represents the ratio of these two: $z = \Delta\lambda/\lambda = (\lambda' - \lambda)/\lambda = \lambda'/\lambda - 1$. But $z+1$ represents a combined effect of the types of wavelength changes mentioned above.

In reality, many simple cases are covered by the equation given in (21.13). Let $z_D$ be the Doppler shift due to motion, let $z_G$ be the gravitational red shift for spherically symmetric masses, and let $z_C$ equal the cosmological red shift. The number $z+1$ represents a combination of these:

$$(z+1) = (z_D + 1)(z_G + 1)(z_C + 1)$$

21.13

With:

$$z_D = \gamma\left(1 + \frac{v}{c}\cos\theta'\right) - 1$$

$$z_G = \frac{1}{\sqrt{1 - 2GM/c^2 r}} - 1$$

$$z_C = \frac{S_0}{S} - 1$$

The reason for this is easy to understand. Each effect will modify a given wavelength by the same factor regardless of effects modifying it previously. This equation holds to a high degree of approximation for observations of radiation coming from distant regions of the universe. To be strictly correct, we should add additional factors for radiation coming to earth: blue shifts by the gravitational field of the Milky Way, the gravitational field of the sun, and the gravitational field of the earth. Neglecting these, (21.13) is a good approximation for many astronomical objects.

## *Specific Cosmological Models*

So far this chapter has explored some general properties of the Robertson-Walker models. Specific models will depend on the values of $\rho, p, k$ and $\Lambda$. Broadly speaking, there are two classes of Robertson-Walker cosmological models: *Lemaitre* (models with a non-zero cosmological term) and *Friedmann* (models with a zero cosmological term). For both Lemaitre and Friedmann models there are three sub-models for $k = -1, k = 0$ and $k = +1$. With $k$ and $\Lambda$ specified, there are two equations (21.5) and (21.6) in three unknowns $S(t)$, $\rho(t), p(t)$. From a mathematical point of view, if any one of these functions is specified, the remaining two are completely determined. Choices for these functions should be physically reasonable. For example, $\rho(t)$ should probably never be negative, and $p(t)$ should be based in believable physics. If pressure is a given function of density—that is, $p = p(\rho)$, then $S(t), \rho(t), p(t)$ are all found from equations (21.5) and (21.6) if $k$ and $\Lambda$ are known. The values of $k, \Lambda$ and $p(\rho)$ are determined from astronomical observations and the laws of physics. Matter, $\rho$, emits radiation resulting in radiation pressure, $p(\rho)$, as a function of other specific laws such as those governing the emission of radiation from objects. The observed values—both measured at the present time—of the Hubble constant, the deceleration parameter, and possibly a cosmological term, are used to infer $k, \rho, p$ and $S$, along with other observations. The terms $k, \rho, p$ and $S$ are inferred from the observational parameters $(H_0, q_0, \Lambda)$. The subscript $_0$ means the present-day values of $H$ and $q$.

Consider an example of the use of the field equations to provide a cosmological model, in this case a Lemaitre model. Imagine a positively closed universe, $k = +1$, without matter or pressure, so that $\rho = 0, p = 0$, and a positive non-zero cosmological constant $\Lambda > 0$ exists. In this case, equations (21.5) and (21.6) become:

$$\dot{S}^2 + c^2 - c^2 \Lambda S^2 / 3 = 0$$

$$2S\ddot{S} + \dot{S}^2 + c^2 - \Lambda S^2 c^2 = 0$$

$S(t)$ can be found from the first equation alone. After separating variables, we obtain:

$$c\sqrt{\frac{\Lambda}{3}} \int_0^t dt = \int_0^S \left. d \middle/ \sqrt{S^2 - 3/\Lambda} \right) dS$$

And after substituting $S = \sqrt{3/\Lambda} \sec u$ and solving for $S$ after integration, we have:

$$S(t) = \frac{1}{2}\sqrt{\frac{3}{\Lambda}} e^{ct\sqrt{\Lambda/3}} + \frac{1}{2}\sqrt{\frac{3}{\Lambda}} e^{-ct\sqrt{\Lambda/3}} = \sqrt{\frac{3}{\Lambda}} \cosh\left(ct\sqrt{\frac{\Lambda}{3}}\right)$$

This model is unusual because it lacks matter and ordinary energy and, at $t = 0$, $S$ starts at $S(0) = \sqrt{3/\Lambda}$ and exponentially expands in deep time. This is a simple example of the generation of cosmological models.

## Modeling the Cosmos

The physics and history of the first one second of the universe is mostly conjectural. At times less than $10^{-4}$ seconds after the big bang the physics of the universe is purely speculative. To understand events occurring at earlier times would require a better understanding of quark-gluon plasmas and unification of the forces of nature.[1] Radiation pressure played a major role in the early evolution of the universe. Fusion, for example, caused radiation pressure, which affected $S(t)$. A few hundred thousand years after the big bang, the universe became transparent to radiation and has been transparent ever since. The amount of time since the big bang is approximately twelve to eighteen billion years. Throughout most of that time, electromagnetic radiation pressure has been negligible in comparison to matter density so setting the pressure equal to zero in equation (21.6) can approximate the general evolution of the universe. (To model earlier times in the universe, the pressure must be non-zero.) If we set the pressure to zero, equation (21.6) becomes:

$$2S\ddot{S} + \dot{S}^2 + kc^2 - \Lambda S^2 c^2 = 0$$

Integrating this equation with respect to time gives:

$$S\dot{S}^2 + Skc^2 - \Lambda c^2 S^3/3 = \mathbb{E}_0$$

Here $\mathbb{E}_0$ is a constant of integration. After factoring out $S$ on the left-hand side of this equation, we get:

$$S\left( \dot{S}^2 + kc^2 - \Lambda c^2 S^2/3 \right) = \mathbb{E}_0$$

21.14

By equation (21.5), the parenthesized expression on the left side is $8\pi G\rho S^2/3c^2$. Subsituting it into equation (21.14) results in the equation:

[1] See Chapter Twenty-Two for discussion of grand unification.

$$\mathbb{E}_0 = \frac{8\pi G}{3c^2} \rho S^3$$

Because $p = 0$, equation (21.7) simplifies to $0 = d(\rho S^3)/dt$. After integration it becomes:

$$\rho_0 S_0^3 = \rho S^3$$

Thus matter density decreases in a manner inversely proportional to the cube of $S$. We would expect this, because as the size of the universe doubles its volume increases eight times, and matter density decreases to one eighth of what it was. The constant $\mathbb{E}_0$ can loosely be thought of as the "matter" of the universe. (Of course, this is not strictly correct, because mass is relative, $S$ is a scale factor, objects in the universe move with cosmic expansion, and so on.) The constant $\mathbb{E}_0$ can be calculated in terms of present time quantities by letting $S = S_0$:

$$\mathbb{E}_0 = \frac{8\pi G}{3c^2} \rho_0 S_0^3 = \frac{8\pi G}{3} \mathbb{M}_0$$

21.15

Solving (21.14) for $\dot{S}^2$ gives:

$$\dot{S}^2 = \frac{\mathbb{E}_0}{S} + \frac{\Lambda c^2 S^2}{3} - kc^2$$

21.16

This equation allows calculation of $S(t)$ if the constants $\mathbb{E}_0$, $k$ and $\Lambda$ is known.

We do not yet know whether $\Lambda \neq 0$. The mechanism and nature of a non-zero cosmological constant are not understood at present, but it is thought that such a cosmological term would result from some kind of new quantum property. Understanding how energy enters and exits the vacuum would help to explain a non-zero cosmological term or a time-varying cosmological-like term. Depending on how energy flows in and out of the vacuum, it may be that there is a varying cosmological term $\Lambda(t)$—presently called *quintessence*— but this is speculation. Perhaps small wormholes transport energy from some other location, making a non-zero cosmological term or quintessence, but, again, no one really knows. There is some evidence, presently being explored by astronomers and cosmologists, that a non-zero cosmological term or a quintessence may apply to the real universe. But because there is no known mechanism in physics to explain a non-zero cosmological term or quintessence, it is possible that $\Lambda = 0$. With no pressure, with $p = 0$, and with the cosmological term zero, equation (21.16) reduces to the Friedmann model with no pressure:

$$\dot{S}^2 = \frac{\mathbb{E}_0}{S} - kc^2$$

21.17

Even with the Friedmann models, the value of $k$ ($-1, 0,$ or $+1$) is still undecided.

Cosmological models obeying equation (21.17) have several properties. If the average density of the universe is *less than* a critical density, then its global space-time curvature is negative—shaped rather like a saddle—and the universe will expand forever, asymptotically approaching some constant speed. And if this is true, the universe contains infinite volume. If the average density of the universe is *exactly equal to* the critical density, then its global space-time structure is like a flat surface, and it will expand forever, with speed of expansion asymptotically approaching zero. A flat universe would also have infinite volume. If the average density of the universe is *greater than* the critical density, the global space-time curvature is positive, like the surface of a sphere. It will expand to a maximum size, momentarily halt, and then re-contract to a big crunch. A universe with positive global curvature would have finite volume and a finite lifetime between big bang and big crunch.

To find the critical density, let $k = 0$ for flat space, so that equation (21.17) becomes:

$$\dot{S}^2 = \frac{\mathbb{E}_0}{S} = \frac{8\pi G}{3} \rho_c S^2$$

Here $\rho_c = \rho / c^2$ is the critical mass density, also called *closure density*. Dividing both sides of this equation by $S^2$, and remembering the equation $H^2 = (\dot{S}^2 / S^2)$, the critical density at any cosmic time is:

$$\rho_c = \frac{3H^2}{8\pi G}$$

21.18

As mentioned earlier, it is customary to denote all variables at the present epoch with a subscript $_0$. At the present epoch the critical density is $\rho_{c0} = 3H_0^2/8\pi G$. Once Hubble's constant is known, the critical density can be calculated by (21.18), and then it is simply a matter of observing the amount of matter in the universe to see if it falls above or below $\rho_{c0}$. Astronomers are still divided as to the present-day value of Hubble's constant. A tentative consensus places it between sixty and eighty kilometers per second per megaparsec. Others argue for a lower value: around fifty kilometers per second per megaparsec, or possibly less.

Studies of galaxies show that there is much more mass both in galaxies and in galaxy clusters than is indicated by visible light. Estimates of this unknown matter, or *dark matter*, place the density of the universe anywhere from one-third to one-half the critical density. Interestingly, the critical density is proportional to the *square* of Hubble's constant. If estimates of Hubble's constant are cut in half, the density needed to close the universe falls to one quarter of its previous value. A reduction of Hubble's constant from seventy to fifty cuts critical density approximately in half. Therefore the density of the universe may be very near the critical density, and the observable universe is nearly flat. Observations of fluctuations in the cosmic background radiation imply that the universe is extremely close to the critical density. In this case the observable universe makes up only a small portion of the whole universe. The true size of the universe is not known but could easily be trillions of times the distance from earth to the farthest observed galaxy.

If the observable universe is indeed very nearly flat then the global shape of the whole universe is something that could be determined if it were possible to see far beyond the most distant observable galaxy, perhaps a billion trillion light years or more. However, it is not possible to see that far because light from those far regions has not yet arrived on earth. Further, because of the tremendous distances and the expansion of space, it would take a comparable amount of time for light from those distant regions to reach the earth. How, then, did the big bang push those regions so far away that no light from them has yet reached the earth? In general relativity, space can expand at speeds far greater than the speed of light. This does not contradict special relativity, because as space expands at those speeds, light in those regions moves with the space. In fact, at the big bang, space could expand infinitely fast which can be seen in the cosmological models below.

If the observable universe is very nearly flat, then it is useful to look at the equations for flat cosmological space. The case where $k = 0$, a flat universe, is called the *Einstein-DeSitter model*. We can easily find $S(t)$:

$$\left(\frac{dS}{dt}\right)^2 = \frac{\mathbb{E}_0}{S}$$

$$\int_0^t \sqrt{\mathbb{E}_0}\,dt = \int_0^S \sqrt{S}\,dt$$

$$t\sqrt{\mathbb{E}_0} = \frac{2}{3}S^{3/2}$$

At the present epoch $t_0$, the size and time of the universe are related by $t_0\sqrt{\mathbb{E}_0} = (2/3)S_0^{3/2}$. The relationship between the present epoch and an arbitrary epoch is just the ratio between these:

$$\frac{S}{S_0} = \left(\frac{t}{t_0}\right)^{2/3}$$

The age of an Einstein-DeSitter universe can be found by differentiating this equation with respect to time, setting $t = t_0$, and solving for $t_0$. This gives $t_0 = (2/3)(1/H_0)$.

## The Friedmann Models

The Friedmann models are governed by the equations in (21.5) and (21.6), with the cosmological term set to zero. With zero pressure, these models are described by the following equations:

$$\frac{\dot{S}^2 + kc^2}{S^2} = \frac{8\pi G}{3c^2}\rho$$

21.19

$$\frac{2S\,\ddot{S}+\dot{S}^2+kc^2}{S^2}=0$$

21.20

We have already solved the case for flat space, $k = 0$. For an open and closed universe $k = -1$ or $k = +1$, respectively. We can put equations (21.19) and (21.20) in terms of $H$ and $q$. Then, by applying the result to the present era, $H_0$ and $q_0$, it is possible to express $\mathbb{E}_0$ in terms of these quantities. Equation (21.17) then has the general form:

$$\dot{S}^2 = \frac{\mathbb{E}_0\,(H_0,\,q_0)}{S}-kc^2$$

The equations in (21.19) and (21.20) become:

$$\frac{kc^2}{S^2}=H^2\,(2q-1)$$

$$\rho=\frac{3c^2}{8\pi G}\left(H^2+\frac{kc^2}{S^2}\right)$$

Substituting $H^2(2q-1)$ for $kc^2/S^2$ into this last equation leaves:

$$\rho=\frac{3c^2}{4\pi G}\,(H^2 q)$$

21.21

At the present time, $t_0$, these equations are:

$$\rho_0=\frac{3c^2}{4\pi G}\,(H_0^2 q_0)$$

$$S_0^2=\frac{kc^2}{H_0^2\,(2q_0-1)}$$

The present values of $(S,\rho,H,q)$ are given by $(S_0,\rho_0,H_0,q_0)$. The constant $\mathbb{E}_0$ is then calculable, leaving three equations used to calculate Friedmann models with no pressure. They are summarized here:

$$\mathbb{E}_0 (H_0, q_0) = \frac{8\pi G}{3c^2} \rho_0 S_0^3 = \frac{2q_0 c^3}{H_0} \left( \frac{2q_0 - 1}{k} \right)^{-\frac{3}{2}}$$

$$S_0 = \sqrt{\frac{kc^2}{H_0^2 (2q_0 - 1)}}$$

$$\dot{S}^2 = \frac{\mathbb{E}_0}{S} - kc^2$$

$$21.22$$

Solutions to (21.17) will be in terms of the Hubble constant, the deceleration parameter, and no other observational parameters. Equation (21.21) can be substituted into the critical density (21.18) to give the following relation:

$$2q = \frac{\rho}{\rho_c} = \Omega$$

$$21.23$$

This means that there is a simple relation between the deceleration parameter $q$ and the ratio of the density of the universe to its critical density $\Omega$. If $q < \frac{1}{2}$, the universe is open and has negative spatial curvature. If $q = \frac{1}{2}$, the universe is flat, and if $q > \frac{1}{2}$, it has positive curvature and is closed. The value of $k$ will be difficult to obtain from observations if the deceleration parameter is very close to $\frac{1}{2}$.

### *An Open Cosmos* $(k = -1)$

For an open universe, let $k = -1$ and separate variables on equation (21.17) to get:

$$\int_0^S d/ \sqrt{c^2 + \mathbb{E}_0 / S} \, dS = \int_0^t dt$$

Substituting $k = -1$ into the other equations in (21.22) gives:

$$\mathbb{E}_0 = \frac{2q_0 c^3}{H_0} (1 - 2q_0)^{-\frac{3}{2}} \qquad\qquad S_0 = \sqrt{\frac{c^2}{H_0^2 (1 - 2q_0)}}$$

$$21.24$$

From these, we solve for $t(S)$, the inverse of the function $S(t)$. Equation (21.17), with $k = -1$, can be integrated by a variable substitution $x = \text{Arctan}\left(\sqrt{c^2 S/\mathbb{E}_0}\right)$, which leaves an easy integral in trigonometric functions. The final result is:

$$t = \frac{\mathbb{E}_0}{c^3}\left[\sqrt{1+\frac{c^2 S}{\mathbb{E}_0}}\sqrt{\frac{c^2 S}{\mathbb{E}_0}} - \log_e\left|\sqrt{1+\frac{c^2 S}{\mathbb{E}_0}}+\sqrt{\frac{c^2 S}{\mathbb{E}_0}}\right|\right]$$

This equation can be solved for the present time by letting all occurrences of $S$ become $S_0$, letting all occurrences of $t$ become $t_0$ (the present time), and substituting the expression for $\mathbb{E}_0 (H_0, q_0)$ of (21.24). After simplifying, the result is:

$$t_0 = \frac{1}{H_0}\left[\frac{1}{(1-2q_0)} - \frac{q_0}{(1-2q_0)^{3/2}}\log_e\left|\frac{1-q_0+\sqrt{1-2q_0}}{q_0}\right|\right]$$

21.25

If the universe is open, its age can be found from the present-day value of the Hubble constant and the deceleration parameter.

## A Closed Cosmos $(k = +1)$

To calculate $t(S)$ for a closed universe, let $k = +1$ in the three equations for (21.22), and separate variables on (21.17) to get:

$$\int_0^S d\!\left/\sqrt{-c^2 + \mathbb{E}_0/S}\right. \, dS = \int_0^t dt$$

The equations in (21.22) become:

$$\mathbb{E}_0 = \frac{2q_0 c^3}{H_0}(2q_0 - 1)^{-3/2} \qquad S_0 = \sqrt{\frac{c^2}{H_0^2(2q_0 - 1)}}$$

21.26

The variable substitution $x \doteq \text{Arcsin}\left(\sqrt{c^2 S/\mathbb{E}_0}\right)$ leaves an integral in sines and cosines, which easily integrates to:

$$t = \frac{\mathbb{E}_0}{c^3} \left[ \text{Arcsin}\left(\sqrt{\frac{c^2 S}{\mathbb{E}_0}}\right) - \sqrt{\frac{c^2 S}{\mathbb{E}_0}} \sqrt{1 - \frac{c^2 S}{\mathbb{E}_0}} \right]$$

21.27

Solving for the amount of time since the big bang $t_0$, let all occurrences of $t$ become $t_0$, let all occurrences of $S$ become $S_0$, and substitute all values from (21.26) into the equation above to get:

$$t_0 = \frac{1}{H_0} \left[ \frac{2q_0}{(2q_0 - 1)^{3/2}} \text{Arcsin}\left(\sqrt{\frac{2q_0 - 1}{2q_0}}\right) - \frac{1}{(2q_0 - 1)} \right]$$

From basic double angle formulas in trigonometry,

$2\,\text{Arcsin}\,(F) = \text{Arccos}\,(1 - 2F^2)$.

Thus $2\,\text{Arcsin}\left(\sqrt{(2q_0 - 1)/(2q_0)}\right) = \text{Arccos}\left((1 - q_0)/q_0\right)$, and the equation above is rewritten as:

$$t_0 = \frac{1}{H_0} \left[ \frac{q_0}{(2q_0 - 1)^{3/2}} \text{Arccos}\left(\frac{1 - q_0}{q_0}\right) - \frac{1}{(2q_0 - 1)} \right]$$

21.28

For a closed cosmos, the time since the big bang $t_0$ is found from the present-day values of the Hubble constant and deceleration parameter. A closed Friedmann universe will eventually expand to a maximum size, halt momentarily, and then contract to a big crunch. What, then, is the size of the universe as it momentarily halts before contracting, $S_{Halt}$, and how much time exists between the big bang and this momentary halting? From equation (21.17), the universe halts when $\dot{S} = 0$. Therefore, setting this term of (21.17) to zero makes it easy to solve for $S$:

$$S_{Halt} = \frac{\mathbb{E}_0}{c^2} = \frac{2q_0 c}{H_0}(2q_0 - 1)^{-3/2}$$

To find $t_{Halt}$, substitute $S_{Halt} = \mathbb{E}_0/c^2$ into (21.27) to get:

$$t_{Halt} = \frac{\pi \mathbb{E}_0}{2c^3} = \frac{\pi q_0}{H_0}(2q_0 - 1)^{-3/2}$$

The total time from big bang to big crunch is $2t_{Halt}$ or:

$$\mathbb{T}_0 = \frac{2\pi q_0}{H_0}(2q_0 - 1)^{-3/2}$$

21.29

These cosmological models show how general relativity governs the behavior of the entire universe.

## General Cosmology

The quantity $1/H_0$, called the *Hubble time*, is an upper limit for the age of the universe in the Friedmann models. It is the amount of time that would have elapsed since the big bang if all galaxies had always traveled at their present speed. In all Friedmann models the galaxies must have traveled faster in the past because they were closer together then, and all had to climb out of the gravity field of the rest of the universe. Another interesting property of the Friedmann models, alluded to earlier, is that if the deceleration parameter is very close to ½ it is difficult to determine whether the universe is open, flat, or closed. If $q_0$ is close to ½, direct experimental determination of global cosmological curvature is very difficult. An indirect way to estimate $q_0$ is to make an estimate of the density of the universe and divide that by twice the critical density.

The evolution of the universe is governed by the total amount of matter it contains. Astronomical observations suggest that the amount of matter in the universe may be anywhere from ten to one hundred times greater than the luminous matter of galaxies. Cosmological models must take into account the fact that galaxies and groups of galaxies have more dark matter than luminous matter. At present it is not known what dark matter is. It may consist of black holes, neutron stars, white dwarfs, scores of Jupiter-like worlds, or something completely unknown. Energy may also reside in the vacuum, the physics of which is also poorly understood at present because there is no grand unified field theory to explain the complete physics of the cosmos. According to quantum field theory, the energy density of the vacuum should be infinite, which would mean that the mass energy residing in a single cubic centimeter would be infinite. Even if it were not infinite, the energy density of the vacuum could be on the order of the *Planck density*, the density range where quantum fluctuations may have strengths comparable to those of black holes. Even this energy density is far too high in comparison to what has actually been observed. If all matter in the observable universe were collapsed to something reaching the Planck density, its size would be comparable to that of about two proton volumes. Such a high vacuum energy contradicts ordinary experience, and even atoms could not exist in that situation. Perhaps there are huge energy densities of this kind in every cubic centimeter of space, but, for physical reasons not yet understood, we simply do not feel them. If so, perhaps the vacuum energy is not actually at its lowest energy level, its true zero point. It may appear to be at its lowest level because the energy density of subatomic particles may be greater than the energy density of the vacuum. And if there were a mechanism allowing some of that energy to be felt suddenly by the cosmos, it could cause the expansion rate of the universe to accelerate. It might behave like a cosmological constant or a time-varying quintessence.

None of this is as far-fetched as it sounds. Remember that only two protons'-worth of this dense Planck energy could double the energy of the entire observable universe! Something similar may have happened in the very early universe: the vacuum dumped huge quantities of its energy into the young universe, causing it to undergo cosmic inflation. What if the energy density of the vacuum were infinite, as quantum theory suggests, but is unfelt by the universe? And what if that infinite energy reserve could eternally dump its energy into the universe, in the form of a cosmological constant, for example? This would mean that the universe would expand exponentially faster throughout an infinite amount of time. An infinite number of years from now, the universe would be infinitely large, expanding infinitely fast, with the galaxies infinitely far apart from each other. As strange as these possibilities sound, some scientists are considering them more seriously. The answer to these questions awaits further astronomical observations and the final grand unification of physics. Einstein's discovery of general relativity, making possible an understanding of the entire cosmos, is one of the greatest triumphs in all science.

## Exercises

(For these exercises, the Hubble constant of 70 corresponds
to $2.27 \times 10^{-18} 1/\text{sec}$)

1.  For an open universe where $k = -1$, find $S(t)$, given that $\rho = p = 0$, $\Lambda > 0$. Do this same calculation for a DeSitter (flat) universe.

2.  Let $S(t)$ be given. Expand $S(t_0 - \tau)$, with $\tau = t_0 - t$, into a Taylor series, and substitute the definition of $H_0 = \dot{S}(t_0) \big/ S(t_0)$ to derive the deceleration parameter. Based on this result, give a physical interpretation of the deceleration parameter.

3.  When the universe was one-third its present size, a neutron star, traveling at one-half the speed of light at an angle of 30 degrees, emitted radiation of a given wavelength. If the star's radius is 10 km and its mass $2.0 \times 10^{30}$ kg, what is the $z$-value for that radiation received on the earth today?

4.  Calculate the age of a flat Friedmann universe with a Hubble constant of 70 and then calculate its age for a Hubble constant of 50 and 60.

5.  For a Friedmann universe at ten percent of the critical density, calculate the age of the universe for the following values of the Hubble constant: $50, 60, 70$ and $80$.

6.  For a Friedmann universe with $\rho_0 = (101/100)\rho_{c0}$, calculate its age for $H_0 = 40, 50, 60, 70$, and $80$.

7.  Assuming that the present density of the universe is twice the critical density $\rho_0 = 2\rho_{c0}$, calculate the age of the universe for the values of $H_0 = 50, 60$, and $70$. For each of these present-day values of Hubble's constant, how much time is there between big bang and big crunch?

8.  Suppose the universe is just barely closed. For the values of $H_0 = 50$ and $70$, calculate the time between big bang and big crunch for each of the relations between the current density of the universe and the critical density: $\rho_0 = \rho_{c0}(1+10^{-4})$, $\rho_0 = \rho_{c0}(1+10^{-60})$, $\rho_0 = \rho_{c0}(1+10^{-600})$.

9.  Consider a type of time-varying vacuum energy, "quintessence", with the property $\rho = p$ in a negatively curved universe $k = -1$ and a zero classical cosmological constant $\Lambda = 0$. Assume that the universe has only this vacuum energy. What is $S(t)$? (Hint: assume that the form of $S(t)$ is given by $\sigma t^p$, where $\sigma$ and $p$ are constants.)

10. Consider a positively closed universe with a zero cosmological constant $\Lambda = 0$ and with pressure related to density by the equation $p = -\rho/3$. What are $S(t)$ and $\rho(t)$? What is $\dot{S}/S$ ?

11. Imagine a universe lacking all matter and energy, $(p = \rho = 0)$, except for a time-varying vacuum energy that varies according to the formula below. Let $\Lambda_0$ and $S_0$ be constants. Find $S(t)$ for an open, flat, and closed universe.

$$\Lambda = \Lambda_0 \left( \frac{S_0}{S} \right)^2$$

12. From the metric in (21.1), calculate the affine connection in (21.2).

13. Calculate (21.3) from (21.2). Then, using (21.4), derive (21.5) and (21.6).

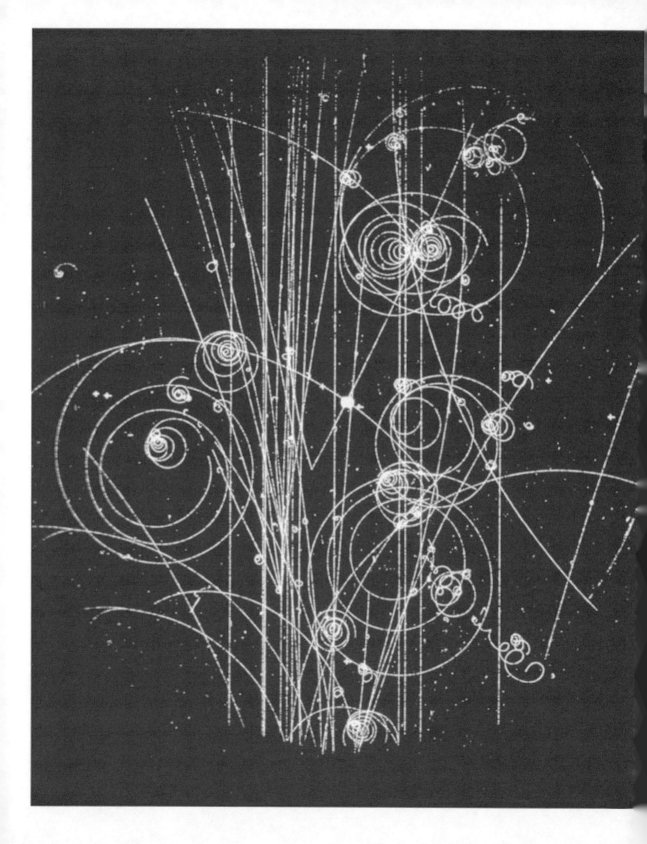

# PART 7

## *The Forces of Nature*

# CHAPTER 22

## *Grand Unification*

THE SUCCESS OF RELATIVITY theory lies not only in the fact that its predictions have been confirmed by experiment, but also in its conceptual simplicity. All of special relativity can be deduced from two simple laws of nature. Likewise, the whole of general relativity, which assumes the truth of special relativity and builds upon it, can be deduced from the principles of equivalence and of general relativity. However, the mathematics embodying curved space-time is fairly involved, as the reader no doubt observes. The shapes that space-time can assume are functions of the properties of matter and energy.

If, for example, the existence of negative mass-energy is allowed, it is possible in general relativity to shape space-time in such a way as to allow backward time travel. To avoid self-contradictions in physical theory, it can simply be assumed that negative mass energy, or negative inertia, does not exist. But certain quantum effects and electrical binding effects can be interpreted as resulting from negative energy density. Even without these, backward time travel cannot be completely ruled out, as global solutions to general relativity may still have closed time-like curves. Therefore, the question of backward time travel is strictly an open issue.

The ultimate character of the whole of space-time is determined by the properties of mass-energy, which, it is presently thought, will be completely uncovered by a grand unified field theory of the forces of nature. One question that concerned Einstein was whether the relativity theory was complete. Although the special and general theories produce a metric that tells the shape of space-time, the metric itself seems to exist as an absolute structure. As Einstein studied the question of relativity's completeness, he turned to *Mach's principle:* the idea that the local properties of matter and energy are functions of the distribution of all mass-energy. (The inertial mass of an object, for example, is determined by all other masses in the universe.) Einstein thought that incorporating Mach's principle would make relativity more complete. If such a "universal theory of relativity" could be formed, then the present theory of relativity is only two-thirds complete. But Einstein abandoned this approach, apparently thinking that the theory need not be extended in this way. He spent the remaining thirty years of his life working in a different direction: trying to unite general relativity to electromagnetism. He failed in this attempt, as has everyone else to date.

The idea that gravity and electromagnetism may be united in a broader theory follows naturally from the history of scientific thought. Maxwell united the electric force to the magnetic force and then related these two to light, showing that light, electricity, and magnetism are three different manifestations of the same thing. With special relativity, Einstein united space to time (the four dimensional world of space-time) and with general relativity he united space-time to gravity (the curvature of four-dimensional space-time). Thus he showed that space, time, and gravity are three different manifestations of the curved four-dimensional space-time. Einstein did for space, time, and gravity what Maxwell had done for light, electricity, and magnetism. If general relativity could now be united to electromagnetism, then the quantites they each unite would be six different manifestations of one underlying reality. Actually, the unification is more comprehensive than this: relativity also unites mass to energy, for example, showing they are two different aspects of the same thing.

The problem of unifying all of the forces of nature is complicated by the fact that quantum mechanics needs to be incorporated into the grand unified field theory. Quantum field theories describe the electromagnetic force, the weak nuclear force, and the strong nuclear force. The electromagnetic force is described by quantum electrodynamics and the weak nuclear force is described by the Electro-weak theory, (which also subsumes quantum electro-dynamics). Quantum chromodynamics accounts for the strong nuclear force, as well as the structure of subatomic particles. All of these field theories are strongly supported by experiment. The only remaining undetected particle in the Electro-weak theory is the Electro-weak Higgs boson, which mediates mass in Electro-weak interactions. Its rest mass is not predicted by the Electro-weak theory, just as the rest masses of quarks and leptons are not predicted by quantum chromodynamics. The so far mentioned field theories do not say whether magnetic monopoles exist, nor do they give predictions for their rest masses if they do exist.

These field theories, clearly not yet complete, are probably approximations of a larger unified field theory. Such a theory will explain how energy can flow into and out of the vacuum and illuminate all the details of vacuum energies. It will uniquely predict all the masses, charges, spins, and other properties of subatomic particles, as well as uniquely predict all the constants of nature. So far such a theory has not yet been found, but there have been many speculative candidates over the past few decades. The favored candidate at present is the *super string theory*, which holds that subatomic particles are tiny loops of energy, analogous to loops of string. It is hoped that the grand unified field theory will be found and, if history is any guide, people should be wise enough to discover it.

One problem may arise if several grand unified theories were put forward, all of which made the same low energy predictions (that is predictions testable in present day particle accelerators) but made different predictions at energies far higher than could ever be achieved terrestrially. Perhaps some day a particle accelerator will be built on the surface of the moon so that its length equals the circumference of the moon. Such a "lunar collider" would be able to probe matter at a far higher energy scale than any particle accelerator existing today but it would not help at very high energies. To test between competing theories, which make different high-energy predictions, a particle accelerator many light years in length would need to be built. A particle accelerator of that size will probably never be built so how would scientists test between competing theories? It is not known if, or how, difficulties of this kind could be overcome. Science may be approaching insurmountable barriers but what relativity and quantum theory shows is certain: the cosmos is accessible to the mind.

# APPENDIX A

## *Newtonian Orbits*

To CALCULATE THE ORBIT of a small mass $m_*$ around a much larger mass $M$, it is useful to express the path in polar coordinates $r(\theta)$, with mass $M$ at the origin. The acceleration vector of $m_*$ can be written as the sum of two vectors in the x-direction and y-direction or as the sum of two vectors in the r-direction and $\theta$-direction: $\bar{a} = \bar{a}_x + \bar{a}_y = \bar{a}_r + \bar{a}_\theta$ .

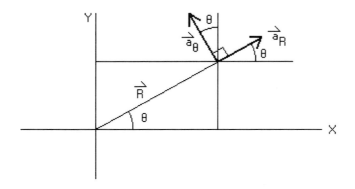

From this diagram, the relationships between the magnitudes of the two decompositions of $\bar{a}$ can easily be seen. Let $a_x, a_y, a_r$, and $a_\theta$ be the magnitudes of the vectors mentioned above. Then the acceleration can be expressed solely as a function of $a_r$ and $a_\theta$:

$$\bar{a} = (a_x, a_y)$$
$$\bar{a} = (a_r \cos\theta - a_\theta \sin\theta, \ a_\theta \cos\theta + a_r \sin\theta)$$
$$\bar{a} = a_\theta (-\sin\theta, \cos\theta) + a_r (\cos\theta, \sin\theta) \qquad \text{A-1}$$

The path in Cartesian coordinates is given by the well-known formula ($r\cos\theta$, $r\sin\theta$), and the coordinates $r$ and $\theta$ are both given as functions of time: $r(t), \theta(t)$. Differentiating $\bar{r} = (r\cos\theta, \ r\sin\theta)$ twice with respect to time gives the acceleration:

$$\bar{a} = \frac{d^2 \bar{r}}{dt^2}$$

$$\bar{a} = \left[ r \frac{d^2\theta}{dt^2} + 2 \frac{dr}{dt} \frac{d\theta}{dt} \right] (-\sin\theta, \cos\theta) + \left[ \frac{d^2 r}{dt^2} - r \left( \frac{d\theta}{dt} \right)^2 \right] (\cos\theta, \sin\theta)$$

Comparing this equation with equation (A-1) shows that acceleration in the $\theta$-direction is given by $a_\theta = r(d^2\theta/dt^2) + 2(dr/dt)(d\theta/dt)$. For a purely radial (or central) force, $a_\theta = 0$ because there is no force in the $\theta$-direction. Setting $a_\theta = 0$, multiplying both sides by $r$, and then factoring gives the following equation:

$$r^2 \frac{d^2\theta}{dt^2} + 2r \frac{dr}{dt} \frac{d\theta}{dt} = \frac{d}{dt} \left( r^2 \frac{d\theta}{dt} \right) = 0$$

Integrating this equation gives:

$$r^2 \frac{d\theta}{dt} = \frac{L_*}{m_*} \qquad \text{A-2}$$

The constant $L_*/m_*$ is the angular momentum of $m_*$ divided by the mass $m_*$, relative to the center of the coordinate system $r = 0$. The tangential speed of $m_*$, $v_T$, is given by $rd\theta/dt$, and equation (A-2) becomes $m_*v_Tr = L_*$. This is just the conservation of angular momentum which simply means the tangential speed of $m_*$ is inversely proportional to the radial distance for purely central forces. Because of this, Kepler's second law holds true. Kepler's second law is the conservation of angular momentum in an unusual guise. To calculate the path followed by $m_*$ around $M$, suppose that $m_*$ is at a distance $r_0$ from the origin and travels at a speed of $v_0$ perpendicular to $r_0$:

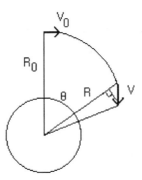

The mass $m_*$ travels on some curved path freely falling in the vacuum, and has some speed $v$ at a new radial distance $r$. From the conservation of energy we can calculate $v$:

$$\frac{1}{2}m_*v^2 = \frac{1}{2}m_*v_0^2 + \int_{r_0}^{r} f(r)dr$$

A-3

This equation is not sufficient to establish $r(\theta)$, but with the conservation of angular momentum $r(\theta)$ is uniquely fixed, as is the tangential speed $v_T$. Because $v$ is established by equation (A-3), the radial speed $v_r$ can be found by the Pythagorean theorem:

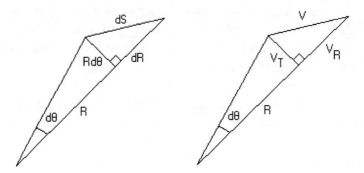

The conservation of angular momentum demands that $m_*rv_T = m_*r_0v_0 = L_*$. Therefore $v_T = r_0v_0/r$, and $v_T$ can be expressed as a function of $v$ by the Pythagorean theorem $(rd\theta)^2 + (dr)^2 = (ds)^2$ and by similar triangles $v_T/v = rd\theta/ds$:

$$v_T = v\left(\frac{rd\theta}{ds}\right) = v\left[\frac{1}{\sqrt{1+\dfrac{1}{r^2}\left(\dfrac{dr}{d\theta}\right)^2}}\right]$$

The equation $rv_T = r_0v_0$ becomes:

$$\frac{vr}{\sqrt{1+\dfrac{1}{r^2}\left(\dfrac{dr}{d\theta}\right)^2}} = v_0r_0$$

Solving for $d\theta/dr$ and integrating gives:

$$\theta = \int_{r_0}^{r}\left(\frac{v_0r_0}{vr^2}\frac{1}{\sqrt{1-\left(v_0^2r_0^2/v^2r^2\right)}}\right)dr$$

A-4

Substituting $f(r) = -GMm_*/r^2$ into equation (A-3) and solving for $v$ gives the formula:

$$v = \sqrt{v_0^2 + \frac{2GM}{r} - \frac{2GM}{r_0}}$$

A-5

Substituting equation (A-5) into (A-4) expresses (A-4) solely as a function of $r$. Completing the square gives:

$$\theta = \int_{r_0}^{r} \left[ \frac{1/r^2}{\sqrt{\left(\frac{1}{r_0} - \frac{GM}{v_0^2 r_0^2}\right)^2 - \left(\frac{1}{r} - \frac{GM}{v_0^2 r_0^2}\right)^2}} \right] dr$$

$$\theta = \text{Arcsin}\,(1) - \text{Arcsin} \left[ \frac{\frac{1}{r} - \frac{GM}{v_0^2 r_0^2}}{\frac{1}{r_0} - \frac{GM}{v_0^2 r_0^2}} \right]$$

Now, $\sin(\text{Arcsin}(1) - \theta) = \cos\theta$. So, after substituting this, the above equation above can be solved for $r$:

$$r(\theta) = \frac{r_0}{\left(1 - \frac{GM}{r_0 v_0^2}\right)\cos\theta + \frac{GM}{r_0 v_0^2}}$$

A-6

The point of closest approach between $m_*$ and $M$ can be found by differentiating this equation with respect to $\theta$ and setting the result equal to zero. Solving for the angle gives the point of closest approach, or perigee, which will be at $r = r_0$. The equation in (A-6) gives conic sections and for elliptical orbits the eccentricity is $e = \left(r_0 v_0^2/GM\right) - 1$. This proves Kepler's first law because $M$ is at the origin. Equation (A-6) can be expressed in terms of $e$:

$$r(\theta) = \frac{v_0^2 r_0^2}{GM(1 + e\cos\theta)}$$

Assume that $r_0$ is the point of closest approach for an elliptical orbit (*i.e.*, perigee). Then $r = r_0$ when $\theta = 0$. The apogee will be at $\theta = 180°$ and its distance from the origin is $r_*$, then perigee and apogee are given by the following equations:

$$r_0 = \frac{v_0^2 r_0^2 / GM}{1 + e}$$

$$r_* = \frac{v_0^2 r_0^2 / GM}{1 - e}$$

The semi-major axis, $a$, for an ellipse is defined as the average of these two:

$$a = \frac{r_0 + r_*}{2} = \frac{v_0^2 r_0^2 / GM}{1 - e^2}$$

A-7

The total area of an ellipse with eccentricity $e$ is:

$$A_{ellipse} = \pi a^2 \sqrt{1 - e^2} = \pi \frac{v_0^4 r_0^4 / G^2 M^2}{(1 - e^2)^{3/2}}$$

A-8

Over a differential element of time, $dt$, the triangular area swept out at perigee is:

$$dA = \frac{1}{2}(r_0)(v_0 dt)$$

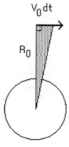

According to Kepler's second law, the rate at which area is swept out is constant, and was just calculated:

$$\frac{dA}{dt} = \frac{r_0 v_0}{2} = \omega_0$$

A-9

Therefore, the time for completion of one elliptical orbit must be equal to the area of the ellipse divided by the constant rate at which area is swept out, or equation (A-8) divided by equation (A-9):

$$\mathbb{T} = \frac{A_{ellipse}}{(r_0 v_0 / 2)} = 2\pi \frac{v_0^3 r_0^3 / G^2 M^2}{(1 - e^2)^{3/2}}$$

Squaring both sides of this equation and substituting in equation (A-7) gives Kepler's third law:

$$\mathbb{T}^2 = \frac{4\pi^2}{GM} a^3$$

A-10

This proves Kepler's third law.

# APPENDIX B

# *The Electromagnetic Spectrum*

| *Type of Light* | *Range of Wavelength* | | |
|---|---|---|---|
| Radio Waves | INFINITY | to | $3.00 \times 10^{-1}$ meters |
| Microwaves | $3.00 \times 10^{-1}$ | to | $1.00 \times 10^{-3}$ meters |
| Infrared Light | $1.00 \times 10^{-3}$ | to | $7.60 \times 10^{-7}$ meters |
| Visible Light | $7.60 \times 10^{-7}$ | to | $3.80 \times 10^{-7}$ meters |
| Ultraviolet Light | $3.80 \times 10^{-7}$ | to | $1.00 \times 10^{-8}$ meters |
| X-Rays | $1.00 \times 10^{-8}$ | to | $1.00 \times 10^{-11}$ meters |
| Gamma Rays | $1.00 \times 10^{-11}$ | to | ZERO meters |

# APPENDIX C

# *Differential Geometry for General Relativity*

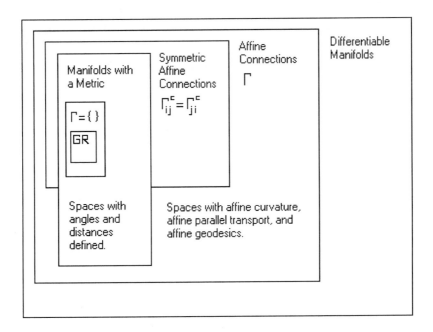

THE GENERAL NOTION of a space is embodied in the idea of a *differentiable manifold*. Of all possible differentiable manifolds, a subset of them have affine connections, called *affine manifolds*. Of all possible affine manifolds, a subset of them are symmetric and are called *symmetric affine manifolds*. Any space with an affine connection has affine curvature, affine geodesics, and affine parallel transport, but for a space to have distances and angles defined it must also have a metric. Manifolds with a metric are called *Riemannian manifolds*. For Riemannian manifolds consider affine spaces with an affine connection equal to the Christoffel symbols of the second kind $\Gamma = \{\ \}$. Of all possible spaces with $\Gamma = \{\ \}$, some subset of them contain all possible solutions to general relativity, indicated in the chart by GR.

It is possible to have a symmetric affine connection a function of the metric, other than $\{\ \}$, but these require that the covariant derivative of the metric is non-zero: $g_{ij;k} \neq 0$. The only symmetric affine connection compatible with $g_{ij;k} = 0$ is the Christoffel symbols of the second kind. It is also possible to have a non-symmetric affine connection, which is a function of the metric, yet satisfies $g_{ij;k} = 0$ but these come with constraints.[1] These bizarre spaces do not apply to general relativity. General relativity takes place solely within spaces described by $\Gamma = \{\ \}$.

[1] See Erwin Schrödinger, *Space-Time Structure*, p. 63, or Hermann Weyl, *Space-Time-Matter*, p.125.

# APPENDIX D

# *Planetary Data*

| Star | Mass (Kilograms) | Polar Radius (Meters) | Equatorial Radius (Meters) | Semi-Major Axis (Meters) | Eccentricity |
|------|------|------|------|------|------|
| Sol | 1.989E+30 | 6.960E+08 | 6.960E+08 | N/A | N/A |

| Planet | Mass (Kilograms) | Polar Radius (Meters) | Equatorial Radius (Meters) | Semi-Major Axis (Meters) | Eccentricity |
|------|------|------|------|------|------|
| Mercury | 3.302E+23 | 2.440E+06 | 2.440E+06 | 5.791E+10 | 0.2056 |
| Venus | 4.869E+24 | 6.052E+06 | 6.052E+06 | 1.082E+11 | 0.0067 |
| Earth | 5.974E+24 | 6.357E+06 | 6.378E+06 | 1.496E+11 | 0.0167 |
| Mars | 6.419E+23 | 3.375E+06 | 3.397E+06 | 2.279E+11 | 0.0935 |
| Jupiter | 1.899E+27 | 6.685E+07 | 7.149E+07 | 7.786E+11 | 0.0489 |
| Saturn | 5.685E+26 | 5.436E+07 | 6.027E+07 | 1.434E+12 | 0.0565 |
| Uranus | 8.683E+25 | 2.497E+07 | 2.556E+07 | 2.872E+12 | 0.0457 |
| Neptune | 1.024E+26 | 2.434E+07 | 2.476E+07 | 4.495E+12 | 0.0113 |
| Pluto | 1.250E+22 | 1.195E+06 | 1.195E+06 | 5.870E+12 | 0.2444 |

| Moon | Mass (Kilograms) | Radius (Meters) | Parent Planet (Name) | Semi-Major Axis (Meters) | Eccentricity |
|---|---|---|---|---|---|
| Luna | 7.349E+22 | 1.737E+06 | Earth | 3.844E+08 | 0.0549 |
| Phobos | 1.060E+16 | 1.120E+04 | Mars | 9.378E+06 | 0.0151 |
| Deimos | 2.400E+15 | 6.100E+03 | Mars | 2.346E+07 | 0.0005 |
| Io | 8.933E+22 | 1.821E+06 | Jupiter | 4.216E+08 | 0.0040 |
| Europa | 4.797E+22 | 1.565E+06 | Jupiter | 6.709E+08 | 0.0090 |
| Ganymede | 1.482E+23 | 2.634E+06 | Jupiter | 1.070E+09 | 0.0020 |
| Callisto | 1.076E+23 | 2.403E+06 | Jupiter | 1.883E+09 | 0.0070 |
| Mimas | 3.750E+19 | 1.987E+05 | Saturn | 1.855E+08 | 0.0202 |
| Enceladus | 7.300E+19 | 2.493E+05 | Saturn | 2.380E+08 | 0.0045 |
| Tethys | 6.220E+20 | 5.300E+05 | Saturn | 2.497E+08 | 0.0000 |
| Dione | 1.100E+21 | 5.600E+05 | Saturn | 3.774E+08 | 0.0022 |
| Rhea | 2.320E+21 | 7.640E+05 | Saturn | 5.270E+08 | 0.0010 |
| Titan | 1.346E+23 | 2.575E+06 | Saturn | 1.222E+09 | 0.0292 |
| Hyperion | 2.000E+19 | 1.460E+05 | Saturn | 1.481E+09 | 0.1042 |
| Iapetus | 1.590E+21 | 7.180E+05 | Saturn | 3.561E+09 | 0.0283 |
| Miranda | 6.600E+19 | 2.357E+05 | Uranus | 1.294E+08 | 0.0027 |
| Ariel | 1.340E+21 | 5.789E+05 | Uranus | 1.910E+08 | 0.0034 |
| Umbriel | 1.170E+21 | 5.847E+05 | Uranus | 2.663E+08 | 0.0050 |
| Titania | 3.520E+21 | 7.889E+05 | Uranus | 4.359E+08 | 0.0022 |
| Oberon | 3.010E+21 | 7.614E+05 | Uranus | 5.835E+08 | 0.0008 |
| Triton | 2.147E+22 | 1.353E+06 | Neptune | 3.548E+08 | 1.6E-05 |
| Nereid | 2.000E+19 | 1.700E+05 | Neptune | 5.513E+09 | 0.7512 |
| Charon | 1.900E+21 | 5.930E+05 | Pluto | 1.960E+07 | 0.0000 |

# APPENDIX E

# *Some Useful Constants of Nature*

## *Electromagnetic Constants*

| | |
|---|---|
| The speed of light ($c$) | $2.99792458 \times 10^8$ m/sec |
| The permittivity constant ($\varepsilon_0$) | $8.85418782 \times 10^{-12}$ C$^2$sec$^2$/kg-m$^3$ |
| The permeability constant ($\mu_0$) | $1.25663706 \times 10^{-6}$ Kg-m/C$^2$ |

## *Atomic Constituents*

| | |
|---|---|
| Electron rest mass ($m_e$) | $9.10938 \times 10^{-31}$ Kg |
| Proton rest mass ($m_p$) | $1.67262 \times 10^{-27}$ Kg |
| Neutron rest mass ($m_n$) | $1.67493 \times 10^{-27}$ Kg |

## *Gravity and Quantum Constants*

| | |
|---|---|
| The gravitational constant ($G$) | $6.67259 \times 10^{-11}$ m$^3$/Kg-sec$^2$ |
| Planck's constant ($h$) | $6.62607 \times 10^{-34}$ Kg-m$^2$/sec |
| Proton and electron charge ($\pm e$) | $1.60218 \times 10^{-19}$ C |

# Answers to Selected Exercises

## Chapter 3

1. ~995m, ~866m, ~493m, ~141m.

2. 99.97998 percent of the speed of light.

3. $6.8873 \times 10^{-5}$ sec.

4. Final result: $\Delta V' = \Delta V \sqrt{1 - v^2/c^2}$

5. ~424.29 years.

6. Two years.

## Chapter 4

1. $(20/29)c$.

2. $(5/19)c$.

3. $\sim \delta_1 \delta_2 / 2c$.

4. $\gamma_{12} \approx 2\gamma_1 \gamma_2$.

5. Final result: $c/n + (1 - 1/n^2)$.

6. $\sqrt{v^2 + u^2 (1 - v^2/c^2)}$ .

7. $L(v)L(w) = I$.

8. Final result: $L(v)L(w) = L[(v + w)/(1 + vw/c^2)]$.

9. Final result: equations (4.18) and (4.19) and the transformations below:

$$x' = \left[ (u_x - v)/(1 - u_x v/c^2) \right] (t' + \gamma v x_0/c^2) + \gamma x_0$$

$$y' = u_y \left[ (t'/\gamma + v x_0/c^2)/(1 - u_x v/c^2) \right] + y_0$$

$$z' = u_z \left[ (t'/\gamma + v x_0/c^2)/(1 - u_x v/c^2) \right] + z_0$$

10. $(-vt', r_0 \sin(v_0 t'/\gamma r_0), r_0 \cos(v_0 t'/\gamma r_0), t')$. *Primed frame:*

$$\left\| d\overline{X'}/dt' \right\| = \sqrt{v^2 (1 - v_0^2/c^2) + v_0^2} \quad \text{when } v_0 = c; \text{ then } \left\| d\overline{X'}/dt' \right\| = c \cdot$$

*Unprimed frame:* $\left\| d\overline{X}/dt \right\| = v_0$ , when $v_0 = c$; then $\left\| d\overline{X}/dt \right\| = c$ .

## Chapter 5

1. $\gamma = (\lambda'^2 + \lambda^2)/2\lambda'\lambda$.

2. $v = c[(\lambda'^2 - \lambda^2)/(\lambda'^2 + \lambda^2)]$.

3. $\theta = \text{Arccos}\left[ (c/v)\sqrt{1 - v^2/c^2} - (c/v) \right]$ .

4. $\lambda' = \gamma\lambda$.

5. $E' = \gamma E$.

6. 0.

7. Time will run slower for the object in circular motion because it is constantly changing inertial frames.

8. $\int \sqrt{1 - v^2/c^2}\, dt$ .

## Chapter 6

1. $\hat{\theta} = (1/2)\log_e\left[(c+v)/(c-v)\right].$

2. $\sqrt{47,200}$ m.

3. $t' = (c/a)\log_e\left[(at/c) + \sqrt{1 + (at/c)^2}\right]$, $x = (c^2/a)\sqrt{1 + (at/c)^2} - (c^2/a).$

4. 299,792,458 m.

5. 0.

6. $\gamma = \cos\theta.$

7. $v = c\sqrt{1 - (dt'/dt)^2}.$

8. $v = c\sqrt{1 - (t_0 k/t)^2}.$

## Chapter 7

1. Final result: equation (7.2)

2. $u(v,n) \approx nv.$

3. $m' \approx 480.39\text{Kg}, p' \approx 1.44 \times 10^{11}$ N-sec.

4. $v = .9999852c.$

5. Approximately $1.00504 m_{earth}, 1.00607 m_{earth}, 1.34164 m_{earth}, 2.1828 m_{earth},$
   $7.124 m_{earth},$

6. $\sim 4.39 \times 10^{18}$ N.

7. $\rho' = \rho\gamma^2.$

8. $v(t) = F_0 t / m\sqrt{1 + (F_0 t/mc)^2}$, $x = (mc^2/F_0)\sqrt{1 + (F_0 t/mc)^2} - (mc^2/F_0).$

9. $F_r = m'v^2/r.$

10. $m(v + w)/\left(\sqrt{1 - v^2/c^2}\sqrt{1 - w^2/c^2}\right).$

## Chapter 8

1. $E_K \approx \frac{1}{2}mv^2.$

2.  18.97406 Kg.

3.  Final result: $dE/dt = mva\gamma^3$.

4.  $E_K = (mc^3/v_0) \operatorname{Arcsin}(v_0/c) - mc^2, mc^2(\operatorname{Arcsin}(1) - 1)$.

5.  Let $p_b = m_b v_b / \sqrt{1 - v_b^2/c^2}$. Then:

$$E = \left( \frac{m_b c^2}{\sqrt{1 - v_b^2/c^2}} - m_b c^2 \right) + m_g c^2 \sqrt{1 + \frac{p_b^2}{m_g^2 c^2}} - m_g c^2$$

6.  Let $K_0 = (E/c^2 + m_1 + m_2)$. Then:

$$v_2 = \frac{\sqrt{(m_2^2 - m_1^2 + K_0^2)^2 - 4(m_2 K_0)^2}}{(m_2^2 - m_1^2 + K_0^2)} c$$

$$v_1 = \frac{m_2 v_2 \gamma_2}{(m_2 \gamma_2 - K_0)}$$

7.  $M_T \approx 2 m_f \gamma_f$.

8.  Let $m$ = the rest mass of the solar sail, let $E$ = the total energy of incoming photons, and let $k$ be a constant of proportionality. $E = kt$ by assumption:

$$v = \left[ \frac{(2E/mc^2 + 1)^2 - 1}{(2E/mc^2 + 1)^2 + 1} \right] c$$

$$\tau = \frac{mc^2}{2k} \log_e \left[ (2kt/mc^2 + 1)^2 + 1 \right] - \frac{mc^2}{2k} \log_e [2]$$

9.  Final result: $E_S = \Delta m_S c^2$.

10. $E_K = (2mc^4/v_0^2) \left[ 1 - \sqrt{1 - v_0^2/c^2} \right] - mc^2, mc^2$.

## Chapter 9

1.  $\mathbf{F} = m'\mathbf{a}$.

2. $v_2 = v_1 r_1 \gamma_1 / \sqrt{r_2^2 + (v_1 r_1 \gamma_1 / c)^2}$ .

3. $\tau = r_0 d(m'v)/dt$.

4. $\boldsymbol{F'} = (-8N/3, 6N, 9N)$.

5. $mvr \sin\theta / \sqrt{1 - v^2/c^2}$ , where $\theta$ is the angle between $\boldsymbol{p}$ and $\boldsymbol{r}$.

6. No.

7. One way to prove these is by substitution.

## Chapter 10

1. Final result:

$$\iint \bar{E} \bullet d\bar{S} = q/\varepsilon_0$$

$$c^2 \int \bar{B} \bullet d\bar{l} - \frac{d\Phi_E}{dt} = i/\varepsilon_0$$

$$c^2 \iint \bar{B} \bullet d\bar{S} = q_m/\varepsilon_0$$

$$-c^2 \int \bar{E} \bullet d\bar{l} - c^2 \frac{d\Phi_B}{dt} = i_m/\varepsilon_0$$

2. Final result: equations (10.21), but with time not set to zero.

3. $j'x = -\gamma\rho_0 v, \rho' = \gamma\rho$.

4. $\bar{B}' \bullet \bar{E}' = \bar{B} \bullet \bar{E}$ .

5. $\bar{B}' \bullet \bar{B}' - (1/c^2)\bar{E}' \bullet \bar{E}' = \bar{B} \bullet \bar{B} - (1/c^2)\bar{E} \bullet \bar{E}$ .

6. $-\iiint v\gamma j_x / c^2 dV'$ .

7. $v = qBr / m\sqrt{1 + (qBr/mc)^2}$

8. $\boldsymbol{B} = (0, \gamma B_0, 0), \boldsymbol{E} = (0, 0, v\gamma B_0)$.

9. Final result: $\boldsymbol{E}$ and $\boldsymbol{B}$ are unaltered by the gauge transformation.

10. $\boldsymbol{S} = 0, u = \varepsilon_0 c^2 B_0^2/2, \boldsymbol{S'} = (1/\mu_0)(-\gamma^2 v B_0^2, 0, 0), u' = (\gamma^2 \varepsilon_0 c^2 B_0^2/2)(1 + v^2/c^2)$.

11.  $\varepsilon_0 c^2 \Box E = -c^2 grad \,(\rho) - \partial \bar{j}/\partial t - curl \,(\bar{j}_m),$
     $\varepsilon_0 c^2 \Box B = -grad \,(\rho_m) - (1/c^2) \partial \bar{j}_m/\partial t + curl \,(\bar{j}).$

12.  Final result: equation (10.14). Their inverses are calculated from (10.13) by direct substitution.

13.  Final result:

$$u = \frac{\gamma^2 q^2}{32\pi^2 \varepsilon_0 r^4} \left( 1 + \frac{v^2}{c^2} \left( 1 - \left( \frac{x+vt}{r} \right)^2 \right) \right)$$

$$\bar{S} = \frac{-\gamma^2 q^2 v}{16\pi^2 \varepsilon_0 r^6} \left( -y^2 - z^2, y\,(x+vt), z\,(x+vt) \right)$$

## Chapter 11

1.  $g = J^2$.

2.  $\overline{g_1} = (\cos\theta, \sin\theta),\ \overline{g_2} = (-r\sin\theta, r\cos\theta)$. The metric is:

$$g_{ik} = \begin{bmatrix} 1 & 0 \\ 0 & r^2 \end{bmatrix}.$$

3.  $g_{ab}g^{ab} = n$.

4.  $g^{ab}\overline{g_b} = \overline{g^a},\quad g_{uv}\overline{g^v} = \overline{g_u}$.

5.  $\overline{g_1} = (\cos x^2, \sin x^2, 0),\quad \overline{g_2} = (-x^1 \sin x^2, x^1 \cos x^2, 0),\quad \overline{g_3} = (0, 0, 1)$,
    $g_{11} = 1, g_{22} = (x^1)^2, g_{33} = 1$, and all others are zero.

6.  Cartesian: $T_{11} = 2, T_{22} = 3, T_{12} = T_{21} = 0$, Polar: $T_{11} = 2 + \sin^2\theta, T_{22} = r^2(2 + \cos^2\theta),$
    $T_{12} = T_{21} = r\sin\theta\cos\theta.$

7.  Cartesian: $T_{1132} = -20$. Cylindrical: $T_{1132} = 4(2\sin x^2 - \cos x^2)(3\sin x^2 + \cos x^2)(7x^1\sin x^2 + 5x^1\cos x^2).$

8.  $\overline{g_1} = (2,1,0),\ \overline{g_2} = (0,1,1),\ \overline{g_3} = (0,0,-2),\ \overline{g_1'} = (\tfrac{1}{2},0,0),\ \overline{g_2'} = (-\tfrac{1}{2},1,0),$
    $\overline{g_3'} = (-\tfrac{1}{4}, \tfrac{1}{2}, -\tfrac{1}{2}), v_1 = 4, v_2 = 5, v_3 = -6, v^1 = 1/2, v^2 = 3/2, v^3 = -3/4.$

## Chapter 12

1. $d^2x^\sigma/ds^2 = 0$ gives $x^\sigma = A^\sigma{}_0 s + B^\sigma{}_0$.

2. Final result: $\vec{a} \otimes \vec{b}\,[v] = \vec{a}\,(\vec{b} \cdot \vec{v})$ is true.

3. The first-order tensor transformation, applied twice, gives
$v''^m = (\partial x''^m / \partial x^l) v^l$.

4. $B_\delta{}^\alpha{}_{op} A_\gamma{}^{j\beta}{}_l, A^{uv} - B^{uv}, F^{uv}$.

5. $mx_i'' + \partial V / \partial x^i = 0$, which is simply $F = ma$.

6. Final result: $y(x) = LOG_{(2/3)}[(x + 1)/(2x - 2)] + 2$.

7. Final result: $y(x) = 0$.

8. Final result: equation (12.19).

## Chapter 13

1. Final result: $[k\,m,l]' = [\alpha\,\beta,b]\dfrac{\partial x^\alpha}{\partial x'^k}\dfrac{\partial x^\beta}{\partial x'^m}\dfrac{\partial x^b}{\partial x'^l} + g_{\gamma\beta}\dfrac{\partial x^b}{\partial x'^l}\dfrac{\partial^2 x^\gamma}{\partial x'^m \partial x'^k}$.

2. Final result: equation (13.14).

3. Cartesian: $grad(\varphi) = \left[ x_*^1 \Big/ \sqrt{(x_*^1)^2 + (x_*^2)^2}\,, x_*^2 \Big/ \sqrt{(x_*^1)^2 + (x_*^2)^2}\,, 0 \right]$,
Cylindrical: $grad(\varphi) = (1, 0, 0)$.

4. $\delta v_k = \Gamma^\sigma{}_{m\,k} v_\sigma \delta x^m$, $\delta v^k = -v^\sigma \Gamma^k{}_{m\,\sigma} \delta x^m$.

5. $P_{ijk;l} = P_{ijk,l} - P_{imk}\Gamma^m{}_{l\,j} - P_{mjk}\Gamma^m{}_{l\,i} - P_{ijm}\Gamma^m{}_{l\,k}$.

6. The result is a tensor product.

7. Direct substitution shows that the Christoffel symbols of the second kind transform according to (13.6).

8. Final result: $v_{a,m} g^{an} - v^n_{,m} = v^\alpha \Gamma^n{}_{m\,\alpha} + g^{kn} v_\sigma \Gamma^\sigma{}_{m\,k}$.

## Chapter 14

1.  Final result: $g^{kp}{}_{;n} = 0$.

2.  Because the covariant derivative of the metric is the third-order zero tensor and because { } was derived from that, it must transform as an affine connection would.

3.  One way to prove $\overline{g_{p,q}} = \Gamma^r{}_{pq}\overline{g_r}$ is to calculate how the $g$-terms transform from Euclidean space.

4.  Final result: $u_{1;1} = 0, u_{2;2} = 3 + 6x^2\tan x^2, u_{3;3} = 4 - 8x^3\cot x^3$. All other terms are zero.

5.  $0, H^{ij}{}_{;j}$.

6.  Final result: equation (14.1).

7.  $\Gamma^i{}_{km} - \Gamma^i{}_{mk}$ is a tensor.

8.  Final result: $g^{ab}\overline{g_{b;c}} = \overline{g^a{}_{;c}}$

## Chapter 15

1.  Direct substitution shows that $T^{uv}g_{uv} = 0$.

2.  Expressed in terms of $E$ and $B$:
    $$\overline{E} = \left(\gamma q / 4\pi\varepsilon_0 r^3\right)[x + vt, y, z], \quad \overline{B} = \left(-\gamma vq / 4\pi\varepsilon_0 c^2 r^3\right)[0, z, -y].$$

3.  Direct substitution shows that $j^a{}_{;a} = 0$.

4.  Result: $T^{jk}u_k = u^i\rho$.

5.  Final result: equations in (15.4).

6.  Final result: equations in (15.5).

7.  Direct substitution gives $d(m'v)/dt = q(\overline{E} + \overline{v} \times \overline{B})$.

8.  Final result: equations (15.5) and (15.6).

9.  $l^{mn} = -l^{nm}$.

10. $f^k = md^2x^k/d\tau^2$.

11. Four-velocity, four-momentum, four-force, proper time, and $x$-coordinate, in order:

$$(c\sqrt{\tau/\tau_0}, 0, 0, c\sqrt{(\tau+\tau_0)/\tau_0})$$

$$(mc\sqrt{\tau/\tau_0}, 0, 0, mc\sqrt{(\tau+\tau_0)/\tau_0})$$

$$((mc/2\tau_0)\sqrt{\tau_0/\tau}, 0, 0, (mc/2\tau_0)\sqrt{\tau/(\tau+\tau_0)})$$

$$t(\tau) = (2/3)\tau_0 ((\tau+\tau_0)/\tau_0)^{3/2} - (2/3)\tau_0$$

$$x(t) = (2/3)\tau_0 c ((3t/2\tau_0)+1)^{2/3} - 1)^{3/2}$$

## Chapter 16

1. A million and one times faster.

2. ~ $1.5 \times 10^{-12}$ m.

3. ~ 49,772.6 Km.

4. $\Delta f = 8.303 \times 10^{-8}$ Hz.

5. Equation (16.7) can be verified by reverse reasoning: because the box is moving in the other direction, the classical Doppler blue-shift formula is used.

6. Even if materials that could withstand the tremendous centrifugal forces existed, the disk would fly apart because of perimeter length contraction.

7. The rod would break apart if each of the thrusters gave a large enough impulse.

8. $\rho = \dfrac{\alpha\beta^2}{4\pi G}\left[x^2 y^2 + x^2 z^2 + y^2 z^2\right] e^{-\beta xyz}$

## Chapter 17

1. Final result: equation (17.10)

2. All terms are zero: $R_{abcd} = 0$, $R_{uv} = 0$, $R = 0$, $G_{uv} = 0$.

3. $ds^2 \approx (1 - 2GM/c^2 r)dw^2 - dx^2 - dy^2 - dz^2$ by substitution of the Newtonian potential. But this approximation is not very good even for very weak gravity fields, because the metric does not account for radial stretching of space.

4. Final result: equation (17.17).

5. $R^a_{\ a} = R_{mn}g^{mn}$.

6. Not generally.

7. Does not approximate Newtonian gravity in the weak-field limit.

8. $-(8\pi G/c^4)T^a_{\ c} = R^a_{\ c} - (1/2)\delta^a_c R + \Lambda\delta^a_c$.

9. $-\Lambda c^4/8\pi G$.

10. Final result: $v^p_{\ ;qr} - v^p_{\ ;rq} = v^\sigma R_{\sigma\ qr}^{\ p}$.

11. 0.

12. The equation can be shown to be true by expressing it in terms of the metric and using the equality of mixed partials.

13. $R^{spqr} = -R^{sprq}, R^{spqr} = -R^{psqr}, R^{spqr} = R^{qrsp}, R^{spqr} = R^{rqps}$.

14. $\lambda' = \lambda(1 + GM/c^2 r)$.

15. Yes.

## Chapter 18

1. Final result: $R_{33} = -R_{44}/g_{44}$.

2. Substitution of the arbitrary metric into (18.1) gives the result.

3. $H = -c^2/a$

4.  $[1\,1,1] = [1\,1,0] = \beta(x-w)e^{-\beta(x-w)^2}$ , $[1\,0,1] = [0\,1,1] = -\beta(x-w)e^{-\beta(x-w)^2}$ ,
    $\Gamma^1_{11} = -\beta(x-w)$ , $\Gamma^1_{10} = \Gamma^1_{01} = +\beta(x-w)$ , $\Gamma^0_{11} = \beta(x-w)e^{-\beta(x-w)^2}$ ,
    $R_{10} = 0, R_{01} = 0, R_{00} = -\beta + \beta^2(x-w)^2, R_{11} = [\beta - \beta^2(x-w)^2]\ e^{-\beta(x-w)^2}$ ,
    $R = -2\beta + 2\beta^2(x-w)^2, G_{uv} = 0.$

5.  $T = 1.34 \text{ Kg/m}^3.$

6.  $\sim 9 \times 10^{15}$ m.

7.  Final result: true by substitution.

8.  $[0\,0,0] = (1/2w_0)\cos(w/w_0), [1\,1,1] = (1/2x_0)\sin(x/x_0), \Gamma^0_{00} = (1/2w_0)\cot(w/w_0),$
    $\Gamma^1_{11} = -(1/2x_0)\tan(x/x_0), R_{ab} = G_{ab} = 0, R = 0.$

## Chapter 19

1.  Final result: true by direct calculation.

2.  $8.86 \times 10^{-3}$ m.

3.  $2.95 \times 10^3$ m

4.  $T' = T(1 - (6.94 \times 10^{-10})).$

5.  Final result: $\sqrt{2GM/r}$ . By conservation of energy, changes in kinetic energy must be equal to the amount of energy gained via blue shift if the object fell down the gravity well in the form of photons.

6.  Final result:

$$s = \sqrt{r_2^2 - \frac{2GM}{c^2}r_2} - \sqrt{r_1^2 - \frac{2GM}{c^2}r_1} + \frac{2GM}{c^2}\log_e\left[\frac{\sqrt{r_2 - \frac{2GM}{c^2}} + \sqrt{r_2}}{\sqrt{r_1 - \frac{2GM}{c^2}} + \sqrt{r_1}}\right]$$

7.  True by substitution.

8.  True by substitution.

9.  The scalar function $g = -r^4\sin^2\theta$.

## *Chapter 20*

1. ~ $8.48 \times 10^{-6}$ radians or ~ 1.75 Arcseconds.

2. Substitution gives the identity 1 = 1.

3. Final result: $d^2r/d\tau^2 = -GM/r^2$.

4. Infinity. Letting $r_1$ equal the Schwarzschild radius gives the result.

$$t = \left[ \frac{r}{c} + \frac{2GM}{c^3} \log_e \left( \frac{c^2 r}{2GM} - 1 \right) \right]\Bigg|_{r_1}^{r_2}.$$

5. $\sqrt{GM/r}$ .

6. $\tau = t\sqrt{1 - 3GM/rc^2}$ .

7. ~ $4.26 \times 10^{-5}$ radians.

8. Final result: $n \approx (1 + e)r_0 c^2/3GM$.

9. Substitution proves the calculation.

## *Chapter 21*

1. $s(t) = \sqrt{3/4\Lambda} \left( e^{ct\sqrt{\Lambda/3}} - e^{-ct\sqrt{\Lambda/3}} \right)$, $S(t) = k_0 e^{ct\sqrt{\Lambda/3}}$ , where $k_0$ is a constant.

2. Direct calculation gives the deceleration parameter, $q$.

3. Z = 4.92.

4. 50: ~ 13.1 billion years, 60: ~ 10.9 billion years, 70: ~ 9.4 billion years.

5. 50: ~ 17.6 billion years, 60: ~ 14.7 billion years, 70: ~ 12.6 billion years,
   80: ~ 11.0 billion years.

6. 40: ~ 16.3 billion years, 50: ~ 13.0 billion years, 60: ~ 10.9 billion years,
   70: ~ 9.3 billion years, 80: ~ 8.2 billion years.

7. 50: ~ 11.2 billion years, 60: ~ 9.3 billion years, 70: ~ 8.0 billion years, $2t_{half}$:
   50: ~ 123 billion years, 60: ~ 103 billion years, 70: ~ 88 billion years.

8. 50: $10^{-4}$: ~ $6.2 \times 10^7$ billion years, $10^{-60}$: ~ $6.2 \times 10^{91}$ billion years,
   $10^{-600}$: ~ $6.2 \times 10^{901}$ billion years,
   70: $10^{-4}$: ~ $4.4 \times 10^7$ billion years, $10^{-60}$: ~ $4.4 \times 10^{91}$ billion years,
   $10^{-600}$: ~ $4.4 \times 10^{901}$ billion years.

9. $S(t) = ct$.

10. $S(t) = A_0 t + B_0$, $\rho(t) = \left(3c^2/8\pi G\right)\left[\left(A_0^2 + c^2\right)\middle/\left(A_0 t + B_0\right)^2\right]$,
    $\dot{S}/S = A_0/\left(A_0 t + B_0\right)$, where $A_0$ and $B_0$ are undetermined constants of
    integration.

11. $S(t) = t\sqrt{\Lambda_0 c^2 S_0^2/3 - kc^2}$

12. Final result: equation (21.2).

13. Final result: equation (21.3) and equations (21.5) and (21.6).

# Recommended Reading

Andrews, Larry C. *Elementary Partial Differential Equations with Boundary Value Problems*. Orlando, Florida: Academic Press, Inc., 1986.

Braun, Martin. *Differential Equations and Their Applications,* 3rd ed. New York: Springer-Verlag, 1983.

Davies Paul C.W. *Quantum Mechanics.* New York: Chapman and Hall Ltd., 1989.

Dunham, William. *Journey Through Genius.* New York: Penguin Books, 1991.

Feynman, Richard P. *QED: The Strange Theory of Light and Matter.* Princeton, N.J.: Princeton University Press, 1985.

Greiner, Walter. *Quantum Mechanics: An Introduction,* 3rd ed. Berlin and New York: Springer-Verlag, 1994.

Greiner, Walter and Berndt Müler. *Quantum Mechanics: Symmetries,* 2nd ed. Berlin: Springer-Verlag, 1994.

Greiner, Walter. *Relativistic Quantum Mechanics: Wave Equations.* Berlin: Springer-Verlag, 1997.

Greiner, Walter and Joachim Reinhardt. *Quantum Electrodynamics,* 2nd ed. Berlin: Springer-Verlag, 1994.

Greiner, Walter and Andreas Schäfer. *Quantum Chromodynamics.* Berlin: Springer-Verlag, 1994.

Gross, Franz. *Relativistic Quantum Mechanics and Field Theory.* New York: John Wiley and Sons, Inc., 1993.

Hawking, Stephen. *A Brief History of Time.* New York: Bantam Books (Bantam Doubleday Dell Publishing Group), 1988.

Henbest, Nigel. *The Planets.* New York: Viking (Penguin Group), 1992.

Knopp, Konrad. *Theory and Application of Infinite Series.* New York: Dover Publications, Inc., 1990.

Peebles, Phillip James Edwin. *Quantum Mechanics.* Princeton, N.J.: Princeton University Press, 1992.

## *Bibliography*

Anton, Howard. *Elementary Linear Algebra,* 3rd ed. New York: John Wiley and Sons, Inc., 1981.

Bergmann, Peter G. *Introduction to the Theory of Relativity.* New York: Dover Publications, 1976.

D'Inverno, Ray. *Introducing Einstein's Relativity.* New York: Oxford University Press, 1992.

Dirac, Paul Adrien Maurice. *General Theory of Relativity.* Princeton, N.J.: Princeton University Press, 1996.

Dobbs, Roland. *Electromagnetic Waves.* Boston, MA: Routledge and Kegan Paul, 1985.

Einstein, Albert. *The Meaning of Relativity,* 5th ed. Princeton, N.J.: Princeton University Press, 1956.

Einstein, Albert. *The Principle of Relativity.* New York: Dover Publications, 1952.

Einstein, Albert. *Relativity: The Special and General Theory.* Wings Books, N.J.: Random House, 1961.

Feynman, Richard P., Robert B. Leighton, and Matthew Sands. *The Feynman Lectures on Physics,* Vols. 1, 2, and 3. Reading, Mass.: Addison-Wesley Publishing Company, 1977.

Folger, Tim. "The Magnificent Mission." *Discover Magazine* 21, no. 5 (May 2000).

Gautreau, Ronald and William Savin. *Schaum's Outline of Theory and Problems of Modern Physics.* New York: McGraw-Hill Publishing Company, 1978.

Goldberg, Samuel. *Difference Equations,* New York: John Wiley and Sons, 1958.

Hans, Christian Von Bayer. "Vacuum Matters." *Discover Magazine* 13, no. 3 (March 1992).

Islam, Jamal N. *An Introduction to Mathematical Cosmology*. Cambridge: Cambridge University Press, 1992.

Kaku, Michio. *Quantum Field Theory: A Modern Introduction*. Oxford: Oxford University Press, Inc., 1993.

Kane, Gordon L. *Modern Elementary Particle Physics*. Reading, Mass.: Addison-Wesley Publishing Co., 1993.

Karttunen, Hannu, Pekka Kröger, Heikki Oja, Markku Poutanen, and Karl J. Donner. *Fundamental Astronomy*. New York: Springer-Verlag, 1987.

Krauss, Lawrence M. "Cosmological Antigravity." *Scientific American Magazine* 280, no. 1 (January 1999).

Lerner, Rita G. and George L. Trigg. *Encyclopedia of Physics*, 2nd ed. New York: VCH Publishers Inc., 1991.

Lindley, David. *The End of Physics: The Myth of a Unified Field Theory*. New York: Basic Books (Harper-Collins, Inc.), 1993.

Marsden, Jerrold E. and Anthony J. Tromba. *Vector Calculus*, 2nd ed. San Francisco: W. H. Freeman and Company, 1981.

Misner, Charles W., Kip S. Thorne, and John A. Wheeler. *Gravitation*. New York: W. H. Freeman and Company, 1973.

Musser, George. "Boomerang Effect." *Scientific American Magazine* 238, no. 1 (July 2000).

NASA, National Space Science Data Center.

Narlikar, Jayant V. *Introduction to Cosmology*, 2nd ed. Cambridge: Cambridge University Press, 1993.

Noble, Ben and James W. Daniel. *Applied Linear Algebra*. Englewood Cliffs, N.J.: Prentice-Hall Inc., 1977.

Pais, Abraham. *Subtle is the Lord*. Oxford: Oxford University Press, 1982.

Pauli, Wolfgang. *Theory of Relativity*. New York: Dover Publications, 1958.

Peebles, Phillip James Edwin. *Principles of Physical Cosmology*. Princeton, N.J.: Princeton University Press, 1993.

Resnick, Robert, David Halliday and Kenneth S. Krane. *Physics*, 4th ed, vols. 1 and 2, New York: John Wiley and Sons, Inc., 1992.

Salas, Saturnino L. and Einar Hille. *Calculus: One and Several Variables*, 3rd ed. New York: John Wiley and Sons, Inc., 1978.

Schrödinger, Erwin. *Space-Time Structure.* Cambridge: Cambridge University Press, 1950.

Schwartz, Melvin. *Principles of Electrodynamics.* New York: Dover Publications, Inc., 1972.

Simmons, George F. *Differential Equations with Applications and Historical Notes,* 2nd ed. New York: McGraw-Hill Inc, 1972.

Straumann, Norbert. *General Relativity and Relativistic Astrophysics.* Berlin: Springer-Verlag, 1984.

Wald, Robert M. *General Relativity.* Chicago: University of Chicago Press, 1984.

Weyl, Hermann. *Space Time Matter.* New York: Dover Publications, Inc., 1952.

# *Index*

Aberration, 4, 14
Absolute:
    motion, 14, 16, 17
    space, 18, 31
    time, 18, 31, 43
Aether, 14, 16
Affine:
    connection, 176-181, 183; symmetric,
        187, 191-192, 197; in general
        relativity, 229, 240; in solving field
        equations, 250-253
    curvature, 177, 331-332
    geodesics, 177, 331-332
    manifolds, 331-332
    parallel transportation, 177, 331-332
Ampère's law, 126-129, 136-137, 140-
    141, 197, 205
Antimatter, 100

Atoms, 285, 310

Bianchi identities, 234-235, 237
Big bang, 18, 285-286, 288, 292, 300, 303-
    304, 308-309
Big crunch, 302, 308-309
Biot-Savart Law, 139
Black holes, 4, 18, 259, 266, 269, 279,
    309-310; rotating and charged,
    267-269
Blue-shift, 222-223, 225, 266, 295-298,
    345
Boyer-Lindquist coordinates, 268

Calculus, 3, 124, 134, 147, 150, 164-166,
    182-183; of variations, 164, 243;
    tensor, 3, 147, 173; vector, 3, 5, 150,
    215, 228